THE
Narrowbo Builder's Book

THE COMPLETE GUIDE TO FITTING OUT A NARROWBOAT
3RD EDITION

by Graham Booth

Waterways World
Burton-on-Trent

Published by Waterways World Ltd,
The Well House, High Street, Burton-on-Trent,
Staffordshire DE14 1JQ, England

First published as a series of supplements by Chris Lloyd and Andy Burnett in
Waterways World magazine in 1984 and 1985
Second edition by Graham Booth and Andy Burnett first published in Waterways World
in 1992 and 1993
This edition first published 1999

British Library Cataloguing In Publication Data
A catalogue record for this book is available from the British Library

ISBN 1 870002 71 7

Design and typesetting by Steve Bellaby
Sketches and diagrams by Graham Booth and Andy Burnett
Colour origination, Derbyshire Colour Services, Alfreton, Derbyshire
Printed and bound in the United Kingdom by Arkle Print Ltd

Contents

Acknowledgements

This book is based on the *New Narrowboat Builder's Book* which I co-wrote with Andy Burnett. I am grateful to Andy for allowing me to incorporate some of his original text and illustrations into this book. I am also grateful to Peter Thompson and Peter Hopley for their sections on engine marinisation and electrical systems in chapters 5, 6 and 9.

CHAPTER 1
INTRODUCTION

Reasons for fitting out
Planning *Rome*
Other layouts

Welcome to the completely revised and updated third edition of The Narrowboat Builder's Book. The original Narrowboat Builder's Book, written by Chris Lloyd and Andy Burnett, appeared in instalments in *Waterways World* in 1984. It was also published separately as a book. In 1992 it was replaced by the New Narrowboat Builder's Book, also serialised in *WW*, written by Andy Burnett and myself, Graham Booth, and traced the design, construction and fitting out of my own 60ft traditional narrowboat, *Rome*.

To satisfy the demand for information about fitting out narrowboats, this third edition of the *Narrowboat Builder's Book* is based on the material of its predecessor but with several important improvements. It still recounts the design and fitting out of *Rome* but the text is arranged in a larger number of chapters for easier reference and the sections on alternative ways of tackling a job have been incorporated into the main narrative. The whole work has been up-dated, particularly the parts dealing with legislation, and a new chapter on maintenance and how *Rome* performed in practice has been added. As in the previous books, it is assumed that readers will buy a shell from a specialist builder and complete the majority of the remaining work him/herself. For the reasons given in chapter 3, DIY shell building is not recommended unless you have the relevant skills and experience.

REASONS FOR FITTING OUT

Before starting to recount my own experiences, it may be useful to ask a few basic questions and try to provide a few answers. Firstly, why embark on such a monumental task in your spare time when you could buy a completed new or second-hand boat? In many cases the answer will be "in order to acquire a new boat without paying the £1,000 per foot prices charged by some boatyards and professional fitters-out". There may also be the hope that, after a couple of seasons, you could sell the boat and show a profit. While I would have to agree that this may be possible, there are several factors which could deny you this hoped for profit or even turn it into a loss.

Skill
First on the list is your own ability to produce a reasonable standard of workmanship. Narrowboat design and specification have become much more sophisticated in the last few years and the public – your future market – now has much higher expectations. Acres of indifferently varnished ply and a secondhand stainless steel sink unit will not impress the punters like they used to. You will require

Narrowboat interiors have become more sophisticated and self-assured in the last decade. This fit-out by Stowe Hill Marine is representative of current professional standards

a variety of skills from woodwork to plumbing, from wiring to painting. Have a look at a few nice, newish, boats and ask yourself honestly whether you could produce that standard. You could, of course, enlist the help of specialists for the bits you don't feel capable of doing yourself. This is sensible but, if you rely on them too much, the cost will start to spiral and you may lose your credibility when people ask "did you do it all yourself?"

Design
Then there is that elusive factor – design. However much writers on the subject may encourage you to 'be different' and 'express yourself', it is pretty certain that a 50–55ft 'floating cottage' with a solid fuel stove and a four poster bed will be a much better investment than a similar length replica of the *Titanic* with an all black interior and flashing disco lights. One of the advantages of fitting out your own boat is that you can afford to spend the time getting it exactly as you want it, but you should always bear in mind that, one day, you will want to sell it. Some surveyors say that a few of the boats they see are worth less than the cost of their basic components – even without taking into account the notional cost of their owner's time.

Costs
You may well be surprised by the cost of all the things which are needed to complete a boat – I always am. Assuming that you aim for a reasonable specification, the cost of the shell, engine, materials and equipment will be at least as much as the price of a good quality five year old

boat of similar specification and may be nearly as expensive as one of the new, economy class boats being built in increasing numbers. A quick leaf through the pages of *Waterways World* will tell you the prices of the more obvious items like the stove, cooker or pump out loo, but what comes as a real surprise is the cost of more mundane items such as wall tiling, bath taps, plywood and even paint. With this in mind, there is a breakdown of the cost of *Rome* into its basic elements in the last chapter. When you see this you may think that the prices charged by boatyards for new boats are not so unreasonable after all. While on the subject of boatyards, another advantage of buying 'complete' is that you may get afloat much quicker. This could save the cost of hiring a boat for a year or two for the family holiday and so could affect your economic equation.

Once the boat is complete it will have to be licensed, insured and an approved mooring found for it. The costs of these could easily set you back £1,500 depending on the length of the boat and where you keep it. These costs are, of course, the same whether you fit out your own boat or buy a ready fitted one, but you could reduce them to a fraction by buying one or more shares in a shared ownership scheme. You won't be able to go off cruising 'at the drop of a hat' but if, like many boaters, you only spend four weeks plus the odd weekend on the boat each year, a combination of shared ownership and a couple of short breaks on a hire boat could make very good economic sense. More information on the costs of owning a boat are contained in the Inland Boat Owner's Book (see appendix 4 for details).

The great enemy
All of which brings us to the next worthy topic – time. I soon got fed up with people coming to visit the new shell, shaking their heads and saying "you've got a lot of work there" – mainly because I knew they were dead right! Just how long all this work takes depends on a number of factors. One is the amount of time your job and family commitments allow you to spend on the project. Another is the nearness of the boat to your home – even a short journey can be quite time consuming and disruptive. Anyone living at a considerable distance from the system should consider having the shell delivered to their garden or nearby hardstanding for the fit-out and then having it low-loaded back to the cut when it is finished. The time and cost

If you live a long way from the system, a low loader could save you a lot of time

saved could well outweigh the transport charge.

Next, what sort of person are you? Do you like to crack on with a job and not rest before it's finished or do you do a bit and then go off and do something else? – only you can say. As well as the cost analysis there is a chart showing how much time I took on each part of the work to give you an idea of how long it might take you.

Manual dexterity?
A more recent consideration is the Recreational Craft Directive (RCD) which came into force fully on June 16th 1998. This requires that boats placed on the European market after that date must conform to a number of Essential Safety Requirements as well as being supplied with a technical manual, an owner's manual and a Declaration of Conformity. The owner's manual must contain a comprehensive specification of the boat including details of materials and equipment used and diagrams showing the layout of the various systems like wiring and plumbing. It must also indicate the ways in which you have satisfied the many Essential Safety Requirements of the RCD.

Boats fitted out by their owners for their own use are exempt from the RCD but only if they are not sold for five years. While it is not beyond the capabilities of a competent writer and draughtsman to produce the manuals, it is a considerable undertaking which some professional fitters are finding difficult and many amateurs may find impossible. You might, as some professionals will, pay someone to produce them for you but this would be yet another expense. It may be better to resolve to keep the boat for five years (in which case you need only to obtain a Boat Safety Certificate) or buy a fully fitted, new or second-hand boat. See chapter 2 for more details.

Fitness for purpose
In addition to the outlay of time and money you will also need to be fairly fit and able. Your baptism of fire will probably be laying the ballast, but even after this is done there are large sheets of 18mm ply to shift and awkwardly placed holes to be drilled in unyielding steelwork which require a fair degree of strength.

Finally
If these thoughts have put you off the idea for good I hope that you will still read on and find my experiences useful when you buy a new or second hand boat, or do a partial refit of your present one. You might even thank me for saving you a lot of heartache later on. Those still determined to carry on can look forward to a great deal of hard work but, at the end of it, the incredible satisfaction and sense of achievement when you take your first holiday on the boat which you have designed and fitted out yourself.

ROME

In 1982 I wrote a series of articles, published in *Waterways World*, about the design, construction and fitting out of our 33ft narrowboat *Bess*. We kept *Bess* for several years until delusions of grandeur, plus the acquisition of a Labrador puppy, persuaded us that we should go for something bigger. We considered fitting out another shell but decided we couldn't really justify the large out-

Bess, the first narrowboat the author fitted-out

lay of cash required. Thumbing through the back pages of *WW*, I saw an advert for a 55ft Colecraft, eighteen months old and, by the owner's estimate, 80% complete. Moving with uncustomary haste, we saw the boat, decided it had potential and bought it all in the space of 24 hours.

Inevitably there was more work in finishing the job than there first appeared, and I eventually opted for the radical solution of stripping it back to the lined shell which Colecraft had originally supplied and incorporating as much of the salvaged chandlery as possible into my own fit out. Fortunately the positions of doors and windows more or less suited what I wanted to do and compromises

The saloon of *George*, his second fit-out

were fairly few. I found fitting out *George*, as we called it, was easier and more enjoyable than *Bess*, probably because of the confidence and experience I had gained in the first fit out, so that, by 1990, I was starting to get cravings for the smell of sawn ply and fresh paint. After much deliberation, and with some reluctance we decided to sell *George* and start this time with a completely bare shell.

Planning

Planning a narrowboat is one of the most difficult and most personal aspects of boatfitting. It is also the one which will haunt you longest if you don't get it right. No matter how well executed the joinery may be, if the boat doesn't feel right or if you always bang your knee on the corner of the bed when you walk through the boat, you will very soon tire of it. If you have never planned a boat before – and even if you have – the best way to pick up the basic principles or some new ideas is to look round as

many completed boats as you can. Most owners of nice private boats are only too pleased to show you over their pride and joy if you show a genuine interest. Hire brochures are a useful source of plans which will give you an idea of how much space to allow for various items. Incidentally, if you have never cruised a boat before, and I am always amazed by the number of people who order shells never having been on one, for goodness sake hire a boat for at least a week and preferably out of season. That way you will find out, before it is too late, whether boating is really for you. Once on a boat try to decide whether you like open plans or ones with lots of separate areas, through galleys or U-shaped galleys, traditional or cruiser sterns and all the other possible variations on the theme of boat design. Then try to put your ideas on paper in as clear a form as possible.

Producing the plan

For basic planning I find it useful to divide the width of the boat into thirds, each just over 2ft wide. (I used metric measurements at work for twenty years but revert instantly to Imperial whenever I do a job at home). Then divide the length of the cabin into sections of about the same width to form a square grid. You will find that most of the things you will need to get in will fit roughly into one or more of these squares. A double bed is 3 by 2 squares whereas a single bed is 3 by 1. A good sized bathroom is 3 by 2 and the corridor, be it in the middle or down one side, is one square in width. Galley units tend to be a bit narrower than 2ft wide but if you allow this in initial planning you will have an inbuilt allowance for the thickness of partitions which otherwise may catch you out. What ever method you use, it is vital to pre-plan as much of the layout and detail as possible so that you don't find you have a 4ft long bed, or a partition in the middle of a window!

The layout of the 55ft Colecraft which I refitted after we sold *Bess* was fairly conventional. Starting at the front with an 11ft saloon there followed a galley, a single bedroom with large wardrobe, a bathroom, a double bedroom with vanity unit and, finally, an engine room containing a boxed-in BMC 1.5 diesel engine. This layout suited us well – so well that for a long time we had no thought of ever changing it. The sight of boatman's cabins and engine

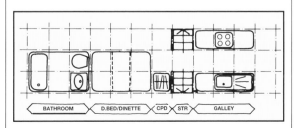
Preliminary planning grid

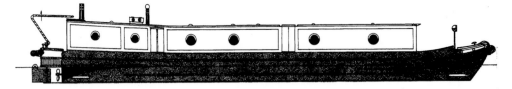

rooms with a vintage diesel on display attracted us, but these, on their own, did not seem to be sufficient reason for going through the upheaval of fitting out another boat. The only thought which irritated me slightly about *George's* layout was that, when we went out on day trips, we were only making use of half of the accommodation.

Inspiration

Sketching around on a piece of paper one day, the idea for a plan which answered all our needs suddenly dawned. At the back would be the replica boatmans cabin and engine room in the traditional manner. Backing onto this would be the bathroom entered from a side corridor. Next would be the bedroom containing a wardrobe and a double bed which would convert to a dinette. A lobby with two small staircases leading to pairs of side doors on opposite sides of the boat would separate the bedroom from the galley. Finally the saloon would be at the front of the boat with access to and from the front deck.

The main advantage of this arrangement was that the boat would have two distinct layouts. In 'holiday mode' the double bed could be left made up and we would eat in the saloon using a table top on the ubiquitous Desmo leg. In 'day trip' mode, or if we wanted a dinner party while on holiday, the bed would be converted to the dinette arrangement, giving us extra day space. The dinette would be well situated next to the galley for easy access for the 'cook' and the bathroom would be in between the two main sleeping areas, ie the bedroom and boatman's cabin.

Although we wanted a fairly open plan we were keen to be able to divide the boat into the public half – the saloon and galley, and the more private half – the bedroom and bathroom. This can be very useful when, after a hard day's locking, one of us could shower and dress in comfort and privacy while the other was free to relax in the saloon or chat to passers-by.

Other features carried forward from *George* and developed slightly were the side steps and doors. The position of the doors was determined by the previous owner and on my plan

they ended up partway along the centre corridored galley. This meant that we could have a proper flight of steps within the depth of the units on either side, rather than the perilous vertical ladder often seen in boats with U-shaped galleys. The side doors are essential for escape but are also useful for access if they happen to face the towpath, or for safe night ventilation if they do not. To avoid this uncertainty we decided to have steps on both sides so that which ever way we moored, we could do both.

This plan could have filled a 70ft shell with no difficulty but I decided, for three reasons, to try to fit it into 60ft. The first was one of economy. Narrowboat shells are nearly always priced by the foot so reducing it by ten feet saved about 14% of the cost. The second was a desire not to restrict our cruising routes. A sixty foot boat can negotiate the Leeds & Liverpool and most other waterways we might want to see. Last was ease of handling. We found no difficulty moving up from 33ft to 55ft but the thought of an extra 15ft when trying to moor the boat against an 'offshore' wind daunted us. It was just possible to fit everything in, but an extra 2ft would have made things a lot easier.

Details

So much for the basic principles – what about the details? The first plan I drew had the side corridor going past the bathroom on the starboard side. This was for no better reason than that most other people seemed to do that way. When we started looking at engines we realised that the majority of them had their exhausts on the starboard side so that a conflict might occur. The engine could be offset by a small amount to reduce this, but the problem could be overcome completely by switching the corridor to the port side. Another advantage of this was that it was now on the same side of the boat as the engine room side doors which traditionally have a hatch over them – the starboard ones being simply doors let into the cabin side. The clincher was that it was also different from our previous boat. We discovered yet another plus as we were building the boatman's cabin. The view from the engine room, instead of being of the bulky table and bed cupboards, is of the space over the side bed. This seems to give the back part of the plan a much more pleasant and spacious feel – my case rests.

Cutaway view of *Rome's* final design

The view from the towpath

Having more or less decided on the internal layout I did a quick check on the external appearance. This largely entailed seeing where the windows came – or in our case, portholes. When I made the first enquiry about *George*, the only drawback I could see was that it had portholes. It wasn't that we did not like the tug-like appearance these gave but, like hundreds of people we later overheard discussing it (isn't it amazing how voices carry over water ?), we thought it must be very dark inside. So much so that I actually talked to Colecraft about the feasibility of replacing the saloon and galley ports with windows. This was before we cruised it home. The trip proved that it wasn't half as dark as we thought and that there were the compensating advantages of security and privacy. By the time we got home I had decided to cut windows in the front bulkhead to give some extra light and views down the cut, and leave the sides just as they were. In five years of use we found no problems with this arrangement and liked it so much that we decided to do exactly the same on *Rome*. The plan seemed to be calling for the portholes to be positioned centrally in the spaces they lit, so I drew a side view of the boat showing this, and with the side doors in their respective positions. It looked fine. The portholes were reasonably spread out along the side and the side doors divided the boat into it's three parts – 'day space', 'private space' and 'boatman's space'. I was starting to think I must be on the right lines.

Services

Back inside then to see how the services would fit in. In order to plan something as complex as a narrowboat, you need to have an appreciation of all the equipment that is available and a good idea which particular piece best satisfies your requirements. Rather than embark on detailed descriptions of the equipment at such an early stage, these have been included in the chapters which describe their installation.

Our previous boat sold me on the idea of solid fuel stoves with back boilers, and calorifiers which use hot water from the engine's cooling system. The only slight drawbacks to these are that you have to light the stove if it suddenly goes chilly on a summer's evening, and you can only have hot water by running the engine for twenty minutes or so. Both these problems can be overcome by installing a diesel or gas-fired boiler to feed a second coil in the calorifier and to supply radiators or finrads throughout the boat. Most private boats over 50ft in length seem to have these nowadays. I decided, however, that since we would not want to run the boiler just to heat the back half of the boat, I would still have a back boiler on the stove to supply a radiator in the bedroom. This meant I would have two totally independent heating systems which may seem a bit over the top, but, for the price of a back boiler, an extra radiator and a length of copper pipe I could reduce my gas and electricity consumption drastically.

Heating

A few quick overlays on the plan indicated that the boiler (assuming it was the 'Alde' gas type) was best located at the side of the wardrobe, about half way down the boat. The ideal place for the calorifier seemed to be under the vanitory unit, half way between its two heat sources – the boiler and the engine. The solid fuel stove fitted in nicely on the port side with straight pipe runs back to a single radiator opposite the double bed and the feed and expansion tank further back on the same side in the engine room.

Water

The bathroom being now on the starboard side meant that the water supply pipe, water pump, and galley sink were most sensibly located on this side as well. That meant that the cooker had to go on the port side. I now had gas appliances on opposite sides of the boat and so would have to run pipes along both sides from the gas locker situated under the forepeak – gas pipes are not allowed in the bilges. This is not the most ideal arrangement for, as a general rule, the less gas piping you have the better. Swapping the positions of the sink and cooker seemed to produce even more problems so I decided to leave things as they were.

Wiring

The wiring layout looked quite straightforward. The batteries – one for the engine and three domestic – fitted in neatly on the starboard side of the engine with the fuse board fixed to the forward engine room bulkhead. From this, most of the wiring would be run in a conduit under the starboard side deck or along each side of the roof.

High voltage

Looking around again at the specifications of 'smart' boats, it seemed that most had 230-volt electricity supplied either by an inverter or a generator. We thought long and hard about this one but eventually decided, for the following reasons, against. Since we were not planning to live on the boat, we would not need a washing machine and most of the equipment we would use can be bought in 12-volt form. I am notorious for my worries about drained batteries, so the idea of an inverter sucking the life out of them did not appeal. Neither did the noise, not to mention the expense, of running a separate generator for hours on end – boating is supposed to be a peaceful activity. Finally, I thought, if Americans consider we Brits are crazy to run 230-volt power into our homes, how sensible is it to use it on a boat surrounded by water? For those who do not go along with this line of thinking, an onboard 230-volt system is described in chapter 9.

OTHER LAYOUTS

That was how the layout of Rome evolved but there are many other ways a boat can be designed and equipped. I have already mentioned the very popular 'floating cottage' layout so let's take a closer look, starting with the specification.

Traditional style, about 50ft long, with shell of 10/6/4mm plating (the metric measurements refer to the thickness of the baseplate, hull sides and superstructure in that order).

Four cylinder water-cooled diesel boxed-in in aft engine room.

Cabin equipment is likely to include a Squirrel solid fuel stove (perhaps with back-boiler to support central heating radiators, and/or Alde gas boiler.

Water heating via a calorifier by the gas boiler or by engine or both.

Gas cooker (free-standing or built-in), 'Batts' type electric fridge. Mansfield fresh-water flush WC on polypropylene holding tank, wash basin, squat bath/shower.

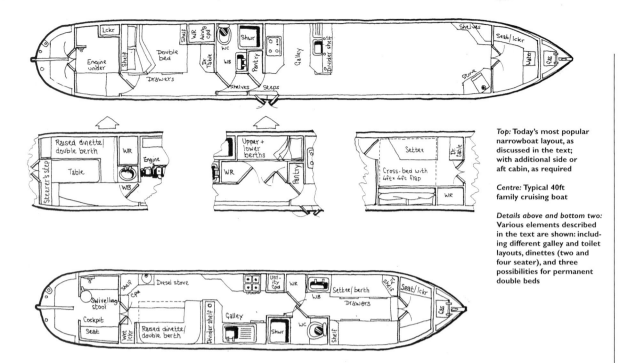

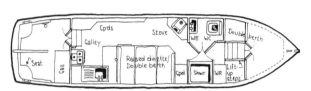

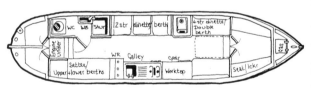

Some DIY owners also appreciated the merits of smaller craft: lower licence and mooring costs, and easier turning – particularly important when planning short evening or weekend trips. Over the years one particular 4-berth/40ft family layout has cropped up regularly on the market. Accommodation is in two cabins so that children can be put to bed early without closing the whole boat down. The 14ft galley/saloon (space-effective but not claustrophobic) is aft to maintain contact between steerer and those in the main cabin (in cruiser-style versions at least). Storage is well thought-out, providing wardrobe, separate wet-hanging locker and utility cupboard or full height pantry.

The settee-berths forward allow day use of that cabin for children to play in or watch TV without annoying others. The berths can also be bridged to make an occasional double bed. The alternative in this space is upper & lower berths on one side with a vanitory unit opposite. If the upper berth folds down, the lower can still be used as a day settee. However, as a berth, the upper invariably has to be 2in-4in narrower than the lower and tends to be unpopular with all except youngsters.

Layout elements
Layout possibilities are so numerous, that it is easier to describe the major components of narrowboat cabins. Variations often hinge on toilet compartment and galley arrangements:

Loo. Today's favoured toilet is approximately 5ft x 4ft and off-set so that a corridor can pass by on the other side. A WC, shower and wash basin fit in comfortably and allow towelling-down space. Sometimes the plan is 'L'-shaped with a wardrobe or airing cupboard completing the rectangle. The corridor need not be wasted – it is often where a side door is sited – and it can be used for table storage and/or shelves.

An alternative that has lost popularity is the toilet that straddles a centre corridor with a shower on one side, wash basin and WC on the other. The compartment doors

The layout shows a basic version. The saloon is empty so that you can furnish it with a free-standing bed-settee, folding chairs and small dining table and, perhaps in later years, install a more convivial built-in dinette. If you need a children's bedroom, insert a private cabin (with upper & lower bunks) off the side corridor, between galley and toilet. If your need is for guest accommodation, you can swap the permanent double bedroom with toilet, and add a guest cabin aft of the engine, resulting in a layout similar to *Rome's*. However that aft cabin does not have to be a traditional boatman's one which incurs a headroom penalty in leaving space for prop-shaft under. A raised dinette/double berth encourages crew to sit sociably close to the steerer, and allows a full headroom passage to one side.

Smaller is better?
The standard layout above evolved in the eighties as the average narrowboat grew longer. At the start of the nineties (and the recession) builders turned again to smaller narrowboats – mainly for the ready fitted-out market.

are usually arranged to close off across the corridor when the shower is in use, making 6ft x 6ft in all. Its obvious disadvantage when in that mode is that it stops others from passing right along the cabin. This disadvantage is shared by the walk-through bathroom but at least its occupant can enjoy a very spacious room. Another alternative is a loo of approximately 7ft x 2ft 6in (shower at one end, WC at the other, compact wash basin in the middle) which can be run along one side of a central corridor, with similarly linear galley on the other side.

Galley. A priority for many cooks is that the he/she should not be disturbed by passers-through. If yours is of that temperament, a galley arrangement based on a centre corridor could cause conflict. An 'L'- or 'U'-shape gives the cook his/her own corner but does not preclude a small additional work surface on the other side of the corridor. DIY fit-outs, particularly, tend to be short of galley storage. High level cupboards, shelves, which can include attractive divider shelves between galley and saloon, or a full height pantry are possible solutions. Small narrowboats usually allow at least 4ft of boat length to the galley, more than 7ft is generous in larger craft.

Loose furnished versus dinette. Eating in a loose-furnished saloon sometimes means perching on the edge of an easy chair and dining off a folding table. Sleeping there entails a bed-settee which invariably requires furniture to be shifted before it can be opened out – lengthways, as they usually won't fit within a cabin width (although you can now buy bed-settees custom-made for narrowboats).

The built-in dinette, therefore, has much to recommend it. The ritual of gathering round one can turn a meal into an 'occasion' and it should convert easily into a double berth. Dinettes can be raised to provide a good view out – a byproduct of which is additional storage under the base for awkward items like folding chairs. A two-seater dinette may be useful in a small cabin – serving as breakfast bar, galley extension, settee and berth. It solves the particular problem in some cramped layouts of not having anywhere to sit when the main bed is made up.

Movable box seats are a flexible alternative to the dinette, offering the choice of double berth or singles and of various seating layouts. A reasonably large cabin is needed to make best use of their permutations

Beds. The permanent double bed, sometimes an inefficient user of space, can also be movable without disturbing its make-up. It can be set across the cabin with its head in a boatman's type bed 'ole. If the bottom end of the duvet is fastened to the mattress, the bottom 4ft of the bed can hinge up into the 'ole, leaving a settee on the opposite side. So instead of giving over 6ft 3in of expensive boat length solely to the bed, 4ft is taken up by bed and day-settee.

In tug-style boats, the permanent double can slide partly under the tug deck, leaving an edge for use as a settee (some deep-draughted tugs actually have a bedroom, with 3ft 4in headroom, under the tug deck – very atmospheric but mind your head when you get up).
The smaller the boat, the more careful planning is needed.

This double bed slides out from under the raised front deck at night and forms the base of a settee during the daytime

You might be tempted to squeeze a permanent double bed into a 30ft narrowboat as part of a 2-berth layout. The only way that could be remotely viable is if the forward cockpit is sacrificed and the berth is run under the deck into the vee of the bow. Removable steps can still provide access over the bed to the foredeck. A temptation in small traditional-style boats is to box the engine in and run 'quarter' berths along each side of it. For this to work the engine must be kept clean, well serviced and ventilated to avoid the adjacent occupants being nauseated by the smell of diesel leaks. As a rough guide, 6ft 3in x 2ft 3in is needed for a comfortable single berth, 6ft 3in x 4ft 0in for a double.

Storage
A sign of boat-fitting experience is not just ample storage but integrated storage throughout the boat – cupboards, shelves and lockers that fit neatly into otherwise unused areas and which ease the awkward starkness of free-standing furniture in saloons. Experience also provides for things like short and long term coal storage, refuse bin recess, airing cupboard, linen storage, wet clothes hanging, utility storage for brooms, ironing board, vacuum cleaner, suitcases, folding bicycles, mini-washing machine. Muckier items can be stored in cockpit seat/lockers (preferably of steel and preferably under a cratch).

CHAPTER 2
LEGISLATION

Boat Safety Scheme
Recreational Craft Directive
Other Legislation

The Boat Safety Scheme

The story so far: British Waterways first introduced a set of Boat Safety Standards in the late 1970s. Without too much fuss or complaint, it made them compulsory for hire craft in 1979. It tried several times to extend the Standards to private boats and succeeded, at last, in 1997. Their introduction caused a furore among boat owners, mainly because of their complexity and the cost of bringing older vessels up to standard. Nevertheless, the scheme passed its first year without too much blood being spilt and, provided BW does not start to change the rules, it should not be long before we wonder what all the fuss was about.

Brass plate to indicate main gas tap below

effect of not complying is much greater for a new boat than for an older one.

The Boat Standards published by BW are reasonably straightforward to follow – particularly for diesel-powered all-steel boats. To certify that your boat meets the Standards it will ultimately have to be checked by a BW-approved surveyor or examiner. Realising that existing surveyors might not be able to cope with the large number of boats needing to be examined at the outset, BW initiated a scheme for training a new breed of 'examiners'. It was envisaged that examiners would be people such as boatyard owners or even long-standing boaters who already had some experience of boats and how they are built. All they would need was a short course to qualify them for the job.

Low level vents in *Rome's* front bulkhead

This fire extinguisher has a built-in pressure gauge so that it can be checked easily.

How does all this affect you? As far as the Boat Safety Scheme (BSS) is concerned, you have an obvious advantage over owners of existing boats in that it will cost you little, if any, more to build your new boat to BW's Standards. In fact you have a positive incentive to comply – the devaluing

In order to ensure consistency between surveyors and examiners, it was necessary to remove some of the discretionary powers which the surveyors previously enjoyed and this caused some resentment.

Exhaust pipe and silencer lagged to prevent accidental burns

It is a good idea to select your surveyor/examiner at the boat's planning stage, so that you can ask him/her to clarify any details in the Standards that you do not understand.

Future changes to British Waterways' Safety Standards might put less stress on hull dimensions – like the height of *Rome's* forward cockpit – because they are now covered by European Directives

When your boat is finally examined, you will then be confident that you have interpreted any moot points to his/her satisfaction.

Revisions, for the next few years anyway, may well put less emphasis on external shell details – for private boats at least. This is because shell design is covered by European Directives. However, although Standards themselves may become less fussy about handrails, safety gear and hull freeboard, you deviate from present requirements at your peril – they may be covered separately by bye-laws.

The Recreational Craft Directive

In the late 1980s, Britain's boat building industry, one of the largest in Europe, foresaw that it might be at a disadvantage in valuable export markets as individual countries adopted their own national standards or, paradoxically, that it might have other countries priorities forced upon it as Europe-wide standards were introduced. So the UK played a major role in formulating the European Recreational Craft Directive. This became law in Britain in June 1996 and all new craft have had to comply with it since June 1998.

In squaring up to the Europeans, Britain's three main waterway authorities attempted to harmonise their slightly differing boat standards. BW and the Environment Agency (in succession to the NRA) now work to the same standards, although their programmes for introducing them vary slightly. The Broads Authority decided to have its own standards which are 95% the same as BW/EA's and are voluntary until April 2000. Boats which satisfy the

BW/EA standards will be accepted by the BA but if you want to use your boat exclusively on the Broads, contact the Broads Authority on 01603 610734.

The European Directive's technical requirements are similar to those of the UK Boat Safety Standards. The major differences are additional sections on hull construction and stability. It places heavy responsibilities on professional boat builders to be able to demonstrate that their products comply with the Directive. While some builders of coastal craft will have to submit them to external examination, inland waterways builders will be able to 'self-certify' their products. They will also be required to keep documentation proving that their boats conform for at least ten years after production and provide the customer with a comprehensive manual showing how the boat and its systems are designed.

Owners of fully fitted boats will know that their boats con-

New style builder's plate complete with the CE mark and ready to have the other necessary information stamped on

form to the RCD by the 'CE' mark it has to display and by the builder's Declaration of Conformity in the boat's manual. The Declaration enables the owner to license the boat for the first four years after which it will have to be surveyed and obtain a Boat Safety Certificate.

One phrase in the RCD is particularly relevant to DIY narrowboat fitters: "Craft built for own use shall be excluded from the scope of the Directive, provided they are not subsequently placed on the Community market for a period of five years". This means that, if an owner wants or needs to sell the completed boat within five years, he would have to produce a technical and owners manual and a declaration of conformity in the same way that a professional boat builder would. Problems arise because, before you can determine when the five year period has finished, you need to know when it started and, to date, there has been no agreement on this point. It may be that the rule is unenforceable but, until it is tested in the courts, no-one can be certain.

In any case, all the major parts that are professionally supplied to a DIY fitter (the shell, for instance), will have to conform to the RCD, and be marked and declared as such by their suppliers.

Other legislation

BS 5482 PART 3 Edition 2

Gas – not locks, weirs or 230-volt electric systems – is probably the most common cause of the few fatal accidents that occur in narrowboats. The type of liquefied petroleum gas (LPG) used in narrowboats is propane, which freezes at a lower temperature than butane, making it more suitable for winter cruising. It is heavier than air and so sinks to the floor, or the bilges, if it leaks out. This is not such a problem in a caravan which can have low level drains but, for obvious reasons, this solution is not possible in a narrowboat.

BW Standards say briefly that gas installations shall comply with BS 5482 'Domestic Butane and Propane Installations, Part 3: Boats'. That simple reference is to a British Standard that is at least as long, and considerably more complicated, than the Boat Safety Standards themselves. The BS has two major ramifications, one that you can tackle readily, the other that – in *WW*'s view – you should not.

Ventilation

Gas can cause explosions and fire; but it is just as likely to kill by carbon monoxide poisoning. Competent installation and maintenance is important in reducing the risk of poisoning. So is ventilation – which the DIY builder can organise him/herself. BS 5482 Part 3 sets out exact requirements for fixed cabin ventilation – that is, in addition to opening windows and adjustable vents. It is presented as a formula, from which the following examples are obtained:

Appliance	Approx.	Min ventilation input (kW) needed – sq in Unflued	Flued
Two burner cooker & grill	7.5	22.5	n/a
Two burner cooker, grill & oven	8.4	28.7	n/a
Four burner cooker grill & oven	15	51	n/a
ALDE central heating boiler	5.2	n/a	3.5

To calculate the needs of an appliance not listed, multiply the input rating in kW by 3.4 if it is unflued, or by 0.7 if flued, to give the size requirement in square inches. Surveyors may also require allowance to be made for solid fuel stoves – as flued appliances. The approximate ratings of Squirrel and Tor Gem, for example, are 4kW and 2.5kW. In addition an allowance of 1 sq in should be made for each crew member. So a typical calculation for total fixed ventilation need would be:

Galley/saloon:

Vanette cooker	51sq in
Tor Gem stove	1.75sq in
Six seated crew, although only two sleep here	6sq in
Total	58.75sq in

Aft cabin:

Two berths	2sq in

Centre cabin:

Two berths	2sq in

In fact, each compartment must have a minimum of 6.5sq in fixed ventilation, so the aft cabin and centre cabin should each be provided with 6.5sq in.

The ventilation should be divided equally between low and high level. Low level ventilation (30sq in) for the open-plan galley/saloon would normally be provided by 8in x 2in vents at each end of the compartment. No other compartment needs more air than this so, to ensure an adequate through supply to both ends of the galley/saloon, vents or air gaps of that size have to be provided in intermediate and outside bulkheads – all as low down as is practicable.

Three 4in diameter fixed ventilators would be sufficient to provide cabin top ventilation in the galley/saloon – the areas of flues have to be additional. Each of the other cabins would need a 3.25sq in cabin top vent in addition to the 8in x 2in through vent at low level. If a centre cabin is fully enclosed (ie, off a side passage), a 3.25sq in low level vent is needed into the corridor.

Many owners are horrified by the size of low level ventilators that BS 5482 Part 3 demands; and not a few surveyors show discretion when calculating ventilation needs. If you are concerned about draughtiness it may be better to introduce air through ducts, perhaps diffused through several grills along the length of the hull side.

Fixed cabin-top ventilators should be just that – not capable of being closed. This is particularly relevant to flue cowls which must also be sturdy enough to resist crushing by impact. Restricted flue outlets can impede complete gas combustion – causing carbon monoxide to enter the cabin – and quite small quantities of that odourless gas can be fatal.

Gas fitting – the law

It is commonly believed that it is illegal for amateur boat fitters to install gas systems in their own boats unless they are CORGI registered. At the time of writing (August 1998), CORGI, the Council for Registered Gas Installers, and BMIF confirm that this is not strictly correct. The Gas

Safety Regulations 1994 only cover hire boats at present, although they may be extended to private boats shortly. So, on the face of it, anyone can install a gas system on a boat provided it is not then used for hire – but read on, it's not quite that simple.

Installing the system in your own boat may not be illegal but, if you get it wrong, it could be a different story. Part B of the Regulation states that 'No person shall carry out work in relation to a gas fitting or gas storage vessel unless he is competent to do so'. Guidance notes in the Approved Code of Practice (ACoP) state that 'Anyone who works on gas fittings must be competent, including DIY installers and those performing favours for friends and relatives'. Competence is defined as belonging to a class of persons approved by the Health & Safety Executive (HSE) and, at the present time, the only body with this approval is CORGI. Suppose, heaven forbid, your system blows up and you could not prove your competence; The HSE is likely to prosecute relentlessly anyone whom they believe might have caused such an incident whether directly or by error of omission. If it proves that the person is not 'competent' in the accepted sense, he could be in serious trouble and possibly face a prison sentence.

There is a lot more to being competent than the ability to make a pipe joint. You should also know how to size the pipework and cylinders, how to select the correct regulator, how to install a flue, how to carry out a soundness test and recognise if the flame patterns are correct to name but a few. You could, of course, do the work yourself and then get it checked by a CORGI registered installer. The moment he puts a spanner on any part of it, he is responsible for the whole system, but don't expect that acceptance of such responsibility will come cheap.

Seen from this point of view, DIY gas fitting loses much of its appeal and paying a CORGI fitter to install the whole system starts to look like a good investment. If you do take this route, make sure that the installer has been accredited to do work on 'LPG – Boats' as someone who only installs natural gas fittings in homes will not have the required expertise. This should be shown on the reverse of his identity card. If you are still determined to do it yourself, check with CORGI or BMIF first to make sure that the law has not been amended by the time you start.

Design considerations

The major change introduced in Edition 2 of BS 5482 Pt 3 is that, with the exception of the cooker, all gas appliances must have a balanced flue. To date, the only pieces of equipment which meet this requirement are the Alde gas boiler and two warm air space heaters. If you are refurbishing an existing boat, you are allowed to maintain equipment which does not comply but, as soon as it gives up the ghost completely, it cannot be replaced like for like. This means that commonly used items like gas fridges and instantaneous water heaters can no longer be installed on new boats, or replaced on existing ones, unless the manufacturer produces an approved balanced flue.

BS 5482 Part 3 requires gas bottles to be stored so that leakage from them cannot enter the hull. Your shell builder should build a suitable sealed locker, with large overboard

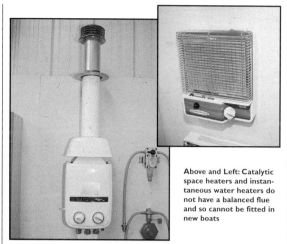

Above and Left: Catalytic space heaters and instantaneous water heaters do not have a balanced flue and so cannot be fitted in new boats

drain holes, into the steel work. If in doubt, check that the locker is large enough (two 13kg propane or 15kg butane bottles is average) and that the locker base will be above the waterline when the boat is complete with its tanks and cupboards full.

Gas from the bottle is reduced to acceptable pressure by a regulator located inside the gas bottle locker. It is then carried to appliances through solid-drawn copper pipe which must be securely fixed and protected against chafing as it passes through bulkheads and conduits. Pipe joints must only be made with compression fittings – not solder, which is vulnerable to vibration and fire. Joints should, in any case, be closely supported on all sides.

Piping has to run as high as possible (usually not below the gunnel and definitely not in the bilge), not through engine rooms (unless sealed in conduit), or alongside wiring. Do not object if your gas fitter takes a pipe over, rather than under, a door – it is conventional practice. The entire system should be accessible for inspection – your BW–approved inspector may not accept assurances that hidden piping is joint-free.

Free-standing cookers are conventionally regarded as 'portable' and connected to the copper supply via approved BS 3212 flexible hose with a cut-off tap at the upstream end. In fact, it is good practice to fit individual cut-off taps to all appliances so that each can be safely isolated for maintenance. If the gas bottle locker is located conventionally in the bow, forward of a cockpit, the lid should be left unlocked all the time that the gas system is in use so that the main valves can be turned off quickly in an emergency.

Gas systems are vulnerable to pressure-drop in the same way that wiring is to voltage drop. The solution is the same – larger pipe. The variables that affect pressure are volume of gas required, distance to be carried, and the number of pipe bends. Pressure drop results in inefficient combustion (which your inspector will assess with a flame test at the appliance). An approved test point is also required in the piping at the furthest extremity from the gas bottles.

CHAPTER 3
DESIGNING THE SHELL

Styles
Anatomy of a shell
Plating specifications
Shell details

STYLES

In an industry that is over-populated, it is surprising that builders have not created more styles to separate themselves from the competition. Interiors have developed out of all recognition in the last fifteen years, shells barely at all. There are seven basic styles. In descending order of popularity they are:

Two original 'Joshers' with fine, doubled-curved bows which a few modern builders seek to replicate

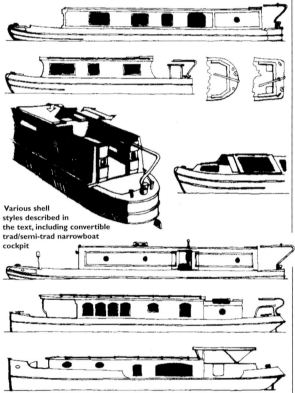
Various shell styles described in the text, including convertible trad/semi-trad narrowboat cockpit

handrails are solid along the cabin edge – and sometimes also referred to as cants. The minutiae of full traditional style are too many to list but the basic characteristics have been honed for over 150 years to produce a boat which is easy and comfortable to operate.

A double curved bow formed by strips of steel welded together where the rubbing strakes occur

The swim of this working boat tapers towards the base plate to allow more water to get to the propeller.

A few builders – often those also specialising in restoration – construct real replicas that are difficult to distinguish from the originals. This even extends to false rivets and double curved bow plating (a time-consuming shape to construct in steel). Advantages of trad-style are good utility storage, weather protection for the steerer's lower regions and the satisfaction of owning a good looking boat. The main disadvantage is that the steerer can be lonely.

Traditional style:
Broadly following the lines of working motorised narrowboats built in the forty years before WWII. Degree of authenticity varies widely – the most basic feature is a cabin that ends about 3ft 6in from the stern. Trad hulls should rise gracefully towards bow and stern. The aft cabin rises in a matching curve. Aft and forward decks are edged by low flat rails called cants. Originally made of timber to serve as a wearing surface and to stop you walking over the edge, they are now always in steel. Cabin top

Cruiser style:
Simpler and more functional, with sociably large but sometimes draughty aft deck (typically 7ft long). Likely to have higher hull sides for good cabin accommodation. Generally less popular than traditional style which affects re-sale value.

Semi-trad:

Looks like a trad-style boat from the side but aft cabin sides actually enclose a largish cockpit. The seats are often used as footrests by the crew who perch on the cabin side. This compromise has gained in popularity over the last decade. It is seldom developed to the obvious conclusion – with large (say 5ft x 4ft) sliding hatch over, into which is set a small hinged hatch. It could then be used in large cockpit mode or, when the weather inclems, as a snug trad.

Tug style:

A variation on trad that looks rather more purposeful but is definitely in the love-'em-or-hate-'em category. While ordinary working boats carried a 14ft cabin on a 72ft hull, a typical tug might have had 30ft cabin on 50ft hull – so, arguably, is easier to replicate in leisure boat form. Because they needed heavy displacement and large propellers for towing, tugs sat fairly deep, with sidedecks about 1ft to 1ft 6in above the waterline. This almost essential characteristic compromises accommodation in modern shallow draught versions. They sometimes compensate with improbably high cabins, above which the head of a short steerer can just peep. Replica tugs often feature a long forward deck instead of cockpit and portholes instead of windows which offer good security and privacy.

Centre cockpit:

Almost extinct variation on cruiser-style, which has a sliding roof (sometimes fabricated in separate port and starboard sections) over a midships saloon. Wheel steering position under windscreen looks out over a low forward cabin. Most have an alternative tiller aft for conventional narrowboat steering. Apart from all-weather steering comfort (particularly appreciated on rivers), the forward steering position also distances the helmsman from the engine's noise.

Inspection launch:

Canal owners did not rough it on working narrowboats to inspect their assets. Instead, they had narrow versions of river launches built with all creature comforts onboard, so replica inspection launches seem appropriate for leisure cruising. Most look beautiful, but if the underwater section is as authentic as the retroussé counter, stopping power on canals can be limited. Also, a line of arched windows might be an embarrassment (lack of privacy, an invitation to stone-throwing vandals). Inspection launches often have forward and aft steering positions – and a fixed roof over the forward cockpit.

Dutch barges:

One style of Dutch barge, the Luxemotor, has been re-proportioned to fit British canals. The Luxemotor looks like a miniaturised ship. Advantages include an all-weather steering position inside the wheel house, and the visual ability to carry a square section cabin – which increases the interior's airiness. Disadvantage: the wheel house has to be squeezed into a overall height of 6ft 6in without looking awkward. Some are built with fold-down wheel houses but the sketch shows one with a soft canopy – to make another point.

Folding canopies make a lot of sense for cruising this country's inland waterways. It may be considered wimpish to shelter from wind and rain, but long hours under the

Steel inland waterways shells for DIY fitting-out can be as small as 20ft ...

... or (particularly if you hanker a floating home under the French sun) as large as this 69ft x 13ft replica Luxemotor

sun now carry real risk from ultra-violet radiation. A soft top can be folded down more quickly (and compactly) than a wheel house for the occasional low bridge. Despite their usefulness, canopies have never been popular on narrowboats but they could suit the lines of a 'Dutch barge' quite well.

THE ANATOMY OF A SHELL

Your choice of shell is probably the most important decision you will make throughout the whole project as it is the only part that you cannot alter at a later date. Whatever you do to it, the quality of the shell will always have a direct bearing on the quality, and therefore the value, of finished boat. The following notes introduce you to considerations in selecting a shell builder and in checking his progress on your boat.

Length:

A narrowboat can be up to 72ft long, a few are as short as 20ft. 60ft allows you to traverse the Leeds & Liverpool Canal and still share locks but 57ft is a fashionable length for larger craft because it looks forward to the reopening of the Rochdale Canal, the spectacular Pennine Ring cruise it will make possible and several other north east waterways.

Beam:

Working narrowboats were 7ft wide; modern ones are 6ft10in to allow for bulging lock walls. If your shell builder is fairly inexperienced, don't take his assurance of 6ft 10in beam for granted – occasionally shells spread during construction and lengthening.

Overall height:

Height from base plate to cabin top is based on internal cabin headroom plus depth of bilge and linings thickness – typically 6ft 7in to 7ft 0in in total. It is also conditioned by maximum height above water (most narrowboats stand between 5ft 6in and 5ft 11in high), by the standard plates sizes that shell builders like to use without trimming, and by draught (the depth of hull below water).

Draught:

To accommodate the average shell height (say 6ft 9in), also allowing for a few inches of stern-down trim, the deepest part of the hull usually draws about 1ft 10in to 2ft in modern narrowboats. That dimension is happily about ideal for the 17in diameter propeller specified for the typical higher-revving diesel engine – it leaves reasonable clearance between blade tip and the steelwork above and

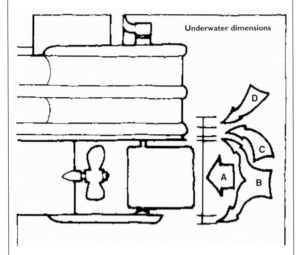

Underwater dimensions

below. In this context, 1ft 10in draught means a stern post of about 1ft 8in height (**A**) the other 2in allows for protrusion of skeg below the bottom plate, and for the counter to be slightly immersed (**B**). When underway the stern will sit deeper, increasing draught by another couple of inches (**C**). Like humans, boats tend to put on weight with age – so, if you specify a 1ft 8in stern post, your stern could well scrape a 2ft 2in underwater obstruction in ten years time (**D**).

Draught is a contentious matter with traditionalists, who are concerned that hulls of average or less draught tend to reduce the cruisability of canals. Working boats, which commonly drew 3ft or more, used to scour a definite channel. Modern narrowboats (suggest the traditionalists) promote a vaguer saucer-shaped section across which they tend to wander with increased likelihood of going aground. Traditionalists, not surprisingly, prefer old-fashioned slow-revving diesels which, even with the help of modern propeller technology, require static draughts in excess of 2ft 3in. They also suspect that, given half an excuse, British Waterways will not dredge canals as deep as required by statute. With care and practice, a boat with a 3ft draught can be steered to any part of the canal system.

A few boatbuilders offer an opposing argument: narrowboats should be no deeper than absolutely necessary – 1ft 5in is possible without compromising headroom and height above water. Heavy displacement hulls, they argue, are slow (particularly on rivers), unresponsive – and more likely to create an anti-social wash. Using artificial ballast, they go on, to pull a boat down in the water, is an offence against good design – especially in this energy-conscious era. Shallower draughts need less engine power, requiring smaller propellers – which will fit shallower stern posts.

Those observing the arguments from the middle ground will comment that low displacement hulls can be tender (prone to roll from side to side), and vulnerable to drift in side winds. And that a draught of 1ft 10in is about right.

Length of swim:

Swim (the part of the underwater hull that tapers from full width to the stem post forward, or to stern post aft) should be as long as practicable. Short, abrupt swims contribute to excessive wash and to poor handling. The aft swim is often a foot or two longer than the forward one. Narrowboats of 60ft or 70ft length can carry swims of 15ft length with advantage but a 40 footer could not, without compromising accommodation and, perhaps, stability. In

British Waterways has developed a design for low-wash bows as seen on this Alvechurch shell ...

practice, a 9ft or 10ft aft swim is average (but less than ideal) in middle market shells. The aft swim should curve gently from full section to a sharp-edged (as against flat-faced) stern post. In fact the builders of working boats in the thirties, and British Waterways' hull design consultants today both agree that if you can persuade your builder to make the aft swim S-shaped in plan, it will be even more efficient. The same design consultants suggest that the extreme bow shouldn't be a sharp stem post but a vertical cylinder of approximately 1ft 6in diameter. In tank tests, this shape, derived from the underwater bulb fitted to many ships, performed well in reducing wash from the

...The same boat has an 'S' shaped swim which is also claimed to reduce wash

bow. Alvechurch Boat Centres have several boats with this type of bow in their hire fleet. The shape caused considerable interest among narrowboaters when it was introduced but, until it is better proven, the conventional sharp bow is a safer bet.

Hull section:

The average main hull section is based on a standard 2m (6ft 6 1/2in) wide flat bottom plate. Hull side plates are joined to the bottom about 1/2in to 1in in from the edge, leaving a valuable flange to withstand wear. As they rise, the hull sides spread out to full boat width (minus the thickness of the rubbing strakes) at the top strake, before coming back in slightly at the side deck. This return above the strake is usually referred to as tumblehome. Hull sides and side decks are often folded (before they arrive at the shell builder) from a single plate. Folding hull sides for all but 16ft of the boat's length can limit the graceful flow of its lines – but in middle market craft it is almost universal.

Variations on this standard section include the Birmingham Canal Navigations style, where hull sides, quite vertical and flat, sit on a 6ft 10in wide bottom plate and side decks are welded on rather than folded-in. This provides extra internal width, at low level and more effective gunwale width – but risks wavy hull sides unless the builder is experienced. A few builders favour vee bottoms, reducing displacement and ballast, allowing easier access to shallow canal sides for mooring – and to the bottom plate for maintenance. The double chine hull, now rarely used for conventional narrowboats, offers some of the same benefits. Both tend to roll more than flat-bottomed craft.

Sidedeck height and width:

Although the overall height of shell averages, as noted above, about 6ft 10in, side-deck height varies according to stylistic preference. Higher sidedecks allow better accommodation (particularly when planning beds across the cabin as in a traditional boatmans cabin); lower sidedecks look better and permit deeper windows. Stepped sidedecks, which solve the accommodation/window depth conflict, are common on hire boats but not popular with private owners. The common width for sidedecks is 4in although 5in feels much safer. Anything less than 4in denies a safe foothold. If hulls do not lean in at the top, the dimension saved can be used to make sidedecks wider – or to increase cabin width.

Cabin section:

Excessively wide sidedecks and/or cabin sides that lean in too much make for claustrophobic interiors. Cabin sides that do not lean in enough look ungainly and are liable to catch bridges. An angle of 1 in 7 seems about average; as does a camber of 3in across the cabin top (flatter cabin tops are prone to waviness and to flexing when jumped on).

PLATING SPECIFICATIONS

Ask what the steel plate thickness of a narrowboat shell is and you will usually be told "10/6/4" – meaning a 10mm thick base plate, 6mm hull sides, 4mm superstructure. The thicker base plate is as much to provide built-in ballast as to combat corrosion (from which hull side plating at waterline level is more at risk). However, the thicker the bottom plate the better wear protection provided by its

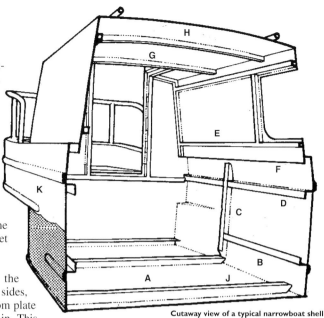

Cutaway view of a typical narrowboat shell

protruding flange. Some owners ask for even thicker bottoms – up to 25mm. Concrete ballast is less expensive than steel plate, so the ultra-thick plate's only real advantage would be in reducing the under floor space needed for ballast. In this way, the main cabin height might be reduced by a valuable 2in or so, if, for instance, a wheelhouse is to be accommodated over the aft cockpit without standing unworkably high. The bottom plate on vee-bottomed hulls is often thinner than 10mm. Smaller conventional shells may be as light as 6/5/3 (which was the norm for all narrowboats fifteen years ago); Springer's 20ft Water Bug, built to be trailable, had 3/3/3 plating.

Plating may be thicker than it used to be – but does it resist corrosion as effectively? Unless protected, modern shells may be thinned by pitting and scaling within five years; while seventy-year old working boats remain corrosion-free. These vintage craft were often built of iron – which is not feasible today – and some modern narrowboat shell builders do skimp on plate quality. The reputable ones specify 43A plate, described as general shipbuilding steel and which conforms to British Standard 4360. This grade provides an optimum balance between wear and corrosion resistance at an affordable price. Should you doubt your builder's claim that he uses 43A plate, you can ask for it to be supplied with certificate from the rolling mill.

FRAMING

Internal frames serve to strengthen the hull, mainly against local impact, and to locate interior linings. Standard sections, as rolled by the mill, are used invariably. Typical abbreviations in quotations are: RSA (L-section steel angle), RSC (C-section channel) and RHS (square tube). Typical provisions are:

Bottom:

Transverse L-section frames spaced at approximately 2ft centres and standing 3in to 5in high (2in, as specified by many builders ten years ago, is too low). The frames, built up by timber noggins if necessary, must be deep enough to allow a decent air gap between under-floor ballast and the floor itself (A). A problem with floor frame centres is that if they are far enough apart to accommodate unbroken 2ft concrete slab ballast without a struggle, they won't coincide with standard 8ft x 4ft ply floor panels. A good solution is to set three frames at 2ft 1in centres and the fourth at 1ft 9in. Longitudinals (keelsons) are sometimes used. They appear to be a leftover from working boat construction, with little function in modern narrowboats with lightish engines. However, they do have a structural function in wide-beam boats.

Hull sides:
Two longitudinal L-section frames (stringers) 2in to 2 $1/2$in wide (**B**) with similar verticals (knees) at 4ft to 8ft centres (**C**). Some builders will pre-drill hull framing which saves hours when you come to fixing noggins for the lining. (**D**)

Cabin sides:
Longitudinal 1in to 1 $1/4$in angle, square tube (or occasionally flat bar) sections clearing the top and bottoms of window apertures by about 1in (**E**). Similar verticals around all windows and door frames usually with the same clearance. If the cabin side plate is produced an inch or so below the side deck, the resulting down-stand is useful for fixing linings and also creating an under-deck service duct (**F**). Some builders prefer to use thicker steel for the cabin sides and reduce the internal framing to a minimum so that weld marks do not mar the outside appearance but this can make the fixing of cabin linings more difficult.

Cabin Top:
Transverse 1in to 1 $1/4$in square tube at 1ft 6in to 2ft centres (**G**). Without a decent camber (about 3in) across the deckhead these will not be sufficient to prevent the roof from flexing underfoot (**H**). Some builders offer C-section frames clenched round timber noggins ready to receive lining attachments.
All framing is stitched rather than continuously welded to minimise heat distortion of the plating. Where frames intersect, the joint should be cut away to avoid building in stresses and to prevent water traps (**J**).

Rubbing strakes:
(**K**) do just that; they provide little hull reinforcement. Most are continuously welded along their top edges and stitched along the bottoms. However, those that descend below the waterline will create corrosion traps if not continuously welded on top and bottom edges. Many builders now continuously weld both. Traditional-style boats often have the top rubbing strake built-up round the bow (called a 'raised guard' or 'flare') . This improves the bow's appearance – but the raised section should be faired on its underside to avoid risk of hanging-up. Many builders use solid bar for the stem post (typically 2in wide) although a hollow C-section with a round capping is usually adequate for medium displacement boats.

Your shell supplier's workshop is not the best place to judge his product. The boats there will be seen from the wrong angle – the eye may pick up hull blemishes that will not be noticed afloat and miss waviness in the superstructure that a glossy livery will emphasise. At that early stage, those flaws are probably masked by grinding marks, matt primer or dust. Try to see fully painted examples of the builder's shell afloat.

Some builders build the superstructure with single lengths of plate, to avoid risk of distortion at welded joints; a few follow marine practice by covering the hidden sides of superstructure joints with butt straps to resist welding stresses. Hull seams of all shells – pricey or cheap – should be welded on both sides below the waterline. If the builder cannot turn the bottom plate over to do this, he may grind the joint out into a vee and build weld up to the plate's thickness from the inside. Above the top rubbing strake, single-side welding is preferable to avoid distortion. Few hulls leak below the waterline; the builder is more likely to slip up with complicated details – like tanks, decorative cants, etc.

If the shell built for you turns out to be less than perfect, bear in mind that that is how the average lower to middle-market narrowboat shell is. It comes from a cottage industry that works cheap because its customers are generally more concerned with price than blemishes. Before you sue, compare the shell with others from similarly priced builders. The secondhand market may be put off by unattractive styling, but not by moderately wavy plating. This argument does not, of course, apply if you have paid above the odds for your shell. A higher price should get you straighter plating, crisper detailing and cleaner welds. Real quality shows in the parts where you are not expected to look – like under decks.

INCLUDED IN THE SHELL

Most shells include the following: rudder, tiller bar, one forward mooring cleat, two mooring cleats aft (or cylindrical dollies), eyes for attaching bow, stern and side fenders, gas bottle locker & lid, self-draining forward cockpit, self-draining aft deck (or in a cruiser-style boat, self-draining cockpit bearers), integral fuel tank (with filler, vent, supply, return and drain fittings), weed hatch, engine beds, skin cooling tank (if a water-cooled engine is to be fitted), cabin-top handrails.

There are good reasons for specifying as many external details in steel as possible. It makes full and honest use of the fabricator's skill, and of the material, which is versatile and durable. By contrast, wooden parts on an otherwise all-steel shell look ephemeral – and really will not last as long. Other items that can be of steel are: door & hatch skins, taffrail, cockpit seat/lockers, cratch-frame, bridge guards, cabin top midships mooring ring, pigeon box, cabin-top vents, plank/pole/boathook rack, window security shutters, aft fender stud, engine silencer, cooling header tank, ventilation ducts, internal bulkheads (as between engine room and main cabin), bulkhead frames, hearth for solid fuel stove, shower tray sump.

Three items sometimes built into the shell are usually better in another material. Integral steel water tanks, with access hatch in the forward cockpit floor, have been common – but are vulnerable to pollution through an imperfect hatch seal; integral WC holding tanks are liable to corrosion; and large engine access hatches are dangerous if dropped on hand or foot – a gas strut is one solution but chequer plate aluminium is a maintenance-free alternative.

SHELL DETAILS

Rudder:

Almost all builders use an industrial-type top bearing – a crude rattle fit is no longer acceptable. Sophisticated rudder design seems to be one sign of a thoughtful builder. Traditional-style rudder posts are not vertical but rake back from bottom to top to encourage a self-centring action. Harborough Marine, through hire experience, has a quick access rudder, in case it becomes bent or unshipped from bottom bearing. Mick Sivewright has experimented with a cylindrical rudder for better steering astern.

Weed hatch:

Almost all weed hatches have a quick release clamp. The lift-off plate should be fitted with a seal and have an extension plate that fairs flush with the bottom when the hatch

is closed. Access to the weed hatch in traditional-style boats is often difficult. Many now offer a separate lid set into the aft deck; South West Durham Steelcraft refined that idea by extending the lid to lip under the cabin doors. This links with engine covers inside to provide exceptional access but ensures immediate security when the lid is trapped shut by the doors.

This detail provides exceptional access to engine and weed hatch in a traditional style boat, without prejudicing security

Handrails:

Traditional-style handrails usually lack a lip for positive grip **(A)**. Welding $1/_4$in square bar along the inside top edge improves grip immensely **(B)**. There are good historical precedences for raised handrails which provide a really good grip and make an extra attachment point for fender or mooring lines. To be authentic, they too,

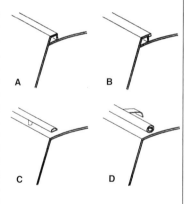

Handrail details – Lip on trad rail provides positive grip; the raised D-section rail has a traditional precedent; cranked stanchions prevent boat pole from rolling against rail.

should run along cabin edge and should be of D section bar **(C)**. You may be denied a finger hold by a boat pole resting against a conventional raised handrail – cranked stanchions make effective spacers to stop this **(D)**.

Pigeon boxes:

Look decorative and make useful cabin ventilators – better over galley than bedroom because they tend to drip condensation.

Security shutters:

Some owners like the idea of recessed cabin sides to reproduce the timber panelling of working boats. These recesses could be made to serve a purpose if they house shutters that slide over cabin windows. In the same way panelled timber forward cabin doors are popular but vulnerable to weather and intruders – they could be installed to open inwards while steel security ones open outwards.

Integrated steel shutters for windows and door

Ventilation ducts:

Although they have been specified by British Waterways Boat Standards for over a decade, low level ventilators are still being fitted as an afterthought – too high up, where they fail to scavenge the floor but cause

An integral low level ventilation duct – more efficient and less draughty than door-mounted vents

draughts. Vents in the rear bulkheads of full-length traditional boats can allow water to enter when descending in a leaky lock. Vent ducts, as incorporated by David Piper, can direct air from cockpit or cabin top to the right height, entering the cabin through several diffused slots. They can also scavenge the under floor space, to the bottom plate's long-term benefit.

BUILDING YOUR OWN SHELL

A word of advice on building your own shell. Don't. A few readers of the original *Narrowboat Builder's Book* complained that no guidance was offered on DIY shell construction. That was because it is more taxing and much more likely to

This narrowboat was built from drawings offered by M&TBS to DIY Shell Builders

go wrong than the fitting-out process. In any case, it really is not worth the trouble. The general level of narrowboat shell prices has always been restrained by a perennial minority of fabricators who seem prepared to work for a pittance. They continue to enter the industry because narrowboat shells are relatively simple to build. If they can do it, why can't you? Well they already have skills in steel fabrication and most of them built three or four shells before they arrived at a marketable product. If you are determined to build your own, only one company (to our knowledge) sells engineering drawings. However, it has been offering that service for some years and its design is in conventional middle-market style (see appendix 5 for details).

CHAPTER 4
BUILDING THE SHELL

Choosing a builder
The contract
Construction stage
Basic hull protection
Anodes
Windows
What's in a name?

CHOOSING A BUILDER

There are many ways of choosing a builder depending on the relative importance you place on those three old favourites – time, cost and quality. The text book method would be to decide exactly what you want, taking into account such points as plate thickness, welding quality, production method and, less tangibly, style. You then seek out as many builders as you can and decide whether you think they are capable of producing what you are looking for. You should also decide whether you think you can work with them on a personal level because a considerable amount of liaison will be required as the job proceeds.

Location
Another consideration which should be added at this stage is location. Unless there is an very good reason for doing so, you would probably be well advised not to choose a builder who is a long way by canal from where you intend to keep the boat. Boatbuilding is a complicated business and, to an extent, every boat produced is a prototype. It is therefore quite likely that the builder will need to make some adjustment or do some remedial work. Most are very happy to do this but, if it means the boat has to be returned to the yard, a long round trip could knock a big hole in your fitting-out schedule. Choosing a local builder will enable you to keep close tabs on the construction stage to answer queries, and give early warning of possible financial troubles. You should ensure that the delivery time being offered is acceptable to you – remembering to add on a couple of months or so to allow for normal builder's optimism.

When you have honed down your list, you send them all your detailed requirements, preferably in the form of drawings and a specification, ensuring that all builders receive the same information. You then sit back and wait for the 'tenders' to arrive and then choose the one offering the lowest price.

The real world
In practice it is seldom that simple. Most builders will try to convince you that your specification, however painstakingly arrived at, is a load of rubbish simply because it would mean them doing something different from what

they have always done. This is a problem which will confront you at all stages. Everyone in the boating business has developed their own ways of doing things which are often diametrically opposed to what others, apparently with equal success, have been doing for years. The only thing you can do is to listen to all sides and then make up your own mind based on common sense and your own requirements. So, when the tenders arrive, you will probably find that some of your stipulations have been ignored in favour of the normal practice of the yard. Some builders will point these out; the less scrupulous ones won't.

Your choice
Even if you avoid all these pitfalls you may well find that the price from the builder you always had a sneaking preference for is not the lowest. In this instance my advice

Some companies built their shells under cover in large sheds

would be, provided the difference is not astronomical, go for the one you want. If in doubt, try working out the difference as a percentage of the likely final cost of the boat and you will see that it is a small price to pay to avoid that nagging feeling that you haven't really got what you wanted. However, this should not be used as an excuse for rejecting the lowest priced builder because you never did like his work. If this is the case, you should not have approached him in the first place and wasted his time.

Our choice
In our own case, we decided that we wanted a well-respected builder who could build a solid, traditional boat that was good to handle and pleasing to the eye. To me, one important factor in this was that the lift or sheer on the

Stern view of *Rome* in Allens' yard shows gradual hull sheer from engine room door

back of the hull should start to rise gracefully from round about the engine room doors – not, as so often seen, from about a foot in front of the rear bulkhead. As noted in Chapter 2, the reason for this latter affliction is that many builders use folded plate to produce their hull sides. Since the folds are made in parallel straight lines it means that the lift has to be achieved, more expensively, by welding the vertical hull side to the horizontal gunwale and covering the join with a 'D' section guard. The longer the folded part and the shorter the welded part, the cheaper the boat – simple. Although one or two of the 'newer' builders are starting to improve their rear hull lines a number of long established yards, mostly around the Black Country, have been welding their hull sides to the gunwales along their whole length for years, so that the position of the start of the rise makes no difference to them. Consequently they have perfected the line it should take.

First call

We decided on the strength of this, and the fact that no-one we spoke to had a bad word to say about their boats, to go to Les Allen & Sons for our first estimate. Finding the yard tucked round the back of a transport firm took us the best part of an hour. We could see it from the towpath opposite but, short of swimming across the canal, we could not see how to get to it. When we eventually worked out the puzzle we almost felt that we had to order a boat to make all the effort worthwhile! Incidentally, if you are tempted to try this for yourself, save yourself the effort – Bob and John Allen retired in April 1997 and the firm is no more.

We did not place an order immediately but went away to 'think about it' which in my case meant phoning up a few comparable (not easy) yards to see what they could offer to make sure I wasn't being taken for a cruise. As expected I could have got a slightly cheaper boat – if I was prepared to wait a bit longer. We had decided by this time that we quite fancied the idea of owning an Allen boat and so went back to confirm our order, only to find that we had lost one place in the queue in the meantime – he who hesitates . . .

The contract

How formally the placing of the order is tied up depends very much on the builder. Some draw up a short contract recording the points agreed – price to be paid, 'Terms of Business' or timing of instalments, the planned start and finish dates plus a few disclaimers. The British Marine Industries Federation (BMIF) offers a well-established form of contract for use by its members. It suggests stages when interim payments should be made and establishes the buyers' ownership of all work paid for – a vital clause should the builders' business collapse during the contract and/or his assets be seized by a third party. It touches on the possibility of penalty payments for late delivery – but don't be surprised if few shell builders take kindly to that idea, late delivery is virtually an established practice in the narrowboat industry.

The BMIF contract has become more common with the establishment of the Canal Boatbuilders Association (CBA) – the representative body for narrowboat builders. The CBA was set up under the aegis of BMIF, the organisation behind almost every aspect of Britain's boat trade. While membership of CBA does not guarantee angelic conduct by the builder, it gives both parties access to arbitration procedures should they fall into dispute.

There is, of course, nothing to stop you producing your own contract if the builder doesn't come up with one – provided you can get him to sign it. We paid a modest deposit with the order for which we eventually received a receipt, and were given a verbal estimate of start and finish dates. While I am wary of contracts drawn up by people with no legal training I have to concede that there is an advantage – even if only a moral one – in having a piece of paper to wave under the builder's nose when the proposed finishing date is reached without any sign of a start being made. It can also prevent confusion about the amount and timing of stage payments once the project is under way.

CONSTRUCTION STAGE

At last the great day arrived and work started on welding up the base plate for the new boat. We had already given the builder a drawing showing the basic dimensions plus positions of doors and portholes. We visited the yard every Saturday morning to see what progress had been made and to answer any queries that had cropped up. Since the yard

Rome's shell during construction, with jigs in place to ensure squareness

was only slightly off my usual route to work I was able to drop in at short notice to discuss anything which could not wait. Having decided to go to a long-established yard, my basic approach was to tell them what I was looking for and leave the method of achieving it to them.

Rome's swim leans in as it tapers. To achieve this, an extra fillet of steel has been added

The swim

One slightly modified feature which I was happy to incorporate was the sloping swim section. I have already mentioned how the length and curve of the swim plates improve the handling of the boat and smooth its passage through the water. This can be further improved by lifting the sides of the hull which form the swim and welding in a triangular piece between them and the base plate to give a sloping cross section. The effect of this is to reduce the mass of the boat below the waterline which gets more water to the propeller and so improves pulling away and stopping.

Bow shape

A more cosmetic modification was to introduce a concave curve into the bow plates as they meet the stem post which

Although bow plates are not curved in two dimensions (a costly process), they blend into stem post for similar effect

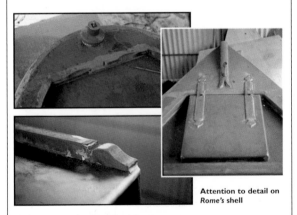

Attention to detail on Rome's shell

gives an appearance as near to the revered Josher bow as you can get without going to the expense of forming it in horizontal strips welded together.

Insulation

As the construction advanced, more options had to be assessed. A lot of Allen's shell buyers have the inside insulated with polyurethane foam, sprayed on by specialists. The advantage of this is that, apart from being an extremely good insulator, the foam bonds to the inside surface of the shell which deadens any vibrations from the engine. It

Sprayed-on foam ready to be trimmed back

also forms a near perfect moisture vapour barrier which reduces the possibility of condensation forming on the inside of the steel.

So much for the advantages. Set against these is the cost which for a boat of our length would have been about £650 compared with about £200 for the conventional preformed insulation. Another drawback is that the foam is difficult to apply evenly and has to be trimmed back with a bread knife or similar to produce a level finish. Depending on how carefully the spraying is done, this process can take days to complete and is extremely arduous work. Taking all this in to account I decided against and spent the money saved on the outside of the shell instead.

Basic hull protection

This important subject required us to make three decisions – the method to be used for preparing the shell prior to painting, the type of paint to be used on the hull and whether or not to invest in anodes.

Preparing the steel

Most shell builders still finish off the shell using an angle grinder which gives a very clean appearance but seldom removes all the mill scale, a thin, bluish coating produced when the steel is made at the steel mill. An increasing

Rome being grit blasted at the Oldbury yard of **BCN** builder **Les Allen & Sons** – a messy job but, in the author's view, well worth while

number of builders are now offering grit blasting as an optional extra. For maximum effect this very messy process should only be done after the shell has started to rust. The steel is left perfectly clean and any paint system laid on top of it does not run the risk of coming off when the mill scale eventually decides that the time is right to jump ship.

The surface is so clean that any dampness in the atmosphere will cause a rust film to develop in an amazingly short time. For this reason it is imperative that the grit blasting is done on a fairly dry day and that the surface is primed immediately afterwards. Prices vary between £500 and £1000 depending on the length of boat and how much the builder still likes you by this stage but it is generally reckoned to be worth doing.

Allens did not grit blast all their shells but Bob recommended it in my case, "knowing what yo'm like" (what could he mean?). We were finally convinced when we saw a six year old grit blasted Allen boat out of the water and showing no signs of pitting. In total contrast to our last cruise on *George,* the construction period was fine and dry. This meant that we had to wait for the shell to start rusting and loosening the mill scale before grit blasting could begin. The weather was so fine that, in the end, Bob had to resort to dilute acid to start the process off. Grit blasting is a messy business and I suspect that we were not popular with the Allen's moorers who were advised not to visit their boats on the appointed day. However, when the dust settled – on about a square mile to the west of Oldbury – I reckoned it was time and money well spent.

Although I opted to have the shell of *Rome* grit blasted from new to provide a better key for the paint scheme, it is sometimes necessary to move the boat to a yard that is set up for blasting. If you are only concerned about blasting the hull, you could leave the job until two or three years after the boat has been completed, when it will need to be slipped for hull painting. Hull corrosion during that time for most 10/6/4 shells is unlikely to be significant. A few builders will offer to build with plate that has been blasted and primed immediately after the rolling process.

Painting it

The majority of hulls are painted with what are known generically, if somewhat confusingly, as bituminous paints. These have the advantage of being fairly easy to apply and touch up, relatively cheap and tend not to chip off as easily as enamel type paints.

There are several types of this paint which may look similar but which have widely varying properties. First are the true bitumen paints such as Sealex. This is quite thick, giving a high build but the steel needs to be primed with a bitumen primer. Its great drawback as far as the canals are concerned is that it dissolves fairly readily in diesel oil.

Comastic vinyl-based bitumen paint and (right) less expensive (but less durable) version

Next are the coal tar types of which Bitumastic Standard Black Solution (SBS) is probably the best known. These are in fact based not on bitumen but on coal tar pitch which is more resistant to diesel oil. The solvent used is more aggressive which means that the paint will adhere to the steel without a primer. Advantages include cheapness and a fairly forgiving nature when it comes to surface preparation. Disadvantages are a thin consistency resulting in a low build and a tendency to succumb quite quickly to the chemical soup which most of us cruise about in.

The current narrowboat industry standard is vinyl modified pitch, typically Comastic, which is more expensive but likely to last longer. It is thicker than SBS so that fewer applications are required to build up a reasonably thick coating. The drawback is the manufacturer's recommendation that the hull should be grit blasted before initial coating as should any patches before recoating during maintenance.

Finally there are the Epoxy pitches, supplied in two tins which are mixed just before they are applied. Because of their more complex composition it is more important than ever to follow the manufacturer's instructions. They also require the steel to be grit blasted but should outlast the other types and, although generally the most expensive, offer good value for money by stretching docking intervals. My advice is to go for the best finish you can afford, it's usually worth it in the long run.

The sight that may confront you at the first dry docking if the hull is not properly protected

Incidentally, none of the paints mentioned above are suitable for painting the insides of water tanks. Intex and Bituros are specially formulated for the job and are manufactured by Wailes Dove. Be very careful to ensure that any paint used in water tanks is suitable or you will have, at the very least, a most unpleasant tasting cuppa.

Whether or not you have any choice about what type of hull paint is used, you should certainly find out, and make a note of, what has been applied. The information is important when you have to repaint the hull. The only way to be sure that you will not have problems of incompatibility is to use the same type of paint, and if you want to be doubly sure, the same make as well. This is particularly important in the case of epoxy pitch paint.

You may decide that the original paint has not lasted very well and want to use something better. Unfortunately it is no use simply going over what remains of the old coating with something from higher up the scale; all trace of the previous paint must be removed otherwise the new will be rejected by the old. The only realistic way to do this is to have the hull grit blasted.

Anodes

Anodes fitted below the waterline at front and rear (and sometimes in recesses at the mid point) are intended to reverse the process of electrolytic action which causes steel to rust. They 'sacrifice' themselves for the good of the hull and therefore, provided they are correctly fixed and are working properly, will need to be replaced about every four years depending on how corrosive your partic-

The pitting on this anode shows that it is doing its job

ular canal water is. When first introduced on the inland waterways they were made of zinc which, although effective in sea water, was too inert for canals. This initially gave anodes a bad name but a switch to magnesium gave the required electrolytic differential and they are now almost universally recommended.

The process by which anodes work is like that in a battery. When two different conductors are immersed in a liquid (the electrolyte), one (the anode) slowly loses particles of itself to the other (the cathode). The cathode in your boat's case can be other parts of the hull (all steel is not exactly of the same composition) or adjacent metals. A set pecking order determines which is cathode and which anode, so if you can introduce a suitable metal that will act as an anode and turn the previously vulnerable parts of your hull into a cathode, corrosion of the hull should all but cease. The battery analogy does not mean that you can recharge boat batteries with the minute current generated between anodes and hull but, if you were to follow car practice and use the hull as a conductor for the boat's electric system, electrolytic corrosion would be likely to be aggravated.

Sacrificial anodes are attached to the hull as lumps of unpainted metal (they must never be painted). They are moulded on a steel strap which is welded or bolted (but must make good electrical contact) to the hull. Typical life of an anode is four years. If they don't erode, the hull is either very well protected by paint or they aren't working. As the surface area is reduced, so is the anode's effectiveness. Manufacturer M G Duff recommends the following sizes:

Wetted Surface Area	Anodes
Up to 300 sq ft (up to 30ft x 2ft draught narrowboat)	4 @ $3\frac{1}{2}$ lb
300 to 450 sq ft (up to 50ft x 2ft)	4 @ 7lb
450 to 550 sq ft (up to 62ft x 2ft)	4 @ 10lb or 6 @ 7lb
Over 550 sq ft, add for every additional 200 sq ft	2 @ 7lb

Anodes are normally mounted on the hull side plates, two on the bow taper, two on the stern. Some builders protect the forward ones with a steel shield to deflect heavy impact by logs, etc. They should be well immersed – an empty water tank can raise high-mounted forward anodes above water. If six anodes are needed the extra two should be midships – either shielded or in fabricated recesses.

BSS requirements

When *Rome* was built, the British Waterways' Boat Standards were looming so we obviously wanted to make sure that all aspects of the shell would comply. The area where the effect was felt most was the bow. The designed draught of about 2ft 2in and our keenness to have the boat trimmed fairly level meant that the front deck was considerably higher than we anticipated in order to keep the drain outlets 250mm above water level. It was so high that we had to abandon our thoughts of having seats along either side – they would have been higher than the side decks.

A less noticeable effect was felt in the gas locker where the floor was about two inches below water level. This is to be avoided of possible but is acceptable provided the gas bottles stand on a platform above water level. The builder did not provide drain holes, reasoning that they were better put in after the final trim had been determined. This also gave me the opportunity to protect the inside of the locker with a good coat of rust resisting paint before holes were drilled and the waters advanced.

Other less obvious items like a separate anchor fixing point were included and, with the diesel filler in the side deck and the vent coming through the roof, at least there would be no doubt about it being 100mm above the filler.

Water tank

Just a few shell builders still offer an integral water tank under the forward cockpit deck (C), with inspection hatch in the deck itself. The hatch has no upstand to deter dirty water from creeping through but depends on the limited efficiency of a gasket or seal. Eventual removal of the hatch often reveals a complete wildlife habitat inside.

Other builders use the bow locker (B) as an integral water tank. As the deck lid has a flange, the tank stays cleaner, and (most importantly) it can be eye-balled for contamination at every fill. The flange still needs a gasket to prevent spray from lock gates from forcing its way in. A less exposed variation is an integral tank (A) across the forward end of the cockpit, raised high enough to form a seat – but again with flanged lid. Mild steel tanks need periodic repainting with the special water tank paint mentioned previously.

Most narrowboats use tanks of polypropylene, stainless steel or galvanised steel, slid under the forward cockpit. Their interiors should be maintenance-free, so are rarely inspected (regular treatment with Milton or sterilising tablets keeps them serviceable). Inflatable tanks, used in smaller craft, are not likely to provide enough capacity for the average narrowboat's needs – typically 150 gallons – although flexible liners can be used to rehabilitate integral tanks. As the difference between full and empty in such a tank is well over half a ton, you may find the effect on bow trim irritating. Tanks can be fitted further aft, under a double bed, where 6ft 3in x 2ft x 1ft 6in fitted along the boat's centre line provides 120 gallons capacity, leaves space alongside for the WC's holding tank to project through from the toilet compartment – and creates a utility locker under the cockpit.

Portholes

One of the few things I don't enjoy about boat fitting is drilling and cutting through steel. I was therefore very pleased to get the yard to fit the portholes and mushroom vents. The spacing of the portholes had been determined at the planning stage and, when we arrived one day to find that the holes had been cut, we reckoned we had got it about right. The portholes themselves are heavy brass castings with a rebate on the inside back edge into which the glass sits. The hole in the cabin side is the same diameter as the inside diameter of the porthole so that the glass is held between the two, bedded in mastic. It is important not to fix the brass surround with nuts and bolts as the nuts would eventually be hidden by the linings and it would be impossible to replace the glass in the event of a breakage. The normal practice is to screw through to 18mm plywood or timber surrounds on the inside of the cabin.

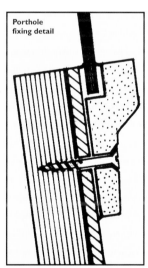

Porthole fixing detail

There is much to be said for you or the builder fixing the doors and portholes or windows at as early a stage as possible, so that the inside of the shell is protected from the weather. Baling out gallons of rainwater before you start your day's work can be very dispiriting and allows rust to set in.

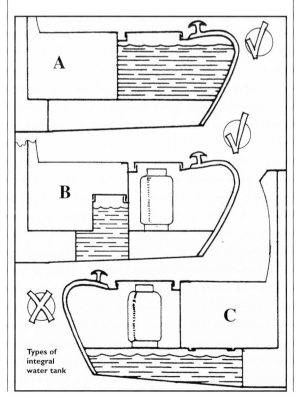

Types of integral water tank

Windows

While I chose portholes to light the interior of *Rome*, narrowboat glazing is usually based on something akin to the bus window. This is seemingly because early conversions did use secondhand windows from buses and because the design is functional, although not necessarily attractive. You might be used to looking at narrowboats but many newcomers still believe them to be cobbled-up conversions – partly because of the window shape. Window design is one area where narrowboat fashions are changing. However, specifying all the latest features can double the typical glazing bill of £850 (or triple it in the case of double glazing).

Shape

Four-rounded corners: The simplest way to improve your narrowboat's elevation is to have all four window corners rounded (rather than just the bottom two). The only disadvantage to this shape was that it did not easily allow the most common opening pattern – a drop back top hopper. However technology seems to have overcome the problem.

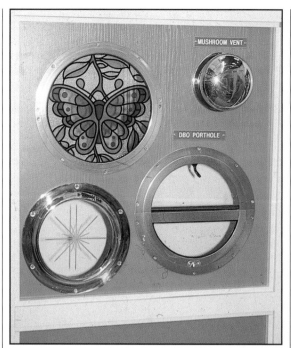

A selection of brass and aluminium portholes

Brass-anodised window with drop back vent; black-anodised unit with four rounded corners; and arch-topped window – typically fitted to replica barges and inspection launches – with combined sliding panel and drop back vent

Rectangular: Not a popular shape, usually used with louvre openings. The mitred lower corners tend to leak.

Arched top: The relatively recent fashion for replica inspection launches and Dutch barges has involved arch-topped windows, to give a distinctive period elevation. At least one builder has tried the shape on a conventional narrowboat – and it didn't look out of place.

Irregular: If your craft is to have the angular lines of a modern cruiser rather than the perpendicular of a narrowboat, window shape will be important to the overall style. Narrowboat window manufacturers will readily quote for

any shape – as long as you provide an accurate pattern.

Round: Aluminium-framed portholes can be of any size. Real brass ones become unviably expensive with size – and the difference increases if they are to open.

Size

The most common narrowboat window measures 36in wide by 21in deep. A depth of 18in used to be popular but is less so now because it looks lost in the cabin sides of most modern narrowboats which have tended to become higher over the last two decades. Shallower windows also let in less light, of course. For that reason, 24in deep windows are preferred by an increasing number of owners. These do not necessarily look ungainly – even at larger widths. A 48in x 24in window lets in 50% more light than 36in x 21in. Typically the largest windows are located in the saloon, and decrease progressively in size through galley, bedroom and toilet.

Port and starboard elevations are often made needlessly identical – you cannot see both elevations at the same time and asymmetry can vary, rather than unbalance, the inside. So, for instance, high level storage, that otherwise might not be practicable, could be fitted in by balancing a 36in wide galley window with an 18in wide unit on the other side.

Opening

Drop back top hopper vents are widely preferred because they can be left open in almost all conditions, without letting in too much draught, any rain – or intruders. Sliding windows provide better ventilation in really hot conditions. They seem to be popular for galleys – presumably so that (environmentally friendly) slops can be thrown into the canal. To cater for all weather possibilities, drop back vent and sliding panel can be combined in one window. A full height hopper maintains good weather protection when open but can provide extra ventilation with the hopper panel lifted out. Louvre windows owe their continued use mainly to hire fleets – the panels are easy to replace when broken. Even in the closed position, they provide some ventilation, because the glass-to-glass contact is by no means air tight. However, when open, the protruding blades tend to catch passing legs on side decks. Unlike almost all other narrowboat windows, which are aluminium-framed, the louvre type is often based on a stainless steel frame. A versatile alternative to louvres might be two shallow drop-back hopper vent panels – one over the other.

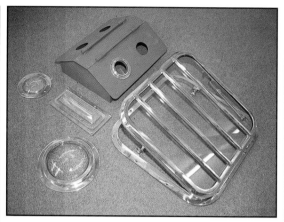

Traditional pigeon box, round and oblong 'bull's eyes' and a modern Houdini hatch

improve portholes or doors. Engraved windows have also received a welcome introduction.

Replacing broken panes (apart from hoppers and louvres) usually requires the window to be removed and taken apart. Channelglaze now has a design that can allow fixed panels to be taken out from inside the cabin without disturbing the frame. The glass is held in place by a rubber gasket.

Trimming off between internal cabin side linings and the window frame causes many DIY fitters-out difficulty yet few resort to the simple and relatively inexpensive solution of ordering internal aluminium trims.

Although expensive, double-glazed narrowboat windows are now well-established. Not really in order to reduce heat loss – narrowboat cabins are not difficult to keep warm – but to do away with steamed-up panes

Glazing – aluminium or hardwood-framed – is often fitted to forward (but not so frequently aft) cabin bulkheads and doors. Glazed opening hatches fitted into the cabin roof increase light levels usefully, particularly where you prefer to fit portholes on the cabin side. A dummy traditional pigeon box provides less light but looks better. It is not unusual to see a sheet of perspex slotted into a side-door aperture so that the doors can be left open in bad weather – you could develop this idea into neat side-hinged windows opening inwards from the side-door.

Window frame details. Brass anodised window with optional covering strip over fixing screws and the thicker section of a double glazed window

Special features
Coloured window frames reduce the starkness of plain aluminium. Gold anodising should look appropriately brasslike but seldom does. Black is, surprisingly, the next favourite choice. Red or green frames could be gruesome – or impressive if set off by a sympathetic painted cabin livery. Tinted glass is a relatively inexpensive way to increase privacy, without darkening the interior too much. However, one owner reports being disconcerted by passers-by who peer in through the tinted glass, thinking the boat to be empty. The same can happen with portholes. Frosted glass is almost universal in toilet windows. Leaded glass (you can buy leading kits) is not uncommon. Decorative stained glass panels are available and can

Fitting
If your shell builder is clearly experienced at fitting windows, get him to do the job – if only temporarily. Otherwise, you may find that the apertures will not accept your windows without further grinding off and that it is almost impossible to drill fixing holes through the aperture edges if they have been hardened by flame-cutting. You may also find the cabin interior filling with rainwater before you start. However, if your builder's skill is limited to steelwork, there is a risk that he will scar the soft aluminium window frame around the fixing holes. If you do have to drill through the frames yourself, impale something soft on the drill bit, to protect the aluminium from impact by the drill chuck if you break through suddenly. Three fixing methods are common: 1) by screw, loosely

through the steelwork to hardwood backing; 2) by self-tapping screws into the steel; 3) by pop rivets, neat but difficult to replace. Screws should be stainless steel or brass but if your windows frames are of unusual colour the manufacturer should be able to supply matching coloured rivets. If you opt for a frame design that has a flexible covering strip over the fixings, bear in mind that cheaper strips tend to shrink and fall out over the years. Above all, the window should be fitted so that it can easily be removed to replace broken panes – although this may not be so important if you choose an internally reglazable type (see above).

Silicone sealer is a favourite bedding material. After the frame has been squeezed down onto the bed, excess sealer should be left to dry then trimmed off with a knife. Butyl sealing tape, typically 3mm thick, is a convenient and less messy alternative. Some mastic sealers, on the other hand, never set, so cause smears when windows are cleaned. If the cabin side is slightly wavy, do not over-tighten the window to make a fit – the anodising is liable to craze if bent. Thin packing material may be needed to fill the worst valleys. A substantial minority of shell builders do not fix internal framing inside cabin sides. The steel surface otherwise hidden by the window frames can be used for securing internal timber noggins – which, in turn and with luck, might be able to pull errant plating reasonably straight. Finally: take care when grinding steel near to windows. The sparks can mark glass permanently.

Roof plan
Since the portholes on *Rome* give no ventilation there would need to be a fair crop of mushroom vents on the roof. In order to avoid an untidy scatter all over the roof I started by locating the position of the vent to the boiler flue as this was the only one whose position I could not alter. It was about 10" in from the handrail so I tried locating the remaining vents the same distance in from the edge and centred over the portholes below. This worked well for the back half of the plan as the vents occurred over the bed/dinette and bathroom, but not so well at the front half.

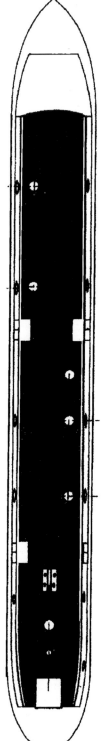

Mushroom ventilator layout on *Rome*'s cabin top. Small circle forward of aft hatch is 'bull's eye' porthole

By switching the front vents to the opposite side of the roof – but still 10in away from the handrail, they occurred over the hob in the galley and near the solid fuel stove in the saloon. This seemed to give the best positions for the vents and also resulted in a tidy, balanced layout on the roof. The next thing to do was to check that there were no roof beams underneath. This is where lack of preplanning let me down a bit as two of the positions had beams partly crossing them so the vents had to be moved slightly to miss them. It shows yet again the value of sorting things out at an early stage but fortunately, in this instance, I just got away with it.

Boatman's stove
One seemingly innocuous item was the subject of some debate. The argument was whether the stove in the Boatman's cabin should be parallel to the centre line of the boat or at an angle following the line of the hull behind it. My instant thought was the latter but Bob assured me that to be properly traditional it had to be set square. After some research I had to admit that I found several examples of stoves installed his way but these all jutted out rather awkwardly in front of the table cupboard. So, risking disapproval yet again, I stuck to my guns and am still glad that I did.

What's in a name?
It was during this period that we finally came up with a name for the new boat. We had just about exhausted the supply of suitable family names (I couldn't quite picture myself on a boat called *Gladys*) and were wondering if we would ever find a name we could both agree on. While I was bemoaning the fact that we were still boatless a friend put his hand on my shoulder and said "Never mind Graham, Rome wasn't built in a day." That was it! It was short, pleasant on the ear and, remembering the working boats Cairo and Vienna, sounded authentic. We looked no further. *Rome's* shell was eventually built, and launched – on Friday the Thirteenth of September 1991 – but at least it didn't rain. We realised that it was now over to us and prepared ourselves for the task ahead.

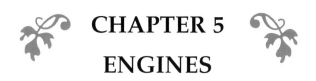

CHAPTER 5
ENGINES

Types of diesel engine
Buying *Rome's* engine
The pitfalls of buying a used engine

DIESELS

The diesel engine is an essential part of narrowboating – almost. Steam, gas, petrol, paraffin, electricity and horses have all been used to propel narrowboats – and some of these are still viable – but diesel engines have almost all of the attributes narrowboats need. They have good pulling power from low speed, are economical, reliable, durable, safe and convenient. They can be either of two things: a shrine at which to celebrate the traditional values of narrowboating (although diesels, as we know them at seventy years old, are a recent phenomenon in the two centuries old canals system), or a virtually silent and invisible means of propulsion. Totally inconspicuous engines are rare in narrowboats although the means of achieving them have existed and been used in other craft for years.

Engine size

How many horsepower will your narrowboat need? This is really the wrong question to ask but the answer is – not many. The average diesel engine installed in narrowboats today can produce around 30hp at its maximum speed but the propeller cannot deliver much more than 3hp into a typical narrow canal without antisocial effect on the bank and moored craft.

Even ploughing against a strong river current, the propeller is probably delivering between 5hp and 10hp (depending on the size of the boat). Substantial power losses are incurred all the way along the transmission line from gearbox to propeller. Gearbox, alternator, water pump, shaft bearings and general misalignment absorb approximately 10% of the engine's power. Efficiency of propellers varies according to relative size and shape: one to fit a 3:1 gearbox reduction may be 60% efficient while the same one on a shaft without any reduction might be less than 45% efficient.

So, to cope with large rivers a small narrowboat needs an engine rated at around 10hp and the largest needs no

Not many narrowboats are powered by outboard motors but this Yanmar diesel version would be suitable for craft up to 6 tons

more than 20hp. However, while the latest generation of diesels sounds less anguished at moderately high speeds than its predecessors, few narrowboat owners would suffer their engines at maximum speed for more than a few seconds. Consequently a generous power margin is usually specified, so that the engine sounds comfortable at river speeds and totally relaxed on canals. Hence the original 30hp.

Torque and engine capacity

The question you should be asking is how much cylinder capacity should your narrowboat engine have. Horsepower as a criteria is misleading because modern lightweight diesels manage high outputs relative to more traditional engines. The Yanmar Shire 25, for instance, produces a maximum of 27hp – considerably more than Russell Newbery's traditional DM2. Yet you would need barely a glance at both engines to realise that the latter will push a 70ft narrowboat and butty without effort, while the former would not find it anything like as easy.

What the Shire 25 lacks, but the DM2 has in aces, is guts. Pure power is useless unless the engine has sufficient guts to accelerate quickly for stopping, starting and manoeuvring. Lack of sufficient guts for heavy duty work puts pressures on the basic innards of the engine that greatly reduces their life.

A vintage Russell Newbery DM2 but brand new versions are still available

The technical term for guts is torque. When shown in engine manufacturers' brochures, it is usually to be found in a graph that shows (in separate curves) both power and torque against engine speed. From these it should be immediately clear that while power increases with speed, torque output varies less – and its maximum is often at quite low rpm. This low speed gutsiness is just what heavy narrowboats appreciate. In fact, it can be taken for granted that if an engine's torque output is high enough, its power output is also bound to be adequate. A couple of marine engine builders quote torque at the propeller, after it is mechanically magnified by the gearbox reduction ratio, rather than at the flywheel. This two- or three-fold magnification is a separate consideration and is misleading for accurate engine comparisons.

Manufacturers do not always reveal torque figures. When they do, the information can be expressed in any of three units of measurement. However torque correlates quite closely to cylinder cubic capacity. The Yanmar Shire 25 produces 32.5lb.ft torque – about a third of the Russell Newbery DM2's figure. Cylinder capacity of the Shire 25 is also around a third that of the DM2. This basic measure of engine size is almost certainly familiar to you as one criteria by which you choose your car and it is readily found in most marine engine brochures.

Boat size
The other variable – size of boat – is not a matter of length but of weight. The momentum of a deep-draughted 45ft traditional tug at 17 tons clearly takes more stopping than a 55ft vee-bottomed Springer narrowboat at perhaps 11 tons.

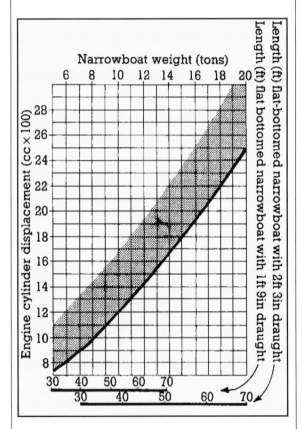

A reasonable minimum seems to be about 125cc cylinder capacity per ton weight, although this might be increased towards 150cc per ton for smaller narrowboats – under 40ft length. Two factors suggest that guidelines for maximum sizes are worthwhile. One is Conspicuous Consumption: during the narrowboat building boom of recent years, owners tended, when in doubt, to specify a larger than necessary tolerance to continuous slow speed

running by the current generation of high-performance diesels. If their lubrication systems fail to reach a reasonable working temperature, sludge can be precipitated into the sump, where its accumulation eventually reduces capacity for lubricating oil to inadequate levels. Bad practice by owners is a contributory factor – running engines off-load for long periods just to charge the batteries promotes sludging. Some engine marinising companies reacted by specifying undersize propellers for vulnerable models to make sure that they ran reasonably fast even when cruising on canals.

A (somewhat arbitrary) guide to maximum engine size is that it should be no more than 25% greater than the minimum. The older the engine design, the more this rule might be relaxed. The erstwhile but still popular BL1.5 diesel, for instance, has little history of sludging, while Lister's even older SR's and ST's have none. The diagram suggests maxima under the 25% rule and minima against different weights – which are then scaled against two combinations of length and draught.

ENGINE CONTENDERS

Almost all narrowboat engines are based on industrial units. The exceptions are one or two, like some traditional diesels in the Norwegian SABB range that was designed from the bottom up for marine use. Even the famous names among vintage narrowboat engines were initially developed for industrial use. Automotive diesels, unless modified for industrial use, may not run without temperament at narrowboat speeds. The industrial version of Ford's XLD diesel, for instance, has a heavier flywheel and flatter torque curve than the original automotive version. Apart from the true marine rarities, narrowboat engines can be divided into two main types:

Light industrial/automotive
Engines designed for light plant use – like fork lift trucks and generating sets – are a main source for modern narrowboat diesels. Designed initially for industrial rather than automotive use they tend to be easier to maintain than modern automotive types – the latter favour more complicated overhead camshafts for higher performance and tend to have circuitous pipework to fit into compact engine compartments. Although industrial units are built in configurations from single to four (or more) cylinders, they rev almost as fast as automotive diesels. Both lend themselves to quiet engine installations although direct injection engines are noisier than the more common indirect injection type (where fuel is injected into a small pre-chamber rather than into the main combustion chamber). Japanese engines appear to have the edge for quiet, smooth running but their spares are relatively expensive.

Large numbers of Mitsubishi diesels have been installed in small and medium sized narrowboats for over a decade. Marinisers are Vetus – a Dutch company with a British subsidiary, Thornycroft, the best known of Mitsubishi marinisers and Watermota. Kubota, another Japanese make, has recently made great inroads into the narrowboat market. Beta Marine offers a spectacular range of ten Kubotas, ranging from a 478cc twin to a 3.3 litre four cylinder unit, but featuring 1.5 litre and 1.85 litre four

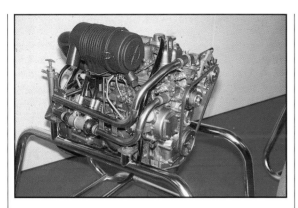
One of the large range of Yanmar 'Shire' engines

cylinder models – the most popular sizes for narrowboats. European mariniser Nannidiesel also offers Kubota-based engines. Yanmar is a major builder world-wide of marine engines. It is well represented in the UK and its products are fitted in British coastal craft. The new Shire range of Yanmar engines suitable for narrowboats has just been introduced.

Perkins' two-litre MC42 is British-built and as quiet as the advanced Kubotas; but it is based on Japanese core parts.

Lister Canal Star 36

Lister's water-cooled Alpha range, introduced in 1988, is lightweight but has many of the easy maintenance features that distinguished its heavier air-cooled predecessors and it is British through-and-through.

The other favourite engine name of the last two decades is BMC, British Leyland or Austin-Rover – the company's various identities during that period. Its 1.5 litre and 1.8 litre diesels, once almost universal in narrowboats, are no longer built in the UK, but imported versions are marinised by two well-established British companies, specifically for narrowboat use. Thornycroft offers a 1.5 and 1.8 of Indian origin; and Calcutt Boats a Turkish 1.8. Although originally automotive engines, the 1.5 and 1.8 are elderly and simple designs.

Ford's XLD 1.8 is the narrowboat diesel with overhead camshaft – the drive belt is not difficult to replace but must be changed every 1,500 hours to avoid expensive engine damage in the event of a failure. The engine is marinised by several companies and has proved itself in narrowboat use but, considering its availability over ten

years and its manufacturer's credibility, has yet to become seriously popular. A few examples of the Volkswagen 1.6 litre diesel have been installed in narrowboats in the past. Comparable Vauxhall and Citroen engines have never been developed for such heavy duty use – and if offered should be treated with suspicion. Most automotive engines have push-on plastic spill racks which must be replaced by a metal one (kits are available) so that they comply with the BSS.

Other names include the sturdy, well-engineered 964cc and 1.45 litre Danish Bukhs – which feature counterbalance weights for smooth running
Although no longer built, Lister's air-cooled SR and ST ranges will surely find their way into new narrowboats – because they are virtually indestructible. Likewise reconditioned versions of the BMC/BL 1.5 and 1.8, Perkins' 1.8 litre 4.108 will also crop up – although it was never really a popular narrowboat engine, despite revamping as the Waterways Four shortly before its demise.

Multi-cylinder engines for really large narrowboats, and their wide-beam variants, have been based on Land-Rover and Peugeot diesels – both 2.5 litre, four-cylinder units. This market may also be taken over by the Japanese.

Heavy industrial engines

These tend to have few cylinders, run at relatively low speed and are heavily constructed. They are gutsy, rugged and easily maintained. They are also a disappearing breed – even the Lister H and S series that earned the company a special place in narrowboating, are out of production. New 'traditional' diesels are drawn from various odd sources – a Ford three-cylinder tractor diesel is the basis of Lister's CRK3 Classic and Beta Marine's BD3 Tug Engine. SABB's mellifluous 10hp true marine engine would grace the engine room of any small narrowboat. Production of the 30hp SABB 2J has just stopped but spares are still available. Major UK manufacturer Perkins is still building a three-cylinder 2.5 litre engine, which Duffields and Calcutt Boats both marinise.

Real engines

If you seek a really impressive centrepiece for your engine room, none of the above pretend-vintage engines will satisfy you. You must then enter the bewildering but absorbing world of Real Engines. The engine that transformed working narrowboats in the early years of this century was the Bolinder semi-diesel. Even if you could find one, it is not an engine for convenience-minded boaters – starting it requires a blowlamp and, to go astern, you must catch the engine just right and make it fire backwards.

The Bolinder's semi diesel engine sounds wonderful but was not designed for convenience

The massive Kelvin K2 is becoming very popular in narrowboats now

Conventional 'traditional' diesels were thought of as modern high-speed designs when they were introduced in the early Thirties. Russell Newbery and National (a closely related engine) were canal pioneers of that time. Lister's CE and JP2 are contemporary designs and the JP2, particularly, is highly regarded by traditionalists.

Two other vintage names of high repute are Kelvin – with superbly perpendicular fishing boat engines – and Gardner, often described as the Rolls-Royce of diesels because of its precise build standard. Most of these vintage engines continued in production after W.W.II, when they were joined by newer models that still look and sound right in engine rooms.

Post-war engines that you might be offered include Ruston & Hornsby, Dorman, Petter, Armstrong Siddeley – and Lister again. That company has kept up a supply of interesting engines until quite recently when the last HRW2 was taken out of production.

Russell Newbery's sixty-year old 2.86 litre twin has survived under several owners to become, for many traditional narrowboaters, the 'ultimate' engine.

The Gardner 2LW, a 'modern' vintage engine

More recently, Gardner has re-introduced its 2LW model giving exceptionally smooth performance for a two cylinder engine – but at a price.

Fuel consumption
Fuel consumption really isn't a consideration in diesel narrowboating – except to settle arguments about how little fuel is burnt. In relation to other running costs – licence, insurance, moorings, maintenance – engine fuel costs, even for a well-cruised boat, are a minor item. Consumption may be lower than manufacturer's brochure figures because narrowboat engines are frequently running slower than any uses projected by the engine manufacturer.

AN ENGINE FOR *ROME*

The order for *Rome's* shell was placed in May 1990 and delivery agreed for April 1991. This gave us about a year to decide on and obtain an engine. It happened that Bob Allen knew of a National engine which was about to be rebuilt and it was agreed that we could have first option on it. In the meantime we looked at some other options.

Alternatives
Having slight worries about the availability of spares for a truly vintage engine I was attracted to the idea of a modern engine with vintage characteristics. The obvious choice was the Russell Newbery DM2 but this was ruled out on grounds of high cost and stories of quality problems at the time – now, reportedly, cured. A more moderately priced alternative was the Beta tug engine but we were disappointed by the light sound and general clatter when we listened to one installed in a boat, so we decided to stick with the vintage option.

Unfortunately, progress on the renovation was extremely slow and about half way through the boat building time it dawned on us that it would never be ready in time to be installed – unless we were prepared to wait a very long time, which we weren't. Looking back we should have realised much sooner but then you can do wonders with 20/20 hindsight.

Last minute substitution
If we were not to be delayed still further, we needed to find a replacement fast. The first port of call was, naturally, the back pages of *WW* where several companies advertise vintage engines. Everyone we spoke to was very helpful – even to the extent of suggesting other people we might try if they could not help.

Essential knowledge
My education was rapid if somewhat superficial and I soon discovered a number of interesting facts. Most of the engines advertised were in their 'original' state – fine if you have the time or ability to work on them but, since we had neither, these were ruled out. The two-cylinder engines we were looking for fell into two categories. There were the pre-war ones of 2.5 to 3 litres developing about 18 HP at 1000 RPM. These included old RNs, Nationals, Gardners and Lister JP2s. Then there were the post-war ones of 1.5 to 2 litres developing 20 HP at 1800

A group of engines in 'original' condition – fine if you have the time and ability to restore them

RPM. Typical examples of these were Lister HAs, HBs, FRs, Armstrong Siddeleys and Petter PH2s.

Within both these categories were industrial engines, built to operate machinery or generators in a factory, and marine engines which may have started life in a fishing boat in the North Sea. As always there were pros and cons. Industrials, we were told, particularly those which originally had two flywheels fitted, sometimes don't take kindly to having one removed and a gearbox grafted on – but at least you know that the inside has not been eaten away by sea water. For marine engines read the reverse.

A fair few had no fuel lift pump and required a high level day tank into which fuel is pumped by hand from the main tank at the start of each day. I did not see any particular disadvantage in this – we were after all seeking authenticity.

In ten days we had assembled a list of about eight possibilities which shows that it is not as difficult to find these engines as we first thought. We listened to as many as possible. Engineers realise that the main reason for buying this type of engine rather than a boringly efficient modern one is for the leisurely tick over and resonant tone and they are generally willing to get one going for you to hear.

The chosen one

In the end our search took us to Marine Engine Services at Uxbridge where Peter Thompson marinised and overhauled old engines, mainly Listers, as well as selling new

Marine Engineer Peter Thompson prepares to run up the Lister HW2 destined for *Rome*

ones. The particular engine was a 1962 Lister HW2 – a water cooled version of the HB2. It had just been overhauled and was about to be sprayed the approved shade of dark green. In its previous existence, it had been a generator on a yacht where it had had a closed cooling system so there were no worries about internal corrosion. Also, being the water-cooled rather than the more common air-cooled version it could be used to feed a calorifier and heat the domestic hot water, and all this for the price of a 'new' BMC 1.5. It seemed a strong possibility – even Bob Allen approved the choice – but to save a long abortive trip from the Midlands, Peter played it to us over the phone first! It passed this test and we sped off down the M40 next morning to clinch the deal. The following day it was on the back of Peter's truck speeding back up the M40 and was soon sitting by the side of the shell ready to be installed.

THE PITFALLS OF BUYING A USED ENGINE

Although I am quite happy to perform the annual oil change and modify engine plumbing, I would not attempt an engine rebuild. If you are more confident and tempted to have a go, Peter Thompson offers the following advice:

A new engine naturally carries a manufacturer's guarantee unless, possibly in the case of an old stock unit, it has already expired. If this is the case I would strongly recommend that you obtain some sort of written cover from the dealer. Generally speaking, where an engine is sold by a private individual, it is a case of Caveat Emptor – let the buyer beware.

A commercial rebuilder will give some sort of cover on a rebuilt unit, although the quality of a rebuild can vary between 'as new' and 'clean off and spray over'. If an engine has been rebuilt properly it will be as clean inside as it is on the outside. Check for cleanliness of oil and with a finger check for presence of dirt or sludge in the rocker cover, oil filler, etc. Observe state of nut/bolt heads – if these are well chewed it generally reflects on the quality of workmanship. Ideally hear the engine running and

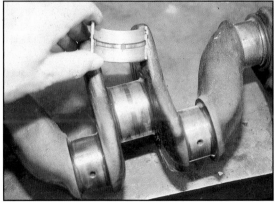

Worn crankshaft bearings

check that exhaust is clean, that there are no mechanical rattles, there is good oil pressure, no leaks etc. Some engines require considerable running under load for the pistons and bores to bed in, and this will sometimes result in a smoky exhaust early in the engine's life. It is worth-

Fuel pump and injector repairs should only be undertaken by specialists

while obtaining a check list of what has been done to the engine from your supplier.

If purchasing a secondhand engine 'as seen', it is very desirable to be able to hear it running, when the points raised in the previous paragraph will give an indication of its condition. To describe an engine as a 'good runner' can mean that it is nearly as new, or could be so worn out that there is not enough power to cause warning rattles!

Repair scar above the left valve on centre cylinder

Looking deeper

There are certain checks that you can carry out on an engine before installing it in a boat that can save a lot of time and trouble later.

First of all drain out the oil and remove the oil filter – inspect the oil for metal particles, etc. Remove the sump or side cover and wash out with paraffin. With any work of this nature, cleanliness is essential. Remove the big end caps and inspect for scoring or wear of the bearing sur-

faces – also that of the crankshaft journals. Assuming that the crank is in good condition and that the bearings are reasonable, it is probable that the main bearings will not require replacement. In some engines these are easy to inspect, in which case I recommend this be done regardless, and new bearing shells fitted if the existing ones show signs of wear. However, in certain engines, especially those of industrial parentage, replacement of main bearings is a major operation and a certain amount of judgement can be applied at this stage.

To check the state of the cylinders, pistons and valves, remove the inlet and exhaust manifolds and turn the flywheel by hand. Compressions should be even and there should not be evidence of gas leakage past the valves, pistons or rings. This may be determined by listening at the ports and in the crankcase area. If significant hissing is evident, the next stage is to remove the cylinder head or heads and investigate further.

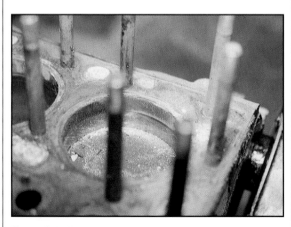

Lip on cylinder bore

If there is leakage on the valves, these should be removed and the seats examined. Inspect carefully for cracks in the head – certain engines are prone to this. Unless the valves and guides appear to be in very good condition, and only require grinding in, I suggest that these should be replaced as a matter of course. If there was leakage past the pistons, it is most probable that a rebore with new pistons will be necessary. Remove the pistons and rods and inspect bores for wear – this will be indicated by the ridge at the uppermost travel of the top ring. Remove the build-up of carbon at this point and run a finger around the bore to get an indication of wear. If this is excessive, then a rebore will be necessary and further examination of the pistons will be unnecessary. If wear is slight or insignificant and the pis-

Corrosion on this water-cooled manifold could have been concealed by paint

tons in good condition, I recommend honing the bores to remove any lip and also deglaze to allow new rings to bed in. Inspect the pistons carefully, especially taking note of side play of the rings in the grooves. If this is excessive, new pistons will be required, in which case I advise a rebore unless the bores are in extremely good condition. If ring grooves are good, it will only be necessary to fit new rings if the old ones are worn – this can be ascertained by removing from the piston and placing in the cylinder bore when the gap can be measured – if there has been leakage it will be most unlikely that the old rings will be satisfactory.

When dismantling, take care to keep all parts identified so that they can be put back in the same place – clean everything thoroughly, and replace with new gaskets and seals – preferably following instructions given in workshop manuals etc. For vehicle engines you should usually refer to the manual for the vehicle from which the engine came. But marine or industrial engines will usually require contact with the relevant manufacturer or dealer. Besides a workshop manual, a suitable workshop and tools of the trade are almost essential.

Fuel equipment will normally require specialist attention (easily found via 'Yellow Pages'). Problems here are usually indicated by presence of whitish smoke in the exhaust – or occasionally black, although this is more often an indication of a worn out engine or overloading. Blue smoke is generally an indication of oil leaking past valve guides or piston rings.

This is not intended to be an exhaustive guide on rebuild-

ing an engine but should give an indication of what might be involved.

Are you – and it – up to it?
It is very important to decide your own level of competence before delving too deeply; as it is easy to cause very expensive damage and possibly end up with something a lot worse than you originally bought. In some cases it can cost more to purchase and rebuild a second-hand engine than to buy a new or overhauled unit – especially if you then have the cost of marinising it using proprietary components. If in doubt take advice from someone who has experience of small diesels – and ideally get them to help or carry out the work as well.

Beware corrosion
Beware of engines that have previously been fitted in seagoing craft as salt water corrosion might well have made them beyond viable repair. Air-cooled marine engines can be a reasonable bet from this area, but look carefully underneath, especially at aluminium castings, sheet metal shrouds etc. All these can be very expensive to repair or replace.

Water-cooled engines can have even more problems – salt water causes significant corrosion damage, especially when different metals are present. To replace the cylinders, heads and manifolds on a small water-cooled Lister will probably cost more than the engine is worth, so it is definitely worth getting an expert to give advice if you are unsure. There can also be problems with seal lands on shafts where corrosion can render oil seals ineffective. These comments are generally aimed at the older direct cooled engines – ie where sea water is passed directly through the engine block or cylinders. If the engine has been fitted with a heat exchanger, it should be a safer buy, providing the sea water has not leaked past the seals into the engine cooling circuit. Excessive corrosion will normally be seen inside the header tank if this has been the case.

Marinisation
Obviously buying an engine which has already been used for marine propulsion will by-pass the problems of marinising an ex-vehicle or industrial engine. Vehicle engines are not usually a problem as most parts are available off-the-shelf for common types such as Leyland and Ford. There is a range of gearboxes, manifolds, etc and discussion with one or more of the engine marinisers should help here.

Industrial engines tend to be more of a problem, especially the older types, and in many cases it is just not worthwhile to proceed along this route. Most dealers are prepared to give advice on this subject. Later engines often have standardised SAE outlets at the flywheel end which lend themselves to attachment of gearbox adapters, mounts, etc.

Peter Thompson's advice on installing engines is included in the next chapter.

CHAPTER 6
INSTALLING THE ENGINE

Gearboxes and reductions
Propellers
Engine installation
Quiet installations

GEARBOXES & REDUCTIONS

The function of a marine gearbox is to provide alternatives of forward and reverse gears while reducing the engine's speed to one that can be more efficiently used by the propeller. In older transmissions, the speed reduction takes place in a separate gearbox bolted to the aft end of the main one. As in a car, changing gear involves a clutch, although it is situated inside the main gearbox and operates automatically. When ordering a new engine, customers can specify from a range of gearbox reduction ratios. In addition to increasing propeller efficiency, stepping down the prop-shaft speed increases torque in proportion to the reduction ratio. However the extra gain achieved by fitting a 3:1 ratio instead of the conventional 2:1 is no real substitute for a gutsy, durable engine.

Large engines like the Beta BD3 Tug Engine have so much torque to spare for pushing relatively light modern narrowboats that they can be installed without any reduction ratio. For the typical modern narrowboat with engine of less than two litres capacity, a 2:1 gearbox reduction is reasonably efficient and allows the appropriate propeller to fit behind an average stern post height of 1ft 8in. The coarser propeller pitch associated with a 3:1 reduction can also magnify the stern's tendency to swing to one side when stopping or trying to steer going astern.

Gearboxes can be mechanically or oil operated. The two makes used by most marinisers of engines for narrowboats are the German Hurth and British PRM – the former mechanical, the latter mostly oil operated. The two Hurth models normally specified are the 100 and 150 although

there are larger and smaller models. PRM's two main contenders are the 150 and 260 (previously known as the Delta and 160) and it has recently introduced the mechanically operated 120. Hurth gearboxes are specified on many private craft but hire operators favour the PRM for its longevity.

Borg-Warner's model 500 mechanically operated gearbox is a relatively recent arrival, competing with Hurth 100 and PRM 150. The Italian-built Technodrive is promoted as an alternative to the Hurth gearbox. Lister gearboxes, both oil operated and mechanical, are no longer built but are sturdy units, often found on seventies-built examples of the company's SR and ST models. Established marine engine suppliers match gearboxes to engines carefully. Before accepting a gearbox from any other source you should make sure that the engine's power/torque output does not exceed the gearbox's capacity – bearing in mind that different gearbox reduction ratios affect that capacity.

PROPELLERS

Narrowboat owners are often dissatisfied with their propellers. Either they are too small, making the engine rev intrusively at canal speeds, or too large, preventing the engine from reaching a reasonable speed, causing the exhaust to emit black smoke during acceleration under load, and making the boat leap forward unreasonably fast as soon as gear is engaged at tickover.

Major propeller suppliers now have considerable experience in specifying narrowboat propeller sizes. Several rely on computer programmes to consider several variables. Their recommendations often differ from the arbitrary sizes laid down by some engine suppliers. A propeller bought from other than an specialist company (you may be offered a secondhand prop by a fellow boater, for instance), may not be of optimum size. If it is only slightly out, a propeller repairer may be able to trim it or dress it up – assuming that this is cost-effective compared to a new propeller. Propshafts do not always turn in the same direction – it depends on the particular combination of engine and gearbox. If your installation is specified for a 'right hand' prop, do not accept assurances that a 'left hand' one can be accommodated simply by selecting what was previously reverse gear to go forward. Some gearboxes are built to allow this, others will – but only for a while.

The standard narrowboat propeller is of 'three-bladed turbine design' with 50% blade area ratio (ie, relative to the

The Newage PRM 120 mechanical gearbox

Propeller shafts are usually 1in diameter – except for larger engines which call for 2in. Prop taper can be 1 in 12 or 1 in 10

area contained in a circle of same diameter as the prop). For heavy-duty work – as in pushing a narrowboat, blade diameter should be as large as possible, with relatively fine pitch. Diameter is limited by the need to allow a clearance of at least 10% of diameter between tip and counter above and skeg below. Arguments for maximum possible tip clearance are that it reduces the likelihood of flotsam jamming between prop and counter, and that it lessens annoying prop drumming on the counter and turbulence immediately aft of the counter.

A conventional 3 bladed propeller

Not uncommonly, owners seek to fit a large traditional-style engine in a modern relatively shallow draught hull. As suggested above, fitting a direct drive (ie, without reduction ratio), allows a smaller propeller. One specialist, Crowther Marine, supplies a propeller with increased blade area ratio (so that what cannot be fitted in outwards is accommodated sideways). As a rough guide for early planning purposes, I offer a propeller chart. It relates to standard blade-area ratio types and its range is limited to modern faster revving engines, but for final size refer to a prop specialist.

On *Rome*, the draught had been designed to accommodate a 22in prop which our first engine choice would have turned with ease. Although I wanted the Lister to operate at as low a speed as possible, it was generally reckoned that there would not be enough torque in this engine for a propeller of this size with a 2:1 reduction gearbox, and it might produce black smoke. Various people approached the problem in different ways from wetted fingers raised in the air to computer programmes. Interestingly they all come up with the same answer – 20in x 16in (diameter x pitch) so that's what we used.

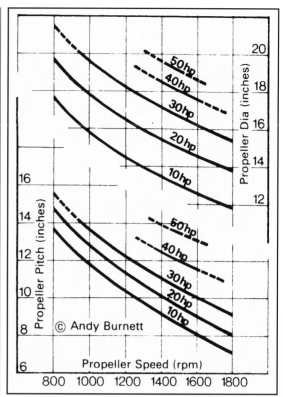

© Andy Burnett

Chart for rough propeller sizing. Consult a specialist for exact dimensions

ENGINE INSTALLATION

Peter Thompson advises on installing an engine –

An installation can be divided into several discrete areas, each of which can be considered separately. As a guide these could be listed as follows:

1. Stern gear and propeller.
2. Engine beds.
3. Cooling arrangements and ventilation.
4. Engine insertion and alignment.
5. Coupling to stern gear.
6. Connection to cooling.
7. Connection to fuel supply and return.
8. Exhaust installation.
9. Control connections
10. Electrical connections.
11. Commissioning – filling with oil, fuel, coolant, bleeding, running up etc.

Normally stern gear, propeller, engine beds, skin tanks etc. would be fitted by the boat builder.

Sizes of propeller and shaft, together with provision of thrust blocks are really a matter of specialist recommendation dealt with above.

With regard to engine beds these should be adequately massive to support the engine, and be cross-braced to the sides of the hull to prevent relative movement. It is amazing how often this is not the case and the engine virtually sits on a little pedestal constructed on the bottom of the boat. In this case the bottom will probably act rather like the diaphragm in a vintage gramophone and amplify the noise and vibration. Always err on the side of strength and rigidity. Obviously the dimensions should suit the engine being installed allowing for final alignment on the mounts, be they solid or flexible.

Lining up

Alignment should satisfy various conditions – the output (gearbox) coupling should be axially true to the stern shaft, the coupling faces should be parallel, and the weight of the engine should be diagonally balanced – ie, the rear feet should be evenly loaded as should the front. There is definitely a knack to this, but quite a good method is to support the engine on the two rear mounts along with a screw jack under the front of the engine on the centre line. The mounts and jack can thus be adjusted to give the correct alignment which may be checked with feeler gauges or dial indicators on the couplings. Then adjust the front mounts or shims so that the gap between the foot and engine bed is just filled. Remove jack, and shim or adjust 'evenly' on each side of the front to return to correct alignment. 'Evenly' means same number of flats on mount nuts, or same thickness of shims on each side. With anti-vibration mounts, try and have the nut below the engine foot as low as possible down the stud – if necessary fit packers below the mount – and if the engine feet are made of aluminium or soft alloy, put a heavy steel washer between nut and foot to spread the load. It is also a good idea to use an inverted Nyloc nut below the foot to make it less likely to come undone. Tighten up all bolts and nuts and recheck the alignment.

This is only necessary when solid or flexible couplings are used. In the case of a Cardan shaft or Aquadrive the requirements are not so critical and in fact Hardy-Spicer joints require misalignment to ensure proper lubrication.

But the points about diagonal balancing should be followed, whatever the method of shaft coupling, as this will go a long way towards improving the smooth running of the installed unit. At this stage the engine may be coupled to the shaft.

Cooling

In the case of an air-cooled engine, sufficient attention must be given to provision of vents to allow ingress of cool air, and the hot air must be ducted outside the boat – either through the side or roof of the boat. It must be arranged such that the cooling air cannot be recirculated through the engine as this will surely lead to overheating.

Water-cooled engines are normally cooled either by skin tank, heat exchanger or direct by canal water.

Skin tanks are normally on the side or bottom of the boat. It is most preferable to use tanks on the side as the volume of coolant required is far less (the tank should not be too thick – 1in is usually adequate) and this set up is more efficient than a tank built on the bottom. The reason for this is that hot water rises to the top of the tank and is therefore not in contact with the cooling surface which is the bottom. To counteract this, the volume of liquid is normally

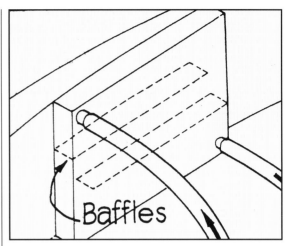

Skin cooling tank with baffles

increased, with consequent increase in cost of anti-freeze, and often a very hot engine room floor! In a traditional engine room layout, I suggest that the space either side of the engine beds is better used for fuel tanks rather than cooling tanks.

Mud box strainer for (less common) fresh or raw water cooling

I pass on, untested, a rule-of-thumb for skin tank size of 1 sq ft of cooling surface for every $3\frac{1}{2}$hp used. For a typical narrowboat with 30hp diesel this could mean a 5ft 0in x 1ft 8in panel – except that most 30hp narrowboat engines never exceed 20hp for more than a few minutes, thus requiring a more typical 3ft 6in x 1ft 8in size in practice. Cooling will also be made more effective if the skin tank is fitted with internal baffles to prevent water taking a short cut from inlet to outlet. Remember that the cool feed to the engine should be taken from the bottom of the tank.

Heat exchanger or direct cooled engines require a water feed from the canal via a stopcock and suitable strainer and/or mud box, cooling water being returned to the canal either directly overboard or through a wet exhaust system.

Exhaust

Most narrowboats use a dry exhaust and the position of this should be considered carefully so as to allow suitable access to batteries, weed hatches, height of outlet above water, etc. It should of course be lagged or guarded. And should try to avoid a side exit from the hull, which has the undesirable effect of causing exhaust fumes to rise up alongside the boat whilst locking – or even sometimes through the ventilation apertures on other craft. Sometimes there is no alternative, but it is worthwhile considering the whole installation with this in mind.

Flexible links

Beware of tight bends in fuel pipes and control cables as this can cause wear or fractures. Support these adequately so that there is no danger of rubbing against moving objects and be aware of the relative movement of items – i.e. insert flexible links where required. 'Flexible' exhaust piping as obtained from many boatyards and motorists shops is designed to be bent into place, not to flex thereafter, although the stainless version will often survive if used with a flexibly mounted engine. Ideally a stainless bellows or similar link is required with this type of installation.

Flexible bellows in the exhaust system help to stop vibration being transmitted to the shell

Beware of mounting heavy items on engines that are flexibly mounted as the inertia might well cause fractures at or near the mounting point. Electrical installation is dealt with in a later chapter – but, again, proper securing of cable looms and neatness are a must.

Other installation equipment

Control systems: the main choice is between single lever control boxes and traditional speedwheel systems but, if your engine is a modern boxed- or decked-in unit, only the single lever type is relevant. Its mechanism is almost foolproof – if set up properly. Boxes have adjustable innards to suit different engines and gearboxes. When set up, your box should, for instance, engage gear fully before the throttle starts to open. The connecting arms of some older

This ingenious speedwheel mechanism (in restored Josher *Hare*) is brazed together from a hand brace and socket-set universal joints

gearboxes move so far and require so much effort that a single lever box is not suitable. The usual solution is a long lever direct from the gearbox to steering position and separate throttle control. When fitting a single lever box, measure cable lengths carefully to ensure economical but smooth runs without tight bends. If your engine is non-standard, a local marine engine shop may be able to contrive a suitable end-fitting kit from its odds-and-ends bin.

Speedwheel systems can range from ingenious (involving VW Beetle steering gear) to horrific (involving cotton reels, fishing line and elastic). The main chandlers do not seem to offer a standard mechanism for the tricky bits. The speedwheel usually controls the throttle with good sensitivity, but slow response. Gear control is normally a push-pull lever linked via cranks. Wheel-operated gear changes have traditional antecedents but may be so slow as to be almost dangerous.

Instruments: when ordering a new engine you will usually be given a choice of standard panel, lacking instruments but fitted with warning lights for individual engine faults – sometimes (and very usefully) backed up by buzzers; or a de luxe panel with various

In-line fuel filter to remove water and/or sediment

analogue instruments. In descending order of priority for a typical skin-tank cooled engine, instruments are: water temperature gauge, oil pressure gauge, voltmeter, hour meter. Tachometers are helpful, but can be misleading – cruising at 1,400rpm may be fine on your home canal but antisocially fast on shallower ones.

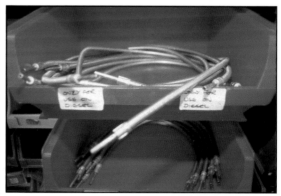

Armoured flexible fuel and gas hoses are not all the same thing

In addition to the engine's fuel filter, an in-line filter is desirable. Different filters take out sediment and water. To avoid your surveyor's disapproval, flexible fuel piping should be of reinforced type and carry the mark 'ISO 7840'. Flexibles should be reasonably short. Fuel tanks are normally built into the boat's counter. With a round stern, this usually results in a tank of 30 to 40 gallons capacity. In addition to filler and raised flame-guarded vent (both on deck), your shell builder should have provided tapped holes at the top (facing into the engine compartment) to connect fuel supply and return pipes, and one at the bottom for a drain.

Finally

Most of the areas involved in installation are a matter of attention to British Waterways recommendations, detail and common sense. The most important thing, if doing a fitting or overhauling an engine yourself, is to have an understanding of what is involved and the way things work. The many considerations in a correct installation are likely to be much more demanding than fitting-out the boat's cabin. If you are almost sure of your ability to fit an engine, several owner's engine courses are run by colleges and training schools.

But if you are in greater doubt, employ an expert – or at least make sure you can call on one for the more difficult jobs. Most professional installers have their own particular ideas and tricks of the trade, many of which may be picked up by talking to your local one.

Peter Thompson runs Marine Engine Services which is now one of the four Lister master distributors.

Installing Rome's engine

Apart from saying which type of controls I wanted (traditional speedwheel and push-pull gear) I was quite happy to leave the whole engine installation to the yard. Although *George* had an aft-mounted BMC 1.5, the previous owner had managed to install traditional controls and we had become thoroughly used to, and liked, using them. The final connections to the engine were by Morse cables but

Rome's speedwheel mechanism at its top junction

the overall impression was good enough to fool many a gongoozler. The engine on *Rome* required no such deception but the gear control needed several cranks and levers to ensure that a forward push on the control resulted in forward motion of the boat.

The engine itself is mounted on solid metal blocks welded to the longitudinal bearers rather than hardwood or Tremco pads. This surprised me but I have to say that the result is a very smooth installation. If you decide to use hardwood bearers, separate bolts should fasten timber to

Final control linkage to gearbox called for several cranks. Also in shot are the engine's metal-to-metal mounts

hull and engine to timber to avoid direct metal-to-metal contact. Also, if you are running short of space in the engine room – perhaps because of a longer three-cylinder engine – it is worth ensuring that the bolts fix down into captive nuts rather than stick up through the hardwood. This will enable you to position the engine much nearer to the front partition because then it can be unbolted and slid back if the flywheel ever has to be removed.

Rome's engine, part installed

QUIET INSTALLATIONS

To the owner of a traditional diesel, the measured 'chuff' is both reassuring and evocative. If you chose a more modern engine, you may take the opposing view and want to eliminate as much of its noise as possible. It is certainly possible, and it is not that difficult to achieve. There are three stages in engine quietening: lining the compartment with sound-deadening foam; specifying low-noise engine installation equipment; and removing the engine to a remote position.

Acoustic foam

Many owners take some steps to insulate engine compartments – if only by sticking carpet to the underside of deck boards. This is now unacceptable as engine insulation must be zero fire rated and have a non-absorbent face. Proper acoustic foam is carefully engineered – typically it is a flexible, open-cell material with a heavy middle membrane of lead or plastic. Most builders of luxury

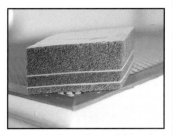

Acoustic foam with a washable surface and two middle membranes of heavy plastic

motor cruisers line their engine rooms comprehensively to eliminate any resonant surface. In a narrowboat, particular attention might be paid to the counter since, when all else is silenced, the propeller's various noises become irritating. Full insulation involves complete enclosure. However the engine needs ventilation – which lets noise out while taking air in. Vents at the aft end of the engine box, or in hull sides, could be muffled by siting foam-lined baffles just inside them.

Quieter equipment

The type of engine you choose is important; modern lightweight engines are easier to insulate than vintage types. In fact some recent models – like Beta Marine's Kubotas, and the Perkins MC42 are impressively quiet.

Proper alignment is also important to vibration-free running. Modern engines are almost always located on flexi-

Different grades of marine flexible engine mount – only one suits your particular engine

ble mounts. These are made in different grades to suit various engine sizes. Despite their flexibility, marine mounts are designed to transmit all the propeller's thrust to the hull. If the engine is flexibly mounted, its connection to the prop shaft should also be flexible. However, most flexible shaft couplings allow for a small amount of angular movement – but not lateral shaking which results from engine vibration. If the distance between coupling and stern bearing (where the shaft passes out through the hull to the prop) is very short, sideways loads will be put on the bearing reducing its life and increasing vibration.

A few builders overcome this by using a water lubricated stern bearing – which is made of neoprene and thus allows the shaft to flex within it without loading. This is usually referred to by the name of the original American design, 'Cutless'. The conventional stern bearing is made of plain metal (phosphor or magnesium bronze) with a seal of seemingly archaic design – the stuffing box. Short lengths of special rope are compressed round the shaft by a screw-adjusted cap; and grease has to be pumped regularly into the space to keep a final seal. This arrangement has greater noise potential than a 'Cutless' bearing but has proven durability. The 'Cutless' bearing is vulnerable to wear by grit par-

Neoprene and plain metal stern propeller shaft bearings

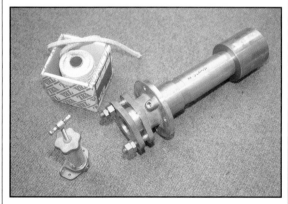

Aft bearing with conventional stuffing box, packing material and greaser

ticles. This is not a problem on sea-going or river craft but units fitted in narrowboats should be supplied with clean water, possibly from a raw water engine cooling system but not a sealed skin tank system.

At the time when *Rome* was fitted out, the alternative to the stuffing box was the Deep Sea Seal, a two-part con-

coction of neoprene and Jubilee clips which makes a drip- and maintenance-free shaft seal with itself. It too is vulnerable to grit wear and, on narrowboats, should receive its lubricating water from the same source as the 'Cutless' bearing.

The American Packless Sealing System, a modern replacement for the archaic stuffing box

Two further propeller shaft seals, both similar in appearance to the Deep Sea Seal, have since come onto the market. The Halyard Marine Industries seal has an oil reservoir mounted at a higher level so that the three lip seals within the rubber gaiter are lubricated and kept in contact with the micron smooth sleeve fixed to the shaft. The American Packless Sealing System, marketed in this country by Sea Otter, has no reservoir and is claimed not to be affected by contaminated water. It relies instead on the mechanical contact, under pressure, between a stationary carbon flange fixed to the stern tube and a stainless steel rotor attached to the shaft.

A plummer block, used to relieve the stern bearing of side loads

Many wear-conscious installations include a 'plummer block' (thrust bearing) just inboard of the stuffing box. It takes side loads off the stern bearing and all thrust loads off the engine. A plummer block will do nothing for the quietness of your engine but its sophisticated cousin, the Aquadrive, certainly will. The Aquadrive, with two constant velocity joints, allows the engine to shake sideways or fore and aft, and its angular tolerance is much greater than a conventional flexible coupling. The unit sits on rubber mounts so reduces transmitted noise and vibration.

When engine clatter, transmission rumble and propeller thrash have been deadened, the exhaust note will remain. One *WW* reader's solution to this was to follow automotive practice by fitting an expansion box upstream of the silencer, with drastic softening to exhaust note. Water-injected exhausts (as used with heat exchanger cooling systems) are not necessarily much quieter than dry ones, and may be regarded as

Aquadrive combines a number of functions to promote quieter transmission

antisocial if they spray sooty water over boats in locks. This problem can be overcome by using a separator silencer which, as its name implies, separates the exhaust gases from the cooling water and emits the former above the water level and the latter, silently, below.

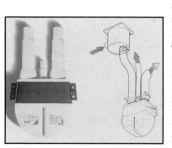

The HMI separator silencer separates water from exhaust gasses to reduce spluttering

Remote installation

If you take all the steps above, and remove yourself to nine or ten feet away from the engine, it will be almost silent. The obvious way to do this is to follow traditional practice with engine room forward of aft cabin – but to box the engine in. If this enclosed engine is moved 2ft sideways, several benefits appear: exhaust outlet and vent grills can be in the hull side at a point where the escaping noise offends no one. The long, angled, drive shaft neces-

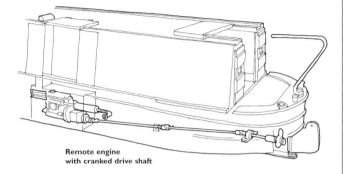

Remote engine with cranked drive shaft

sary between engine and tail shaft, can go under the side furniture in a traditional boatmans (or other) cabin – allowing full headroom instead of more usual raised floor over prop shaft. Also, the engine room space can be put to additional use – say with centre corridor between engine box and narrow toilet compartment. The cranked drive shaft is well established practice. Wilson Drive Shafts of Nottingham make assemblies primarily for lorries, but has supplied several to narrowboat owners over the years. The universal joints involved can work at up to 23 degrees out of line. Linked drive lines have included up to three shafts; and a sliding joint can be incorporated to allow for fore-and-aft movement of the engine/gearbox.

A more drastic step (but also well proven) is to move the engine to the forward end of the boat using hydraulic transmission to connect engine and propeller. Long straight pipe runs down the length of the hull are made with ordinary steel tube without significant power losses. Hydraulic transmission is substantially more expensive than, say, a cranked drive shaft system; but once installed the hydraulic pump can also be (and has been) used to drive a 230-volt generator and/or bow thruster. ARS Marine is an inland hydraulic transmission specialist.

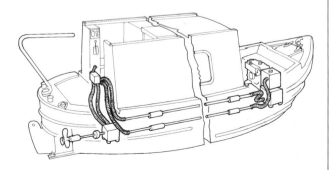

Forward mounted engine with hydraulic drive

Diesel-electric

Many modern narrowboats demand so much cabin electric power that they carry a built-in diesel generator in addition to the diesel propulsion engine. This is because the propulsion engine is too large to run just for generating electric power, without risk of increased internal wear through light-load running.

On the other hand a relatively small diesel could generate cabin power efficiently; and, by driving an electric motor on the prop shaft, could replace a larger engine for propulsion. The electric transmission is a superb torque converter, endowing the little engine with torque to start and stop a large narrowboat confidently.

That small diesel will be set to run constantly at its most efficient speed, reducing exhaust pollution considerably over the tickover-plus-400rpm regime of existing narrowboat engines. The constant note and relatively light weight of the engine, mechanically isolated from the shell, should be easy to insulate to near silence and the compact unit can be moved to a position remote from both cockpits. This is diesel-electric propulsion and it is already in use: several builders have now completed craft based on an HFL drive/generating package. The HFL system is based on 380-volt three-phase output to the propulsion motor, which makes it particularly efficient.

Diesel/electric

Replacing the hyphen between 'diesel' and 'electric' with an oblique slash signifies that drive can either be by diesel or electric. This might be based on a diesel-electric system (more-or-less as above) but with a bank of batteries for occasional engine-off propulsion (as when working a flight of locks in fume-free silence). For this to work simply, the propulsion motor has to be relatively low voltage DC.

Recent developments

Beta Marine has a new package called the Prop Gen. The aim is to provide a single power source capable, simultaneously, of propelling the boat and producing enough electricity to enable it to be completely gasless. It does this with a 30hp BV 2203 or 40hp BF 2803 engine set to a fixed speed of 1500rpm and coupled, at the forward end, to an 11.3 kVA Genko generator. A Newage hydraulic gearbox is connected to the flywheel and the propeller speed can be varied from 0 to 750 rpm by a Newage trolling valve/feathering device which bleeds the clutches of oil pressure. The smaller engine is for boats up to 55 or 60ft and the larger is for boats of 60 to 70ft.

The engine speed remains constant regardless of whether AC power is being generated or not. The whole unit is housed in an acoustic enclosure which reduces the noise level to about 68dbA at one metre. Although the concept is new to the inland waterways it is fairly common on fishing boats which need power for auxiliary equipment like winches while, at the same time, the boat is being manoeuvred about.

CHAPTER 7

BALLASTING AND LINING OUT

Tools of the trade
Ballasting
Laying the floor
Insulation
Lining the interior

TOOLS OF THE TRADE

Before we get down to the real business of fitting out the boat, let us look at the tools that you will need for the job. If you are ambitious enough to be thinking about a project like this then the chances are you will already have amassed a reasonable collection. As far as hand tools are concerned, you will need a good range of screwdrivers, chisels, pliers, files, G-cramps, hammer, tenon and panel saws, and a plane. Also very useful are a Stanley knife, keyhole saw, adjustable trisquare and a number of steel tape measures – I am always losing mine. Most of these are pretty straightforward but two deserve a special mention.

Saws
There are some very good hardened steel saws on the market now – both tenon and panel types. These are extremely sharp from new, stay sharp for a long time but, because they cannot be re-sharpened in the normal way, then have to be thrown away. They are fairly reasonably priced so the occasional cost of a new one is outweighed by the advantage of having a really sharp saw.

Planes
Another product of the throwaway age, but one which does not seem to have caught on to the same extent is the Stanley RB10 replaceable blade plane. This can be used as a smoothing plane or, because the blade goes right to the edge of the sole plate, as a rebate plane. The smoothing blades have a slight camber to prevent the corners from digging in while the rebate ones are straight. I now have a Stanley honing guide and find this makes sharpening conventional plane blades and chisels a lot easier. Even so, it still surprises me that the RB10 is not more popular – a fact which you will discover when you try to buy replacement blades.

Power tools
The core of essential power tools is a half inch drill, circular saw, jig saw, planer and sander. Most of my tools are Black & Decker Proline standard. These, as their name implies are a cut above the basic DIY range but even these are only just man enough for the work involved in fitting out a narrowboat. If I had to replace them I would think in terms of a B & D industrial, Makita or Elu. All the pundits who try to persuade you to buy the best you can afford are, on this occasion, dead right.

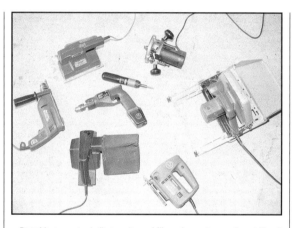

Portable power tools: jigsaw, planer, drill, sander, router, cordless drill and screwdriver, circular saw (in Triton Workcentre mount)

The drill I use is a Black & Decker 550watt D155RT which copes with most of the heavy work. As I have already said, my one bugbear about fitting out boats is drilling through steel. I have tried various types of drill bit and various techniques but just when I think I have cracked the problem I find another part which is seemingly impossible to drill through. A slow speed and plenty of oil to lubricate the bit seems to give the best results.

The circular saw has a 7 $^1/_4$in blade and a 1100watt motor which is about as big as you can conveniently use hand held. Tungsten carbide tipped (TCT) blades are expensive but essential as the resin in plywood and chipboard soon blunt ordinary steel blades and make them impossible to steer in a straight line. Jigsaws are useful for curved cuts but not very good for straight ones. In the time taken sawing and then truing up the line with a plane you can usually make the cut dead straight first time with a hand saw – and get some exercise into the bargain. Pendulum action, which causes the blade to swing backwards and forwards as it goes up and down makes for faster cutting but gives a rougher edge, especially when cutting across the grain of plywood. With the right blade my Proline jigsaw will cut through 5mm steel, handy for cutting holes for chimney collars and the like. However I have to admit that it is not as good as the AEG which I borrowed to cut the windows in the front bulkheads on *George*. This went through the 4mm steel as though it was plywood.

Optional extras

To these basics I have recently added a router. This really does come into the category of 'how did I ever manage without one?' It will not only add decorative mouldings to the edges of solid timber, saving pounds on strip mouldings from the DIY store, but will also cut rebates and trenches which will raise the whole standard of your woodwork.

Since I fitted out the last boat the cordless revolution has arrived – well, with me it has anyway, and I now have a cordless drill and screwdriver. I must admit that I always thought of these screwdrivers as little more than toys given as Christmas presents to the man who has everything. That was before I tried one. Not only do they save physical effort – and that has got to be good – they allow you to fix screws single-handedly in positions that would be impossible with a conventional screwdriver. I have a Black and Decker 3.5volt model which copes with screws up to about an inch and a half in length. Anything bigger or meatier than that and I use the Bosch 9.6volt drill. This really came into its own fixing the two layers of 3in x 2in floor bearers using 4in screws. The clamping action as the screws went home was a joy to behold. The drill is also very useful for drilling the millions of small holes without the inconvenience of having a lead trailing round, and of course, if you don't have a land-line, it means that more work can be done without running the generator. In addition, a small, variable speed cordless drill is very useful for pilot holes and countersinks and saves you having constantly to change bits.

Third hand

For a job as big as this, a second Workmate has proved it's worth but the new tool which has had the greatest impact is the Triton Workcentre. This is an all metal work stand into which you fit your own power tools so that it becomes a saw table, spindle moulder or, less commonly, a bench jigsaw. There is also the facility to work with the tools sliding between parallel guides over the top of the workpiece. It is to wood what word and food processors are to words and food. I have only used a few of its many functions so far but it has already saved time, effort and money as well as producing a far

The Triton Workcentre

better finish than would otherwise have been possible. The cost is close on £300 but the benefits are enormous and I reckon it paid for itself just by enabling me to make the galley doors and drawers; so you could say that, from then on, it cost nothing.

Second hand

If you have the space, a radial arm saw and a planer thicknesser will make the job easier still. The radial arm saw complements the Triton very well and means that you are not forever adjusting from one mode to another. The planer thicknesser will save you money by enabling you to buy sawn instead of planed wood. It does, however, have the slight drawbacks of being very noisy and producing mountains of shavings. Keep your eye on the private ads in *Traditional Woodworking* magazine and you will probably find a bargain.

Hired hand

These tools should see you through the woodwork part of the job but if you are also planning to tackle the services you will need a few specialist tools. These include a blow lamp, spanners and a pipe spring for plumbing and a crimper for fixing connectors to the ends of electrical flex. For some of these tools which may only be used for a very limited time it is worth considering hiring rather than buying. I hired a 28mm pipe bender for the solid fuel central heating pipework. It cost about £10 a week but I completed the job over a weekend and paid only the 48 hour rate.

BALLASTING

Ballasting is a subject shrouded in mystery, folklore and the usual helping of conflicting advice. We ballasted *Rome* while it was still at the yard so that we could cruise it home with a reasonable trim. The boatyard recommended using engineering bricks which have the advantage of being very dense, relatively non-moisture absorbent and small in size so that they can be packed into awkward spaces. This seemed to make good sense so it was agreed that the yard would order some seconds for us. We dispensed with estimating weights of materials and complicated formulae in favour of putting in a layer of bricks and seeing what effect it had. Our only concession to science was to lay the starboard side bricks on their edges, to pack more in, in order to counteract the slightly lopsided final layout of the boat.

The first layer went down well once we had got into a routine with one on the bank passing the bricks to the other on the boat packing them in. When we had completed this we stood back and were dismayed to see that the counter was still about 6" out of the water and the bow was much too high. Much stroking of chins and scratching of heads later it was agreed that, even allowing for the weight of water, diesel and fitting out materials, a second layer of bricks would be needed. So, more bricks were ordered and we went back the next weekend to finish the job. The second load completely covered the first layer and the stiffening angles and gave the inside of the boat the appearance of a brick-paved patio. The garden table and chairs brought on to make our homecoming trip more comfortable only added to the illusion. This second layer did however have the desired effect and, allowing for the water, diesel etc. it was generally felt that we had got it about right this time.

While we decided to use engineering bricks on *Rome*, most boat builders use concrete slabs, even though they are slightly less dense and more liable to absorb moisture.

The problem of barely finding enough space for under floor ballast is less likely to arise in medium draught narrowboats. Shorter boats need less ballast (in relation to their length) than longer ones.

Typical size and weight for concrete slabs is 2ft x 2ft x 2in x 90lb. As Chapter Three suggested, fitting them, mainly unbroken, between bearers is easier if you specify bearer centres at 2ft1in, 2ft 1in, 2ft 1in and 1ft 9in – to make 8ft for standard ply floor panels. Bilge-to-floor dimensions of 4in or 5in are common today – the latter allows two layers of slabs and an air gap over. This dimension is typically made up by a 3in steel frame and 2in timber bearer.

Finnegan's Waxoyl is the definitive protector of the cabin bilge. It is thick, tenacious and tends to self-mend any damage to its surface – particularly useful for getting into nooks and crannies. Some fitters-out apply Waxoyl to bare steel. If you want to paint the bilge first, use zinc phosphate primer rather than bitumen paint because Waxoyl dissolves the latter.

Washed gravel seems a convenient way to ballast – but actually retains water and any contaminants that enter the bilge. Concrete, poured wet, has been used as ballast – and (topped by asphalt) as a floor in narrowboats. The argument for it has been that it almost bonds with the bottom plate to preclude any damp action. However you must get your ballast calculations right first time or you will have to add a pneumatic drill to your tool kit. The Waxoyl/air gap route seems altogether safer.

Underlay
It is fairly common practice these days to lay the ballast on a layer of building felt which is supposed to stop it rubbing the paint off the base plate if it moves around. Fine in theory but it seemed to me that there was a danger that, if condensation or a spillage resulted in water getting into the bilge, it would settle under the felt and take much longer to evaporate. Subsequent experience with other boats has proved this theory correct.

The Rolls-Royce solution to overcome this is to lay the ballast on plastic blocks to provide a half inch or so gap underneath the ballast to allow the base plate to dry out quicker, but this is only feasible if you use concrete paving slabs. I decided to dispense with the felt, put my faith in the Waxoyl which the yard had already sprayed around the bilge and made sure that the bricks were well packed in so that they were unlikely to move too much. Periodic lifting of floor panels has supported this theory as well.

How much will it weigh?
If you want to be more scientific about ballasting, how do you calculate the final design weight of your boat? Follow this example of a 50ft narrow boat (waterline length 46ft) with 12ft aft swim and 10ft forward swim:

Approximate bottom plate area of swims
(calculated by treating them as simple triangles)
= (12 x 6.5 / 2) + (10 x 6.5 / 2)   = 71.5 sq ft

Bottom plate area of section in between (24ft)
= 24 x 6.5   = 156 sq ft

Total bottom plate area
= 71.5 + 156   = 227.5 sq ft

Displaced volume of water
= bottom plate area x average draught
= 227.5 x 1.5   = 341 cu ft

As 1 cu ft of water weighs 62.5lb,
the boat's final weight will be 341 x 62.5
= 23,750lb   = 10.6 tons

A half-ton (or twelve slab) error in ballasting would alter the waterline by $3/4$in. As narrowboats are rarely ballasted as precisely as this, it is hardly an exact science.

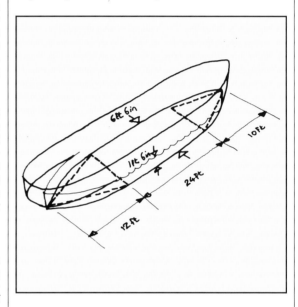

You can roughly calculate the ballast needed by adding weights of shell (available from your builder), engine (typically half-a-ton, including installation equipment), fuel and water (use half-full figures – at 9lb and 10lb a gallon respectively), fitting-out materials and cabin equipment. The difference between this total and the design weight above is your approximate ballast requirement.

Guide weights for standard 8ft x 4ft sheets:

6mm WBP (exterior) ply	19lb
9mm WBP (exterior) ply	29lb
12mm WBP (exterior) ply	39lb
12mm birch ply	43lb
18mm WBP ply	58lb
18mm birch ply or shuttering ply for floors)	73lb
18mm hardwood core blockboard	77lb
18mm softwood core blockboard	57lb

An average water tank varies 3/4 ton between full and empty. As the tank is usually located in the bow, it affects forward trim by several inches. To avoid bow-down trim with full tank (and for one or two other reasons), narrowboats are usually ballasted to sit between two and six inches bow-high; although, for best swimming purposes, they are ideally trimmed level.

LINING OUT

The trip home in October showed that the engine generally performed well. When we did finally get home I took a fortnight of my saved-up leave to make a good start and encourage myself.

THE FLOOR

The first job was to fit the floor bearers which provide a fixing for the floor boards as well as increasing the height of the bilge to accommodate the ballast and allow some ventilation space. My original plan, assuming one layer of bricks, was to fix 3in x 2in timber bearers at right angles

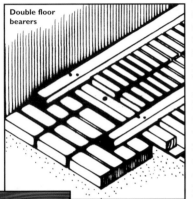

Double floor bearers

to the steel cross stiffeners to ensure good under floor ventilation from front to back. The alternative of laying the bearers parallel to the stiffeners would have resulted in a series of almost airtight compartments down the length of the boat. Since we now had two layers of bricks totalling 7 $\frac{1}{2}$ inches thick on the starboard side, I had to fix one set of bearers parallel to the stiffeners, and then a second set at right angles and on top of these to give the required under floor depth and maintain the ventilation. Apart from the extra work involved this also had the disadvantage of taking two inches off the internal floor to ceiling height which was now 6ft 2in maximum.

Floor bearers down

It is obviously a good idea to make as much of the floor as possible removable so that the under floor space can be inspected and ballast adjusted if necessary. I do not subscribe to the theory that the partitions and fittings should go in first and the floorboards dropped in afterwards. This seems to be an open invitation to the possibility of rot creeping up the partitions, not to mention the difficulty of working in the boat before the floor goes down. On the other hand I think that cutting a

Under floor access is particularly important in the back cabin

couple of holes in the floorboards after they have been fixed, although better than nothing, is a bit half-hearted. I therefore decided to arrange the floor bearers so that any section of floor which did not have anything permanent sitting on it would be removable.

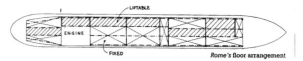

Rome's floor arrangement

Liftable floorboards

My plan for *Rome* divided itself naturally into three two foot wide strips running the length of the boat so I positioned the main timber bearers at the edges of these strips. I then made sure that the short edges of the boards were supported by adding more 3in x 2in bearers half housed at right angles into the long ones. In some cases these had ventilation holes drilled through them to prevent air tight compartments being formed. The main cabin is just over 33ft long so four 8ft boards plus an offcut in the middle fitted the plan very well with minimal waste.

Floor in place

For the boarding I used 18mm Far Eastern WBP (water and boil proof) plywood. This was not the cheapest but worth the extra over the cost of shuttering ply for ease of working and smoothness of finish. The undersides were treated with Cuprinol preservative before being screwed down with brass screws (thank goodness for the cordless screwdriver). I had deliberately not run any services under the floor so this stage was completed fairly quickly. Moving about the boat suddenly became much easier now that the risk of twisted ankles had been eliminated.

SHELL LINING

Insulation

The next job was to insulate and line the hull. Apart from reducing heat loss in winter, insulation prevents the cabin from becoming an oven in summer and it dampens noise transmitted through the shell. It is not regular practice to insulate below the floor boards as this restricts under floor air space and heat loss is, in any case, mainly upwards. The two most popular pre-formed materials are expanded polystyrene slab, and glass/rock wool. Common thicknesses are 2in to 3in on hull sides, $\frac{3}{4}$in to 1 $\frac{1}{2}$in inside the superstructure. A small air gap ($\frac{1}{4}$in to $\frac{1}{2}$in) between insulation and the cabin linings is healthy for the latter. Whichever material you choose you are not likely to notice any difference in insulating properties but each has its advantages.

Polystyrene is very easy to handle and not expensive to buy. However, in 1990, surveyors discovered that, when in contact with the PVC coating over electric wire, it causes that coating to become brittle with consequent risk of shorting to the steel shell. Elementary discipline in keeping the materials apart overcomes the problem. Only flame retardant grades of polystyrene should be used – and they are not fully fire resistant.

Glass/rock wool, however, presents no fire risk. So you might prefer to fit it behind hull side linings where, in the fullness of time, welding could be needed (fitting sacrificial anodes, replating, etc). Both glass and rock wool are made in different densities, from pliable to rigid. The latter can often be cut, like polystyrene, with a knife, but tends to be more expensive (Pilkington actually makes Crown Navy Board specifically for marine insulation). Glass/rock wool needs to be packed in firmly to prevent long term sagging. If wet, it is likely to become soggily ineffective – unlike polystyrene which has closed cell construction. Face masks and gloves should be worn when fitting either wool type.

Hull insulation

I decided to use 2in fire retardant expanded polystyrene slabs for the hull and 1in slabs for the cabin sides and roof. This can be cut quite easily with a bread knife without producing too much mess. With practice you can cut the slabs to the exact size to ensure that they fit snugly between the stiffeners. This snug fit is important as it discourages moisture vapour

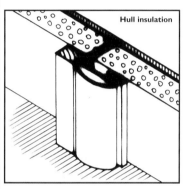

Hull insulation

from getting round the insulation and condensing on the steel behind it. With the 2in slabs pressed firmly against the inside of the hull about 1in of the leg of the stiffening angle was left projecting into the boat. This had to be insulated to prevent a cold bridge occurring which would attract condensate. It also had to have a timber batten or noggin fixed to it to receive the ply lining. For this insulation I used 2mm thick expanded polystyrene sheet obtainable in rolls from DIY and decorating stores. It is rather fragile but can be cut with a sharp knife and bent, with care, round a right angle.

I devised a fixing method whereby the 2in x 1in batten was held by screws through pre-drilled holes in the angles. The polystyrene was cut into 6in wide strips and one edge clamped between the angle and the batten. The other edge was held between the angle and the polystyrene slab by a half-inch thick strip of polystyrene. After a couple of practice runs it worked quite well but would have been much more difficult without the newly acquired cordless screwdriver. The battens were fixed through their short sides leaving a minimal clearance between the face of the angle and the ply hull lining. The alternatives of fixing through the long sides or of bolting the batten to the face of the angle would have meant that the internal width of the hull would have been reduced, which I was keen to avoid. This point is particularly worth watching if you are planning a cross-bed layout.

Cabin insulation

Cabin and roof lining came next using the slightly easier to handle 1in slabs. I discovered that by pressing the slabs against the ply surrounds to the portholes a shallow

impression was made which, when cut round with the trusty bread knife allowed the slab to be pushed in place around the porthole with great accuracy. I was saved the job of fixing cabin and roof battens because the builder, as is his usual practice, had already clenched battens into the 2in x 1in channel sections which stiffen the superstructure. The battens finished slightly proud of the face of the polystyrene but did not leave enough of a gap for wiring.

The next task was therefore to mark out the positions of all light fittings, switches and the like, and run oval plastic conduit set into grooves cut into the slabs to each one of them. The grooves are easily formed by slicing down either side of the line to the required depth with a sharp knife and then removing the waste in between with an old chisel. I then drew the wires through the conduits leaving enough at each end to allow the fittings to be connected

Insulation fitted and hull lining started

later. The conduits not only prevent the wiring from coming into contact with the polystyrene, as required by BW Boat Safety Standards, but also allow you to remove and replace wire if you find you have a problem in future. All the internal framing was then covered with 4in strips of 2mm expanded polystyrene sheet stuck with heavy duty wall paper paste – a boring job but essential to stop cold bridges allowing condensation to form. A quick check to see that everything which needed to be behind the lining was in place, and it was then time to think about covering up all that polystyrene.

Providing evidence

When your Certificate of Compliance surveyor asks if PVC-coated wire is in contact with polystyrene insulation, you could answer no – even if it is. However, he might well find you out on Certificate renewal in four years time because he can test for leakage. If, on the other hand, you feel conscientious, you could take photos of your wiring to show the surveyor before concealing it. One surveyor actually suggests bringing him along at this stage to inspect the wiring and to make helpful general suggestions that could save you corrective work when your boat is finally submitted for a Certificate.

T&G vs Panels

The lining can be done in many ways depending on your personal taste. Our first narrowboat, like most boats built in those days, was lined in knotty pine tongued and grooved boarding. This looked alright at the time, partly because the boat was relatively short. In longer boats, the boarding tends to accentuate the length and narrowness of the interior which is exactly what you don't want. The cabin sides of *George* were already lined in parana pine boards which were much too well executed for me to even consider replacing but on the partitions I experimented with a different treatment. I fixed half-inch thick boards around the edges of the plywood partitions to imitate framed construction. Beading was then glued to the inside edges of the boards and the face of the plywood remaining in the middle covered with hessian or cork tiles. The boarding was generally 4in wide increasing to 6in for the middle and bottom rails. This gave a pleasant atmosphere to the interior so I decided to use the technique throughout the new boat.

Hull lining
For the basic hull lining I used 12mm WBP plywood. Most of this went up very quickly, being simply rectangular sheets screwed back to the battens. Inevitably the spacing of the battens did not quite suit the 8ft length of the linings but the amount of trimming required to ensure that all edges were supported was minimal. The boatman's cabin however took a bit longer as the fixing points for battens seemed to peter out at this end. Fortunately the curved shape provided added stiffness to the sides and once the triangular pieces which covered the swim were glued and screwed to the sides the whole thing became very solid. If you are really short of fixing battens, try gluing them to the inside of the shell with Gripfill or a similar, gun-applied adhesive. I have never done this but those who have swear by it.

Cabin lining
Next came the cabin lining – less easy because of the combined effects of gravity and the fact that I am cursed with having only one pair of hands. One thing which you will discover quite early on is that no matter how many offers

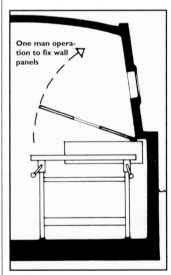

One man operation to fix wall panels

of help you might receive, the kindly souls are very often not to be seen when you want them. It is therefore a good idea to start developing some crafty ways of doing things single-handedly.

In the case of the cabin sides I cut the boards – 9mm this time – to the correct height, saving the off-cuts to use under the gunwales. I then positioned two Workmates at right angles to the hull side and near to each end of where the board was to be fixed. Plywood off-cuts were clamped into the Workmates and set at the height of the bottom edge of the cabin lining. It was then simply a matter of resting the board across the offcuts and pivoting it up into place against the insulation. To keep it in place while the screws were driven in, it was propped with suitable lengths of timber wedged against the opposite side of the hull.

Where the portholes occurred, I measured and marked the position of the centre onto the lining board and cut a hole centred on this, about one inch less in diameter than the porthole itself. The board was then offered up again and, using a short pencil, the outline of the porthole was traced

onto the back of the board. Down onto the benches again, a quick run round with the jig saw and voilà! Had the port-holes not been permanently fixed by this stage, I could have removed them and drawn the line from outside the boat.

The only part of the cabin side which was not lined with ply was the part which would eventually be behind the stove in the Boatman's cabin. For this section I used 6mm Masterboard. This contains no asbestos but has similar heat resisting properties. It cuts and drills well but crumbles just as easily so care is needed when fitting it.

Wiring channel
Since the majority of the wiring was to be run down the length of the boat at gunwale level it occurred to me that I could form an integral 'conduit' there to contain it. Before the cabin lining was finally screwed in place I fixed a 9mm ply gunwale liner, supported by a soft-wood batten to the top of the hull lining. After the cabin lining had been fixed I screwed another soft-wood batten behind the bottom edge of this lining so as to support the front edge of the gunwale lining. This formed an inverted channel section, with no exposed polystyrene, into which the wiring could be fixed before another strip of ply-

Under gunwale duct

wood was screwed to the underside of the battens to complete the box.

Roof lining
The roof lining was 6mm oak-faced ply. As this would simply be varnished rather than covered with another material I had to be more careful about the positioning of joints. The roof itself is about 4ft 6in wide. This allows a 4ft wide board to be fixed centrally leaving just enough space either side for conduits where they are needed. These are then covered with 4in wide strips of the same oak-faced plywood with oak moulding glued against the edge, rather like the partitions.

Our previous boat had Colecraft's familiar dummy roof beams in the saloon but on *Rome* I decided that the entire length of the roof should be divided up at intervals by 4in wide ply strips edged by oak moulding to form a coffered effect. These strips would generally occur where one area of the boat met another, but larger areas like the saloon would be divided by intermediate strips. These would coincide with the vertical framing on the cabin sides. It never ceases to amaze me how many good boatfitters miss this point and have divisions in the ceiling which are total-ly unrelated to what goes on below.

Lining up divisions in cabin side and ceiling

The only area longer than the length of a board was the saloon, but fortunately one of the intermediate strips came in just the right place to cover the joint. Incidentally, if you want to divide anything like this into three parts it usually looks better if you make the middle part slightly wider than the outside parts. All the other areas being less than one board long had their roof boards cut to the right length and the offcuts used for edge strips.

When it came to fixing the ceiling panels Evelyn, the Fitter's Mate, came to my rescue but even with two people this job can be tricky. We found it useful to have two pieces of 3in x 2in timber cut to about 1 $^{1}/_{2}$in shorter than the height of the cabin at its highest point. The technique was to raise the board to ceiling level with one person supporting either end. Each person then positioned one of the props a little way in from the end with the 1 $^{1}/_{2}$in gap being made up with a piece of polystyrene so that the surface of the panel was not damaged. The board is then screwed through pre-drilled holes into the timber battens above. The smaller panels can be put in place by one person using this method.

Boatman's cabin
The boatman's cabin and engine room ceilings were a slightly different problem. We had opted for traditional speedwheel and push-pull gear control which meant that there were several guides projecting through the ceiling – not to mention the exhaust pipe, fuel vent and stovepipe. The engine controls had been thoughtfully detailed so that the rods could be removed easily but I still did not fancy trying to manhandle a piece of plywood up there and get

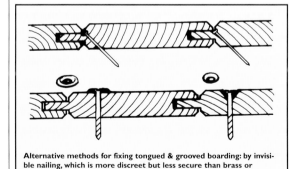

Alternative methods for fixing tongued & grooved boarding: by invisible nailing, which is more discreet but less secure than brass or stainless steel screws. Housing the screws in countersunk, rather than raised, cup washers provides a neater finish

all the holes in precisely the right place. I therefore decided to use T&G boarding for the ceiling over these areas. The planks were far easier to handle and I could deal with

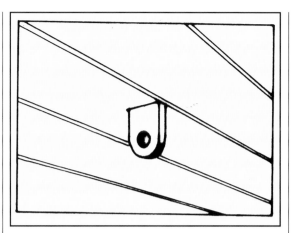

T&G boarding makes it easier to accommodate obstructions

the obstructions one by one. They also give this part of the boat a different and more traditional atmosphere. The backs of the boards were given a coat of varnish to seal them and were fixed with panel pins through the face since I intended to paint rather than varnish this ceiling. The wall treatment was basically the same as the rest of the boat except that the edge strips were plain plywood as they would eventually be scumbled.

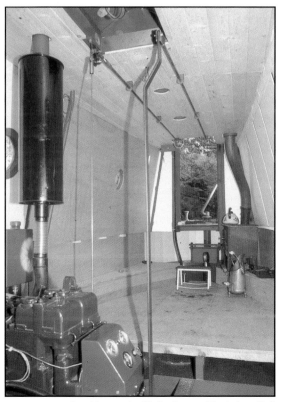

Rome's boatman's cabin, lined-out, awaiting its 'scumbled' (grained) finish

CHAPTER 8

SETTING OUT & BASIC SERVICES

The bathroom
Hot and cold water
Heating systems
Engine/calorifier
Wiring

With the lining out complete, the interior became easier to move about in and much warmer – which was greatly appreciated as winter was fast approaching. The first job was to set to with a piece of chalk and mark out the position of partitions and fittings. My layout, and ideas on internal finishing treatment, relied heavily on symmetry and the lining up of various features in the boat. I had to take this into account when I prepared the drawing for the builder. Now was the time to discover whether they, and I, had got it right. As expected the overall length of the cabin and positions of doors and portholes were within a fraction of an inch of where I had drawn them.

Grasping the nettle
The most critical areas were those containing bought in equipment like the bathroom and galley, or built-in furniture of fixed length like the bed/dinette, so that's where I decided to start. When tackling any problem of this sort I find it useful to start with the parts you are certain about or cannot change and work round to the parts you are less certain about or which can be altered.

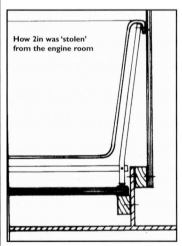

How 2in was 'stolen' from the engine room

With this in mind, I started with the bathroom. I soon discovered that the bath we both liked was 2in or 3in wider than I had allowed for, and that the Midland Chandlers' standard loo tank – which is considerably cheaper than a made-to-measure one – was an inch or two longer than I had hoped. The result of this was that, if I set out the bathroom starting from the back of the boat and the dinette starting from the centre line of the porthole as I planned, I ended up with a dining table 11in wide with a very wide seat on one side of it!

We considered other types of baths or shower trays but we did not really like the narrower ones. Then I remembered that when we switched to the smaller engine I only reduced the length of the engine room by about 3in (which went into the boatman's cabin) and there was still surplus space in front of the engine. If I could start the bathroom a couple of inches further back I might just make the plan work after all.

The engine room is separated from the main cabin by a 9in high steel upstand. Normally the ply bulkhead would be fixed directly to this but, by bolting a 2in thick timber to the back of the upstand and fixing the bulkhead to this, the bathroom gained the 2in it needed to accommodate the wider bath. A quick check with MC confirmed that the supporting cradle for the bath could be modified to allow the rim to oversail the upstand, and things were looking up. If I made the cladding around the loo tank as close fitting as possible, the width of the dining table increased to 20in – not as much as I would have liked but reasonable.

All of this serves to show that thorough pre-planning, so that the mistakes happen on paper – not in steel, is essential. It also shows that with a bit of flexibility and ingenuity most problems can be overcome – which is just as well because I found I had a similar, but not quite so serious problem when I got to the galley . . .

Dimensions across the boat are best set out from a centre line so that slight discrepancies in the line of the hull lining are minimised. Once again the bath was the determining factor, leaving just enough space for the corridor alongside the bathroom. Since *Rome's* cabin side has a reasonable amount of tumblehome (lean in) I also checked

Rome's toilet compartment. Note Hep^{2}O plastic plumbing, horizontal lagged calorifier, polypropylene **WC** holding tank (with Mansfield freshwater flush **WC** already mounted on it) – and the bath that caused a space problem

the width of the corridor at shoulder height. It was just alright but had the corridor been any longer it might have felt too tight. It is very difficult to give a hard and fast rule for this as it depends on so many factors, not least how wide the occupants of the boat are! The best advice is to make a mock up of the space, either with an odd piece of plywood or the actual partition fixed temporarily, and sound out your crew.

Services

Having completed chalking the layout on the floor and walls I was ready to start installing the basic service runs. In my layout, most of these run down the starboard side of the boat and are much better installed at this stage before the partitions go up. My basic aim was that the pipes should be out of sight but as accessible as possible in case of problems. The plan of the boat suited this aim and I was able to arrive at a simple arrangement which resulted in the minimum number of pipes crossing one another.

Hot and cold water

On *Bess* I used solvent-welded pipes which were fine provided you got everything right first time and never had a burst pipe – they were not easy to adapt or repair. On *George* I used copper, mainly because I was more familiar with it and because the previous owner had started using it. Copper is more forgiving, provided you use compression fittings, is neat and precise but prone to frost damage if you can't drain it down completely. Nevertheless I was quite happy to use it again – until I visited Midland Chandlers that is. They persuaded me that copper was the plumbing equivalent of wattle and daub and that what I should be using was push-fit plastic.

The advantages of this, they said, are that it is easy to install, leak free, frost resistant (but not frost proof) and costs little more than copper pipes with compression fittings. My doubts were based mainly on the rather knobbly appearance of the fittings. However, I decided that, as all my pipework would be concealed and since I knew a number of people who had used push-fit more than once, I would give it a try.

Hep^{2}0 elbow showing the '0' ring and a brass elbow with an olive

There are now several manufacturers making their own versions. One of the first on the market was Bartol whose brand name 'Acorn' has been adopted by the industry and become a household name. This is unfortunate as the company has been taken over by Hepworth Building Products and the Acorn name has been dropped in favour of Hep ^{2}O.

Hepworth recommends that the pipes should be supported at about 18in centres. I therefore marked out the length of the boat at 18in intervals and made a template showing the heights of the various pipes. This enabled me to fix the pipe clips at the correct heights and at a regular spacing – not vitally important as they would eventually be covered up but it seemed a good idea to start off in a neat and tidy

way. The spacing of the clips is certainly the maximum that should be used, and the 15mm pipes in particular sag in between them. In places where they might be seen or if you are more fussy, 12in centres would be a better bet.

I must confess I did not enjoy using the system very much. This was partly because of unfamiliarity – I kept having to open the joints to make sure I had remembered the support ring – and partly because I was using coiled pipe which stays banana shaped, making it more difficult to use in tight situations such as around the water pump. The answer to this would have been to buy some lengths of straight pipe for the tricky bits and use the coil for the long runs. My other worry was the thought that if a joint did leak there did not seem to be much I could do about it – with compression copper you can always give it an extra quarter turn. However, my fears were groundless and I am pleased to report that, when I did eventually fill and pressurise the system, the only leaks were from brass fittings.

HEATING SYSTEMS

Gas

You may recall that I decided to have two independent heating systems on *Rome* – one from a solid fuel stove and one from a boiler. A review of the different types of boilers is included in chapter 12. The Alde gas boiler which we chose is thermostatically controlled so push-fit plumbing is able to cope with the likely temperature range. It has a pump but this is so small – I assumed at first that the stated wattage was a misprint – that the system must be designed for minimum resistance. For this reason 22mm pipe is normally used.

So far so good – we next had to decide on the type of radiator. Here I encountered another batch of conflicting advice. One camp said that the boiler was designed for 'finrads' – lengths of copper pipe with aluminium fins threaded on to dissipate the heat – as these offer minimum resistance to the flow of water. The oppo-

A short length of Finrad – 22 mm copper pipe with aluminium fins to dissipate the heat

site camp said that in order to take all the available heat from the boiler you would need an inordinate length of finrad so ordinary domestic radiators were the only answer. Assuming 500 watts per metre it would, in fact, need about ten metres of finrad which is not that easy to accommodate unless you can install it down the whole of one side of the cabin.

My response to this particular dilemma was the, by now, familiar compromise. I settled on a radiator in the saloon where we would want maximum heat and finrads built into the step of the raised dinette and the bench seat of the boatman's cabin (cries of sacrilege!). There is also one in the bathroom but more of that later. The gas boiler also heats one of the coils in the calorifier. As the coil is made of 15mm pipe I used 15mm pipework for the branch which serves it. Most diagrams of these dual systems show each side – heating and calorifier – with its own isolating valve. I could imagine wanting to heat the calorifier without heating the cabin but not the other way round. I therefore put a valve only on the heating circuit so that restrictions were minimised and the heat from the boiler always has somewhere to go.

Solid fuel

The solid fuel side is another kettle of fish. It is unlikely that the stove would be deliberately run at anything like maximum output in the confines of a narrowboat but there

Linings complete and services started

is always the chance that it may get very hot for brief periods. At these times, a plug of near boiling water can enter the system so it is imperative to use copper pipe. Most systems work by what is known as gravity flow. Water is heated in the back boiler, becomes less dense, rises in the flow pipe which is carefully angled to allow this to happen, drops through the radiator, cooling as it goes, and is sucked back along the return pipe by the vacuum formed when the water is heated in the back boiler, becomes less dense and . . . you get the idea. It is an ideal system for a boat being simple, quiet and relatively maintenance free. Getting the water to flow needs even larger diameter pipes than the gas fired system – 28mm is the norm. You can install a pump to circulate the water through smaller bore pipes or a less than perfectly designed system, but do you really want to settle down on a nice calm evening listening to a pump whirring away and thinking how much battery power it is consuming?

I decided to use just one radiator in this system. This was based on the experience of *George* where, possibly due to the layout of the pipework, the near radiator was generally by-passed and only the far one ever got really warm. This was no real problem as the additional heat was more appreciated the further one got from the stove. The radiator on *Rome* is 4ft 6in x 2ft 6in, big enough to cope with a fair amount of heat from the stove.

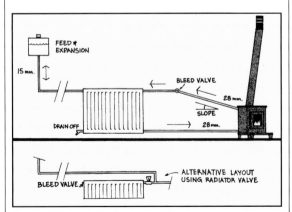
Simple solid fuel central heating layout – driven by convection rather than pump

I reckoned that if it was cold enough to light the stove it was unlikely that we would not want heat in the bedroom as well so I dispensed with radiator valves. This had the advantage of removing two severe restrictions from the system and so improved the flow. If you don't believe this, take a look into the end of a fully open valve next time you're in a plumber's mer-

Rome's solid fuel stove; curved pipes were achieved with a hired pipe bender

chant. Another advantage was that I could run the feed and expansion pipe directly out of the far side of the radiator instead of coming out of a tee upstream of the valve.

The pipework runs half behind the galley units and half along the bedroom wall. I decided to confine the slope on the pipe to the part behind the galley units so that the exposed part could be parallel to the gunwale and therefore less noticeable. Had *Rome* been trimmed to a more nose up attitude and the boiler been positioned further forward I might have had more of a problem achieving a reasonable rise on the pipe. My layout meant I needed to form something like a 15° bend in the pipe – not possible using standard fittings – so I hired a pipe bender. This also enabled me to form the 45° bends at the back of the boiler without using fittings and to make small offsets needed where different lining thicknesses were encountered. Using the bender required some practice but, after a rather buckled first attempt, I soon found that a firm continuous pull on the lever resulted in a smooth professional looking bend.

Engine/calorifier

The pipework between the engine and calorifier is a mixture of copper and plastic – copper where it is visible in the engine room and plastic where it is hidden. It may seem strange to owners of flexibly mounted engines to plumb to the engine in rigid copper but the Lister had been mounted on solid metal pads – not even hardwood or Tremco – and when it is running you can almost balance an upturned pencil on the cylinder head. I therefore had no fears about the pipework which, because of its length, would accommodate a small amount of movement anyway.

Plumbing-in the calorifier was done on a rather trial and error basis. The flow side was easy. Peter Thompson had installed a blanked-off tee fitting between the engine block and the thermostat. To one side of this the fragile mercury filled pipe to the temperature gauge was connected, while the other side was for the 12mm flow to the calorifier. I eventually managed to find a plumber's merchant who stocked a $3/_8$th male to 12mm compression fitting which enabled me to connect to the tee and keep the pipe

Hot water connections on *Rome's* Lister HW2 engine to and from calorifier – supply from between block and thermostat

Return downstream of oil cooler, via an unequal copper tee joint

well away from the front bulkhead and not foul the fuse board cupboard door.

The return pipe was more of a problem. Ideally this should rejoin the main engine plumbing downstream of the gearbox oil cooler but this would have meant a difficult connection into Peter's neatly soldered but tight pipework, and yet another pipe spanning the gap between the engine and the hull lining. All these problems could apparently be solved by making the connection into the main return just as it leaves the keel cooler but before the oil cooler. The only problem with this was that the cooling of the gearbox oil could be impaired. Expert opinion seemed to be that, although this was not the textbook solution, it would probably be OK in a relatively lightly stressed canal installation. I was tempted enough to try it. After completing the job and refilling the system I ran the engine under load to see what would happen. For some time nothing did and I started to wonder if I had an airlock. Then suddenly I could feel warm water coursing along the pipe on its way to, and then back, from the calorifier. Being the eternal pessimist I had removed all the duct covers and panels along the route so that I could immediately detect any leaks but fortunately there were none.

What did alarm me was that the temperature of the water returning to the engine was not a great deal cooler than the water coming from it. On the credit side I had proved that, in spite of doubts expressed by some of my 'experts', an older engine can produce enough hot water to supply a remote calorifier but in the process I had turned the oil cooler into an oil heater.

In one of those blinding flashes of inspiration which only occur when it is too late I realised that I might have avoided this problem just as easily by taking the calorifier return pipe into the main flow pipe from the engine to the keel cooler. Fortunately I consulted Peter before embarking on this modification and his advice was that, while the idea

might work and may be worth a try, I would be effectively bypassing the thermostat and this may increase the engine warm-up time. Faced with the prospect of another abortive drain down I decided to bite the bullet and do the job properly this time.

There was no convenient length of pipe where I could simply add a tee so I decided to replace one of the existing 'Yorkshire' elbows with an unequal tee and connect to that. Luckily I was able to remove the pipework from the engine and clamp it in the Workmate well away from the boat thus avoiding a possible fire hazard. Unsoldering the joint was not as difficult as I imagined it might be and the distance between the redundant joint and the next one along the pipe meant that the latter was not disturbed by the conducted heat. Getting the pipework back on the engine with the new 12mm leg soldered in place was a tight squeeze but it finally went in and I made up the compression and Jubilee clip/hose connections and refilled the system.

To my relief the soldered joints were sound – a leak at this stage would have signalled another drain down as I would have had no chance of heating up the joint sufficiently while it was full of water. Running up the engine in gear again showed that the water entering the oil cooler was cold, so I reckoned that I had got it right this time.

Bathroom heating

Where all the pipework, including the calorifier pipes passed through the bathroom, my original plan was to include a length of finrad heated from the Alde boiler. Because of the very limited length available I had bought twice the length of finrad with the idea of cutting it in two and twinning it behind the panel. As I worked, my 'policy of continuous improvement' lead me to realise that, if I had just one length of finrad on the boiler circuit, the other length could be let into the return pipe from the calorifier to the engine (a height restriction would not allow me to get three lengths in, one on top of the other). This arrangement would give me background heating in the bathroom whenever the engine was running which would help to dry towels and reduce condensation. Being on the return side it would not rob heat from the calorifier but would make use of any surplus heat when it was up to temperature.

Gas piping

As I said in chapter 2, DIY gas fitting is not strictly illegal at the time of writing but there are strong arguments for getting a CORGI fitter to do it. I will therefore not describe how to fit the pipework but simply mention some general points to consider when making provision for gas.

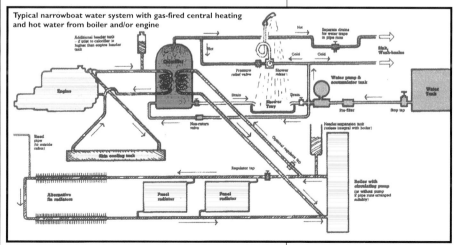
Typical narrowboat water system with gas-fired central heating and hot water from boiler and/or engine

The deepish draught of our boat meant that the bottom of the gas locker was below water level. For this reason the yard had not cut any ventilation holes as the final water-line was not known at the time. I was hoping that there was another way of doing it but eventually had to accept that holes would have to be drilled to let water into the locker so that this would force gas out of another set of holes higher up. In order to resist rusting, the inside of the locker was given two good coats of Smoothrite and the gas bottles stood on a slatted duckboard. The Smoothrite did not perform as hoped and I have since painted the lower part of the locker with the two part epoxy paint I used on the hull.

There are three extras to the gas system itself that you might consider specifying. One is the automatic changeover gas regulator. Two bottles are hooked up to it and both valves opened. When one empties the regulator automatically switches to the other – unless that too is empty. A variation on this is a regulator with pressure gauge – which indicates when a bottle is approaching empty. The gauge can also check for system leaks: if its reading drops after all appliances and gas bottle are turned off, gas must be escaping from the piping.

Another way of testing for leaks is to install a bubble tester near to the regulator so that you can monitor the system every time you turn the gas on. Electronic gas detectors give early warning of leaks via transducers mounted at floor level close to gas appliances. However some can 'cry wolf' by being too sensitive, sniffing other gases – from hair spray to flatulent dogs.

Wiring

When I fitted out *Bess* I opted out completely from this task and got the builder to wire the boat. I had to replace and modify so much wiring on *George* that I felt reasonably confident to tackle the whole job on *Rome* – except for the engine wiring which was done by the builder. My wiring was all done in a fairly piecemeal way – made possible by the under gunwale ducts which I had built in. A certain amount of wiring was put in before the linings went in and ends were left hanging to be connected up at a later date. After lining out I added a few more links and built up the remainder as I went along.

My attitude to wiring is very basic. You have a fuse, a piece of red wire, possibly a switch, some more red wire, a fitting and a black wire which goes back to the negative pole on the fuse board. Wire the fuse board up to a suitable battery and you're in business. Simple but it works. In order to reduce the number of wires coming into the fuse board I adopted the 'tree' principal of having thicker main trunk wires with a number of branches coming off these further up. I was tempted to use this method for the entire lighting system but realised that, if all the lighting went back to one wire, the fuse needed to cope with the total load would be so large as to offer little or no protection to individual fittings.

Fuse boards

I was rather surprised by the lack of suitable fuse boards on the market at the time . My usual chandler could offer only one, which would have looked a bit puny even in a caravan. I reckoned something meatier was called for and ended up using a house-type board. There are a number of types of these available, some with rewirable fuses right up to some really expensive ones with circuit breakers. After I had completed the installation I discovered that house-type boards can have disadvantages. This is not simply because they could be confused with the 230-volt board on a boat fitted with a mains system – they would be clearly marked in any case. The greater culprit is DC arcing: when a switch designed to carry alternating current (AC) is used in a direct current (DC) system, a spark is liable to arc between the contacts as they separate. This reduces the capacity of the switch or circuit breaker considerably. However, in five years of use, this has not caused me any problems.

Wiring sizes

For sizing the wiring I used the formula in *Marine Electrical Systems* by Colin Mudie, published by Lucas Marine Limited. Where the choice was borderline I went to the next size up to be sure that there would be no over-heating or voltage drop – the big problem with 12-volt systems. Why not use 24-volts? I did consider this but thought I might have difficulty getting all the equipment I needed in 24-volt form. The only item for which I did not have to do a wiring calculation was the electric fridge because the manufacturer had already done it for me. These fridges have low voltage cut-out mechanism so the wiring has to be particularly beefy to ensure that minor voltage drops do not set it off. The normally well stocked Midland Chandlers confused me with their range of wiring sizes. Instead of the 1.5, 2.5, 4, 6 and 10mm^2 sizes I had calculated, their stock is sized in the number of 0.3mm^2 strands and equate to 1.5, 3, 4.5. and 6mm^2.

Intercom

I always used to think that having an intercom on a boat was the ultimate in waterborne posing but when we started cruising *George* I soon realised how useful one would be. Any boat over about 45ft in length and particularly traditional-style ones would probably benefit from having one of these devices so that the steerer can speak to or attract the attention of other crew members without resorting to shouting at the top of his/her voice. We used a very cheap but effective system bought from Tandy on *George* and, since we had discovered nothing better in the meantime, used the same thing on *Rome*. It is battery operated but has the advantage that the call signal can be given before the units are switched on so that power consumption is kept to a minimum. This is unfortunately not so with the potentially more convenient radio transceivers also sold by Tandy. These have to be switched on before the call signal can be used and consequently have to be left on all the time and last only about a day between recharges. The intercom units are supplied with about 60ft of very light twin core cable with jack plugs permanently fitted. This cable was installed along with the power cables with one end in the soap'ole (more cries of sacrilege), and the other in the saloon area.

CHAPTER 9
ELECTRIC SYSTEMS

12, 24 and 230-volts
Inverters, converters and chargers
Engine electrics
Cabin electrics
Batteries and battery capacity
Cables and voltage drop
Voltage regulators
Generators
Wind and solar power

Narrowboats electrics is a specialised subject so we asked Peter Hopley of Acorn Engineering to give some guidelines on the design of a typical installation and the equipment that it might include. Here is his account:

As the design of narrowboats has evolved over the last two decades, so the complexity of their associated systems has increased – almost always adding to the demands on boat electrics. Features like elaborate plumbing systems with central heating, flushing toilets, and even built-in washing machines, have to be catered for by efficient 12-volt or 24-volt DC and (increasingly) 230-volt AC services. Before getting down to the 'how to do it' stage, let me recommend some reading matter. Despite much debate, British Waterways formally introduced mandatory Boat Safety Standards from January 1st 1997. They are here to stay, and cannot be avoided, so obtain a copy of the Standards from BW – and work to them. For those starting from scratch, the Standards are not difficult to follow, and in the main are common sense. Where there have been difficulties, these were often to do with the non-availability of suitable parts, but that has now been resolved, and virtually everything you need to comply is now easily and widely available. Ironically, the section in the B.S.Standards on low voltage electrics is brief, and, on 230-volt systems, non existent. But another publication is now available, entitled *BMEA Code of Practice for Electrical and Electronic Installations in Small Craft (Third Edition)*.

The BMEA (British Marine Electronics Association) is a member of the BMIF (British Marine Industries Federation) which is the lead body in all matters to do with boatbuilding in the UK. Another BMIF member group, the CBA (Canal Boatbuilders Association), has already agreed to be guided by this Code of Practice. It is comprehensive, and covers much that would not concern narrowboat builders, but it still contains considerable useful information for DIY fitters-out, and it would make sense to obtain a copy, and work to it as far as possible.

There is some history to this Code of Practice. It was first published in the mid 1990's, which was before the full effects of the then proposed European Recreational Craft Directive (RCD) were known. Most boat users are now probably aware of the RCD, as so much has been published about it in the boating press. The RCD contains a number of 'Essential Safety Requirements' which craft must comply with in order to be CE marked. One of the 'Essential Safety Requirements' concerns a craft's electrical systems, and it may be worthwhile quoting it here in full.

'Electrical systems shall be designed and installed so as to ensure proper operation of the craft under normal conditions of use and shall be such as to minimise the risk of fire and electric shock.

Attention shall be paid to the provision of overload and short circuit protection of all circuits supplied from batteries, except engine starting circuits.

Ventilation shall be provided to prevent the accumulation of gases which might be emitted from batteries. Batteries shall be firmly secured and protected from ingress of water'.

So there you have it! The three sentences above determine everything that shall be done, electrically speaking, on your boat. But how do you know if you have complied with the electrical 'Essential Safety Requirement'? The simplest method is to follow the new technical standards which have been drafted in order to support the RCD. They are ISO 10133:1994 (Extra low voltage DC installations) and ISO 13297:1995 (Electrical system – Alternating current installations). The BMEA Code of Practice incorporates these standards in full, as Sections 2 and 3 of the COP respectively.

The Code is likely to become more widespread with time, and to become the industry standard for electrical installations. The following sections aim to cover most of the considerations in planning your electrical system, but I have deliberately avoided detailing such basics as how to wire a light fitting, crimp connectors, decipher mains wire colours, etc. If these tasks are beyond you, call in a professional or competent colleague to take the job over. You could save yourself much trouble and heartache.

System voltages

Let me first clarify some definitions of low voltage. Surprisingly ISO 13297 describes a 'Low Voltage Alternating Current Electrical System' as one operating at voltages **less than** 250 volts single phase on small craft of up to 24m hull length. (24m = 78ft 9in). All shore, genset and inverter supplies are usually between 220v and 240v and therefore are classed as '**low voltage**'.

On the other hand, ISO 10133 describes an 'Extra Low Voltage Direct current (DC) electrical system' as one operating at 'nominal potentials of 50v DC or less on small craft up to 24m length of hull.

So briefly, your mains system is, strictly speaking, **low** voltage and your battery system **extra low** voltage.

Extra low voltage (or battery) systems

A 12-volt battery based DC supply is the normal basis of narrowboat electrics, just as it is with motor cars. All systems normally work from it, eg engine starting, lighting, pumps. Sometimes the supply may be 24-volts rather than 12-volts, reflecting practice in trucks and buses! Quite a few narrowboats nowadays are wired to use the higher voltage, and virtually all Marine equipment is available in either 12-volt or 24-volt format. The advantage of a 24-volt system is that, for any given size of appliance, the current running through the cables will be half that of a 12-volt installation. Because voltage drop, which is the bane of low voltage

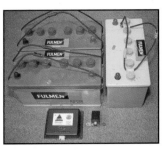

The basis of a sound electrical system – Heavy duty engine start battery (right), deep cycle cabin batteries (left), a heavy duty relay to keep the systems apart and a battery management system to ensure full recharging – in this case an Adverc

systems (particularly in narrowboats with their long cabins), is determined by 'cable size (area)', 'amps' and 'length of cable' then halving the amps will halve the voltage drop. Alternatively, one could use cables of half the area, and accept the same amount of volt drop. Either way, there is a benefit. One disadvantage of a 24-volt system is that your chosen engine will invariably be fitted with a 12-volt starter motor and alternator. Changing them to 24-volts may be prohibitively expensive or not even be possible. Proceeding with a 24-volt system for the cabin then requires two separate electric supplies – ie, a 12-volt alternator and battery to operate the engine electrics, and a separate 24-volt alternator and 24-volt batteries (usually two 12-volt batteries wired in series) to run the cabin services. This arrangement is not uncommon and, if it appeals to you, the only consideration is whether your engine can be fitted with the extra alternator and a pulley to drive it. But for most installations, a simple 12-volt system is perfectly adequate. Providing care is taken over cable sizes, it has

few disadvantages, so this is the scheme which will be discussed in more detail later.

Because of their low voltage, 12 and 24-volt systems are inherently safe in terms of electrocution. There is no risk to life from simply touching battery terminals, or bare wires, not even if you touch a positive wire with one hand and a negative wire with the other (but please DO NOT DO THIS UNDER ANY CIRCUMSTANCES with 230v wires – it will almost certainly kill you!). However, 12 and 24-volt systems are not entirely hazard-free. Undersize cables or bad joints may overheat and destroy insulation to cause short circuits and fires. Low-voltage sparks are easily capable of igniting flammable petrol vapour or L.P. gas, or the hydrogen gas given off by batteries under charge. Batteries contain acid which can cause damage or burns if spilled. And perhaps potentially most dangerous of all is the risk of a dead short across battery terminals, caused by, say, a spanner or tool being dropped across the terminals. Such a dead short would cause a massive current to flow through the offending object. It could act much like a welding current – the spanner would literally 'stick' to the terminals, it would then resist attempts to pull it off, and would very quickly become too hot to grab hold of, and if the current were high enough, the battery might not be able to cope with the rate of discharge, and could eventually explode, showering gas, acid and bits everywhere! Sounds nice, doesn't it. Of course, none of these things will ever happen to you, but haven't we all have heard of some poor unfortunate who has experienced the pleasure? Yes, battery systems are perfectly safe when installed and used correctly, but treat them with respect as they have the potential to cause a lot of damage if abused.

Low voltage systems (or 'mains') systems

Battery voltage can't kill you by electrocution, but 230-volts certainly can, and the proximity of water makes the risk greater. Installing a 230-volt system is not difficult, but does need care. Always fit protective devices such as an RCD (Residual Current Device) as well as fuses or circuit breakers. This is an area where the BMEA Code of Practice will be of great help, as it prescribes equipment and circuitry for 230-volt systems in detail, including such topics as non-current carrying parts, earthing metallic hulls, earthing non-metallic hulls, providing for different power sources (shoreline, generator, inverter/converter), design of switchboards, provision of voltmeters and mains present indicators.

230-volt circuit breaker panel with RCD protection against electrocution: distinctively different 12-volt panel avoids confusion

Integrated 230-volt and 12-volt control panel, increasingly used on narrowboats

Mains and battery voltage systems must not share components, cables or enclosures. They should have their distribution from separate panel boards, but can share a common one if there is a partition or other positive means provided to clearly separate the AC and DC sections from each other, with each being clearly identified.

Installation guidelines

Unfortunately it is not possible to reproduce all the information given in the BMEA COP and the two ISO standards. However, certain items should be mentioned because they are fundamental to the whole installation, and mistakes with these could be difficult, or indeed impossible, to correct at a later stage. These have been included in appendix 3 .

INVERTERS, CONVERTERS AND CHARGERS

Chargers operate from a 230-volt supply (mains or generator) to provide a nominal 14-volt output to recharge batteries. They come in a wide range of types and sizes – their size is expressed in the amperage charge rate they can deliver. Chargers are not all the same. The simpler, less expensive ones, are called 'maintenance' or 'float' chargers. They work at fixed voltage, typically 13.5 to 13.8 volts. They will prevent batteries from going flat, but will not lift them to a very high state of charge. Better quality chargers have programmed outputs, setting the voltage at a high initial level enabling a high charging current, before reducing to the lower one. This lower level (the 13.5 to 13.8-volts region) is called the 'float charge voltage', and is the voltage that can be applied permanently to the battery without risk of damage. In effect, the battery stops the charge of its own accord, once the terminal voltage has risen to this level so it is, for instance, an inherently safe voltage to leave applied to the battery while unattended.

Rediline converter and (behind) Victron combined inverter/charger. Simpler inverters can be much smaller

Inverters and converters work in opposite mode to a charger. They draw low voltage DC power from the batteries and transform it into 230-volt AC power. Inverters are solid state electronic devices, producing stable outputs to closely regulated limits. The better ones have protection against reverse battery polarity, overloading, overheat, and will switch off if the batteries become too flat. The AC of 230-volt mains power means 'alternating current' – the current changes direction 50 times a second in a wave pattern. In household mains power, the pattern is a true wave shape, technically called a 'sine save'. All inverters try to mimic the Sine Wave, with varying degrees of success. Cheaper inverters simply chop up the wave pattern into a rectangular path, called a 'square wave' which will not run

some electronic appliances. More expensive ones simulate the sine wave much more closely and are often called 'modified sine wave' or 'trapezoidal wave'. The very best type simulate the sine wave closely, and will be used in very demanding applications such as aerospace, telecommunications etc. In practice the 'modified sine wave' usually works quite well enough to run most appliances on a narrow boat.

Converters, on the other hand, are electromechanical devices. A 12-volt electric motor simply drives a 230-volt generator. Converters produce pure sine wave output and are usually considerably cheaper than comparably sized inverters. Disadvantages: the output is not regulated, so voltage and frequency can be outside normally acceptable limits; and low-load efficiency is poor. Whilst converters are excellent for running power tools, microwaves or vacuum cleaners, they are not suited to small appliances like televisions.

You can buy a solid state inverter and a charger as a combined unit – called a 'combi'. A combi is normally a much lower cost than purchasing an inverter and charger separately. However there can be disadvantages. A combi has only one set of battery cables, the current going down the cables to the battery when it is in charging mode, and up the cables to the combi when it is in inverting mode. This is fine if there is just one large domestic battery bank, but will be problem if the batteries have been divided into sub groups, eg, cabin batteries, inverter batteries, fridge battery. The combi cannot be arranged to draw power from only the inverter batteries, but replace power into all of them if they are arranged with isolation between them such as split charging relays or blocking diodes.

In any case, installing a charger or combi really only makes sense if you have available an alternative mains supply, such as a shore line supply to your mooring, or an on board generator. You definitely can't use an inverter to create mains power with which to run a battery charger. The inverter will always take more out of the battery than the charger puts back in!

ENGINE ELECTRICS

My diagrams show basic layouts for a typical narrowboat. A few specialist suppliers can sell you more detailed ones. One diagram illustrates the engine's electrical system, the other shows the one for the cabin services. To some extent the engine electrics may be decided for you; although the specifications of engines vary slightly, most new ones are pre-wired in the same fundamental way, complete with cable loom extending to control panel. Control panels also vary. A basic one will probably have a four-position key-switch (off, on, heaters, start), a charge warning light, oil pressure warning light, temperature gauge, and, possibly, a voltmeter. Panels can also include an ammeter to show charging rate, oil pressure gauge (with mechanical or electronic transmitter) and tachometer. The engine supplier probably assumes that you are only interested in the engine and a single battery to start it. In a typical installation, you will have to provide additional circuitry to run instruments for monitoring the condition and charging of cabin batteries.

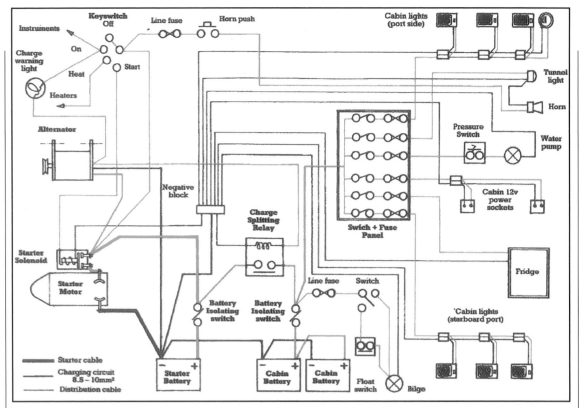

Typical 12-volt wiring diagram for a narrowboat

CABIN ELECTRICS

At the heart of engine electrics are the starter motor, starter battery, and alternator. A heavy cable passes from the positive battery terminal, via an alternator switch, to the starter solenoid, which is usually mounted piggy-back on the starter motor. This solenoid terminal is quite important, as it is generally used as the 'nerve centre' for a lot of other connections. The output cable from the alternator usually attaches here – so when charging starts the current flows via this terminal to the battery. A medium duty cable also runs from this terminal up the cable loom to the engine key switch, from where it may branch off to the instruments. The solenoid's other terminal connects direct to the starter motor (which it serves effectively as a heavy duty switch)

This is a useful point at which to explain the difference between 'insulated return' and 'frame return' installations. On older engines and engines with automotive origins (the BL 1.5 for example), the cylinder block is used as a negative conductor and current from such items as heater plugs, alternator, and starter motor flows through the engine cylinder block. To complete the circuit to the battery a heavy starter-grade cable has to be bolted to convenient point on the engine – typically under the bolts securing the starter motor. It then connects to the starter battery's negative terminal. In an insulated return system, current is not allowed to flow through the engine. While on frame return alternators, there is only one heavy cable running into the back, on insulated return models there are two – one positive, one negative. Most commercially built engines today are fitted with insulated return, although it may still be possible that the engine cylinder block is used as a negative terminal and thus have a heavy cable running back to the battery.

You could, of course, hook cabin appliances to the engine battery. In simple installations with basic cabin services (two lights, one water pump, for instance), this might work. But if you accidentally leave a light on and flatten the battery, then you can't start the engine to begin recharging (OK, so you've got an engine with hand start – you can skip the next bit). The standard arrangement is separate batteries for starting and for the cabin services, with charging from the engine alternator via either a 'selective battery master switch' or a 'split charging system'. The former replaces the individual isolating switches to engine and cabin batteries and has four positions: 'off'- '1'- '2'- 'both'. You have to remember to turn the engine battery off at night, and the cabin batteries on to recharge while cruising.

Split charging systems are completely automatic. There are two types: diode splitter and relay splitter. Diodes must only be used if the engine alternator is battery sensing. So it is safest to go for a relay, which will work efficiently with any alternator – battery or machine sensing. The charge splitting relay most often used is the Lucas 33RA (or SRB600). It has a rating of 60amps, so if your alternator output is close to this (or larger – like the Lucas A127 70amp alternator), you should fit a larger capacity relay. Relays up to 120 or even 180amp capacity are available. The wiring diagram shows how to install the relay.

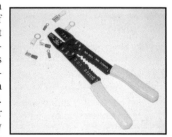

A crimper and the correctly sized connectors make it much easier to install the wiring

Left: selective battery master switch; top: blocking diode; bottom: relay – as recommended in text. The selective switch, if used, would simply replace isolator switches and relay in diagram above

It links the positive terminals of engine and cabin batteries. The relay coil is attached to the alternator's charge warning light terminal. So when the alternator starts charging, the relay's contacts close, completing the connection between engine and cabin batteries. And, vice versa, when you stop the engine, it protects the starter battery. The supply from cabin batteries to cabin is fairly straightforward. It travels from the battery positive terminal via an isolating switch to a distribution panel which can contain either fuses or circuit breakers (except for bilge pump and burglar alarm, which may by-pass the isolator but which must be then individually fused). From the panel the individual circuits run out to the cabin appliances, with return cables coming back – all circuits must be two wire, so you will have lots of negative wires returning with nowhere to go. A commoning block is needed as a means of connecting them all together, with a single large cable returning from the commoning block to the battery.

We mentioned near the beginning of this section about the possibility of fitting a second alternator to the engine, where a 24-volt cabin electrical system was wanted. It is also quite often that a second 12-volt alternator is fitted, dedicated to charging the cabin batteries where these remain at 12-volt. This system makes the cabin electrics completely independent of the engine electrics, and removes the need for a split charging device. One 12-volt alternator charges the starter battery, and another (usually the additional one) charges the cabin batteries.

BATTERIES AND BATTERY CAPACITY

Batteries suited to starting engines are not the same as those designed for long duration cabin loads. For maximum service life the appropriate battery type should be chosen for each job. Any heavy duty 'lorry' type battery will give good service for engine starting. For most narrowboat diesels around 95amp-hours will suffice (although you are just as likely to be

Leak-proof battery boxes

quoted 650amps cold cranking performance over 30 seconds, 475amps cold starting performance over one minute or 175 minutes reserve capacity for a 25amp drain).

'Deep Cycle' batteries are better for cabin services. These are designed to give up their charge over a long

A battery isolator switch

period and then be recharged for a similar time. They are constructed to withstand repeated charges and discharges without suffering internal damage. There are several other battery types on the market: Freedom batteries, leisure batteries, gel batteries, traction batteries and semi-traction batteries. The differences between them are beyond the scope of this feature; but your battery supplier will give guidance on the best type for you – if you tell him the purpose for which you want the battery. One class you may be offered is the sealed type, which has no vents and cannot be topped up or checked with a hydrometer. Gas generated during recharging cannot escape and recombines with the electrolyte. But these batteries cannot be charged at enhanced rates, so are not suitable for use with some of the electronic voltage regulators that can be fitted to alternators.

How do you work out what size batteries are needed for your cabin system? From experience, the quick answer is that one medium size service battery (say 90amp-hours) is sufficient for smaller, simple narrowboats; two batteries for medium length craft with average specification (maybe three if you have an electric fridge and watch a lot of TV). But boats fitted with lots of power-hungry gadgets (bow thrusters, inverters, colour TV, fridge, freezer, etc) may need between four and six batteries, or even more. Incidentally, bow thrusters usually have a dedicated battery located in the bow near the motor. Recharging such a battery can be a problem due to the length of the cable run from the alternator at the rear, to the battery at the front, and back again. Carrying out a volt drop calculation usually leads to the conclusion that a very heavy cable, of around $45mm^2$ section will be needed if charging is to be successful. This may seem excessive, but doing the sums will prove the point.

THE ENERGY AUDIT

A more accurate way to calculate cabin battery needs is to do an energy audit – which establishes how many amp-hours are likely to be used each day. This means looking at each appliance to see how many amps it draws, then estimating how many hours it will be working. The rating plate on most appliances quotes their consumption in amps or watts. Divide the watts by 12 (or 24 if a 24-volt appliance) to obtain amps.

Audit example -

	Load (amps)	Time on (hours)	Audit (amp-hours)
5 fluorescent lights @ 1.3amps	6.5	2	13
2 filament lamps @ 2 amps	4	2	8
Water pump	10	0.25	2.5
Central heating pump	2	4	8
Electric fridge	4.5	12	54
Colour TV	5	2	10
TOTAL			95.5

Multiply the total audit figure by three to obtain the battery capacity needed – in this case 286.5 amp-hours, which could be achieved by linking three 100 amp-hour batteries in parallel. Omitting the fridge (in favour of a gas one) would reduce the audit total to 41.5 amp-hours and the battery requirement to 124.5 amp-hours. The typical electric fridge draws 4.5 amps when the compressor is on, but as it is thermostatically controlled we have assumed it only runs for 30 minutes in every hour. Nevertheless its relative appetite for electricity may explain why electric fridges can cause problems and why it is important to install them with masses of ventilation at the rear to dissipate the heat given out by the condenser, and to obviously keep the thermostat as low as practicable.

CABLES AND VOLTAGE DROP

I have already mentioned that multi-stranded cable should be used. Voltage drop is a particular problem of low voltage systems, requiring cable sizes to be calculated to avoid its consequences. If the voltage to an appliance is too low, it simply may not function adequately, and some equipment may be damaged by grossly low voltage. Having said that, you will see in Appendix 3 that the Guidence note in the DC installations section, says equipment should operate at voltages between 10.5 and 15.5 volts. This is to reflect the fact that when your engine is running, the alternator will raise the voltage of the whole electrical system to about 14.5 volts, so obviously equipment has to work at that voltage at least. But when the engine is stationary and the alternator is not charging, then the electrical system drops back to whatever voltage the battery stands at, which for a fully charged battery should be at least 12.8 volts.

However, when the battery supplies power to the circuits, its voltage will drop below the 'standing' voltage by an amount which will vary, depending upon how much power is being supplied, and what state of charge the battery happens to be in. The higher the load, and the flatter the battery, the more the battery voltage will be 'pulled

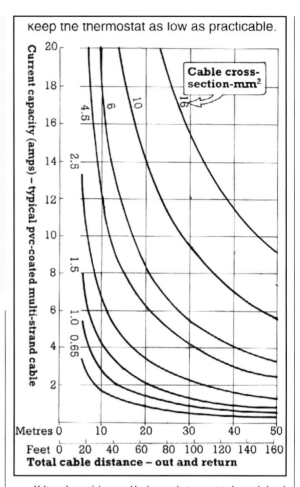

Voltage drop: minimum cable sizes, against current to be carried, and cable length for a 12-volt system with 0.5 volt drop

down' when you switch things on. When a lot of equipment is working, you may see your voltmeter (if you have one) drop down to a level which might alarm you, say 11 or 10 volts, or even less. This does not necessarily mean your battery is flat, because if you switch off some loads, particularly heavy one's, then your battery voltage will recover, and you will see it rise to nearer its normal level. Obviously, in time the voltage will fall further, as the battery charge diminishes, so the choice of 10.5 volts for the level at which equipment should still function normally is simply an attempt to take account of the variation in voltage which will inevitably occur when the system is operating.

Rome's battery monitor shows a healthy voltage on its Adverc Digital Circuit Monitor (DCM)

This is why cable sizing is so important, particularly on voltage sensitive equipment like an electric fridge or a TV. How many people have experienced the annoyance of the low voltage alarm on their fridge sounding continuously, even though the battery is not flat. If the cable is badly undersized, the fridge could be experiencing, say, a 1 volt drop, which means the alarm will sound off much sooner than if there was no volt drop!

In all cases a larger cable than one sized simply on its nominal current carrying capacity will always be needed . As an example, a colour TV takes 5 amps and may be, say twelve metres from the battery. The out-and-back distance is therefore 24 metres (79ft). A cable of $2.5mm^2$ cross section has a current carrying capacity of 15amps, which is obviously more than enough for the TV, but it also has a resistance which will cause a volt drop of 0.0075v per amp per metre. Hence 0.0075 x 5 x 24 = 0.9 volts. On a TV this amount of volt drop could be unacceptable. So then try a $4.5mm^2$ cable (25-amp capacity) which has a volt drop figure of 0.0041v per amp per metre. The same calculation produces a more acceptable figure of 0.49 volts dropped, while a $6mm^2$ cable (current carrying capacity 30amps and volt drop 0.0031v per amp per metre) would reduce the figure even further to 0.37 volts dropped. As I said, to avoid voltage drop much larger cables are needed than you might think. So that you do not have to make individual calculations, I show a graph of appliance consumptions against cable distance and cross section.

VOLTAGE REGULATORS

In the section under batteries, I mentioned the use of electronic voltage regulators. These devices work in conjunction with the alternator to improve its charging characteristics. Almost all alternators have a built-in regulator, which stops the charging voltage from rising above a nominal value of about 14 1/4 volts. This is fine for recharging a slightly discharged battery – as in engine starting. When used with heavily discharged batteries, initial recharging will be satisfactory – but it will taper down to a trickle after a period, even though the batteries are not fully charged. This is because of the extended time needed to replenish heavily discharged batteries: they build up a surface resistance between the plates and the electrolyte; and the increase in resistance effectively stops any further current from flowing. By providing a temporary increase in applied voltage, the extra resistance can be overcome and charging can continue.

The function of the external electronic voltage regulator is to provide this temporary increase to enable full recharging. Without its assistance, the cabin service batteries are unlikely to be charged beyond about 80% full and, as the battery voltage will have fallen off considerably by the time the batteries have discharged to about 50% full (to the extent that lights start to go dim and pumps struggle to run) the batteries are effectively cycling between 50% and 80% full. So in effect you are utilising just 30% of their apparent capacity. This is why you need an actual battery capacity of three times your total daily consumption, as explained above. With an external electronic voltage regulator, you will be able to be charge the batteries to about 95% full. As they will now be cycling between 50% and 95%, 45% of their apparent capacity becomes available – half as much again as in the 'before' situation. Furthermore the batteries themselves benefit from being almost fully recharged as this prevents the formation of sulphate on the plates. Electronic voltage regulators are offered on the market under various descriptions from 'alternators controllers' to 'battery management systems'.

PETER HOPLEY IS PROPRIETOR OF ACORN ENGINEERING WHICH SPECIALISES IN MARINE ELECTRICS AND SYSTEM DESIGN.

FURTHER THOUGHTS ON BOAT ELECTRICS

The main way of producing electricity on a boat is to use the alternator but it is not the only way –

GENERATORS

In the beginning was the portable Honda generator – inexpensive and invaluable for running power tools when no other power source is to hand. After the boat is completed, the Honda travels on board to power the colour TV, teenagers' hair dryer and, perhaps eventually, microwave oven. The Honda/Yamaha/Suzuki/Kawasaki, with typical output of 600 watts to 1,200 watts, is a simple and cost-effective way to ensure an independent 230-volt supply. but it can also be a mighty nuisance. The petrol engine needs plenty of fresh and open air to run safely and reliably. So, despite the best efforts of Japan's acoustic engineers, it sits on cabin or bank making a buzz that is guaranteed to irritate neighbouring moorers.

Honda portable generator

The obvious solution is a generator compartment – designed into the steel shell. If the generator is, like all inexpensive portable models, petrol-powered, the compartment should be sealed and drained overboard as if carrying gas bottles. But it must also be well ventilated – demanding sizeable vent grilles that face out through hull or cabin side. As such grilles are at risk of damage if located on the forward hull taper, the best position for the compartment is in the aft cockpit of a semi-trad or cruiser-style boat – it might, for instance, occupy a locker under a cockpit seat with vent out through the cabin side. The compartment will benefit from acoustic lining and should have a lift-off lid so that you can reach in easily to yank the start cord.

A large diameter welded spigot could be positioned to line up with your generator's exhaust outlet and direct the gases overboard. Generator compartments like this are not uncommon, although a major Honda agent went into sharp-intake-of-breath mode at the idea, and hinted at coked valves or melted pistons caused by reingested exhaust gases. Certainly if you modify the exhaust itself, the guarantee would be invalidated.

Despite the simple advantage of a petrol portable – if every battery dies, you can restore power by pulling a handle – the trend towards more sophisticated built-in generators seems irresistible. However there is an intermediate step – the portable diesel generator. Typically this uses a Yanmar engine but is still easy to fire up because decompressers operate automatically as the start cord is pulled. The range of power outputs (approximately 1 kVA to 3kVA) tends to be higher than for petrol portables, and is more realistic for the cabin needs of largish narrowboats. As the fuel is less volatile than petrol, diesel generators can be installed semi-permanently in a traditional engine room. However in basic form this type is air-cooled, and not insulated, so can be very noisy. Nevertheless it offers good value for money.

What boat owners really want though is unobtrusive 230-volt – just like at home. Many have a persistent reservation that an inverter might flatten the batteries at a vital moment. The built-in diesel generator starts at the touch of a remote button, or even decides for itself whether it needs to be started, and never needs topping up with fuel as it draws on the engine fuel tank. Most are water-cooled and can be linked to a skin cooling tank. They are offered, usually as an option, with an acoustic cocoon; although they may work better if installed cocoonless in a specially insulated and ventilated compartment – as for the petrol portable above. Moral: buy a cheap generator initially but design its compartment to take a built-in type when you can afford one. The typical output range is 2kVA to 6kVA. Budget for between £3,000 and £6,000 before installation.

WIND & SOLAR POWER

The idea of running your home on free power from the wind and sun may be attractive, but for most it is made impractical by the cost of buying sufficient generating capacity. However the largest narrowboat could be supported by a 50-watt wind generator and 60-watt solar panel – if the occupants are sufficiently committed to careful consumption; ie, a diametrically opposite philosophy to the built-in generator faction. For a start these power sources will only run a 12-volt system – apart from low-demand 230-volt appliances via a small inverter. The cabin's electric system should be planned to allow for limited resources – Thorn 2D compact fluorescent lights are particularly useful as they give a warm light, as bright as a 75-watt filament bulb, for a consumption of 16 watts. If the boat is to be occu-

Glass-faced solar panel and smaller, more durable, plastic unit

Rutland wind generators

pied for long periods without running the engine – as in residential use, electric fridges and forced combustion diesel heaters (like the Eberspacher) are not viable.

As the wind generator and solar panel between them would cost slightly more than a 1kVA portable petrol generator, they appear, on the face of it, to

Control panel for solar and wind generators, with shunt regulators and fuses

offer poor value. Particularly as, in most conditions, they are producing considerably less than their combined potential of 110 watts. However one or both is likely to be generating some power almost all of the time – while the petrol portable is probably running for less than an hour a day. If between them, the wind generator and solar panel can produce a third of their potential during daylight hours alone, they would support half a dozen 2D lights, water and shower pumps, and a small TV. You might even be able to run the system on either – wind chargers seem to be more popular at the moment. But fitting both reduces the risk of betrayal by one of the fickle elements.

Low consumption 2D lighting

Solar panels are unobtrusive and narrowboat cabin tops offer plenty of space for mounting them – a 60 watt panel measures 3ft 8in x 1ft 8in. However they work best at lower temperatures, so need insulating and an air gap from the hot steel surface. You might consider a wind generator to be an eyesore on your new narrowboat (unless your beholding eye is charmed by the Green message it signals). The higher it is mounted, the more wind it will catch. That 50-watt wind generator probably stands on a 12ft high mast of 2in galvanised water pipe – and it needs lowering every time you cast off. Your shell builder should be able to make a step for the mast, probably with three mounting points for wire shrouds to brace the assembly. You may be able to order a mast from the generator supplier. The two major names in wind generators, Marlec (Rutland) and Ampair, also market solar panels and low consumption cabin appliances. But Wind & Sun of Oxford offers a wide range of renewable energy equipment, which includes a narrowboat mast for the Rutland Windcharger. Wind & Sun also publishes a catalogue that includes much advice on efficient low consumption installations – from calculating energy needs to selecting solar panels, wind generators and ancillary equipment.

CHAPTER 10

PARTITIONS AND THE BATHROOM

Water heating
Bath and toilet
Holding tanks
Tiling

PARTITIONS

I installed the basic services during the dark depressing months of winter and, by the time I had finished, I had definitely had enough. What kept me going was the thought that the next stage was to add some partitions which would start to transform what looked like the cargo hold of a transport plane into the series of spaces that I had tried to imagine all those months ago. The materials used for the partitioning depend somewhat on the finishes that are planned but the chances are that it will be plywood of some description. None of the other boards – chipboard, blockboard, or even MDF (medium density fibreboard) have any advantages over ply and some have distinct disadvantages. My plan, as you may recall, was to stick timber framing and mouldings to the edges of the walls. These would add some stiffness to the board so I reckoned that 12mm would be quite adequate. Some builders, particularly those used to fitting out hire boats, recommend 18mm but, unless you have a really long partition, not supported on four sides, and are in the habit of inviting the local Rugby team for cruises, 12mm should do the job.

Fixing

Rigidity increases enormously when two partitions are fixed at right angles. When it comes to fixing partitions to the lining we are back to the two schools of thought syndrome. One school says erect the partition before the linings so that the edges are trapped between the linings on either side and so cannot move. This also enables you to remove the linings to get at the inner face of the shell. The other school says rubbish! - (it always does) - having the exposed ends of the partitions poking into the space between the lining and the inside of the shell is asking for them to become damp and eventually rot. My framing method of wall treatment gave me almost the best of both worlds for once. The lining protects the edge of the partition but by the time the framing

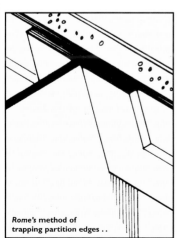

Rome's method of trapping partition edges ..

is added, in most cases to both sides, the edges are trapped and therefore firmly fixed. A further advantage is that you don't have to be quite so accurate cutting the partition to fit as the edge is eventually covered.

There are several methods of fixing partitions where you don't have the benefit of framing.

compared with conventional batten fixing

The simplest is to fix a timber batten to the lining to one side of the line of the partition and then glue and screw the partition to this. It has to be said, however, that this method is a bit crude and wherever possible the batten should be fixed on the less visible side of the wall, preferably in a cupboard or wardrobe. Another way is to use a Kreg Mini-jig. This enables you to drill a hole obliquely through to the edge of the partition so that you can screw it directly to the cabin side without a batten. There are two possible snags. One is the fact that the jig only really works on material of minimum $3/4$in thickness. This can be pushed down to $5/8$in with care but this is still thicker than most partitions. The other is the rather elongated holes left on the face of the partition but these can be filled with dowel or special plastic caps.

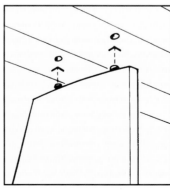

Concealed partition fixing

A method of secretly fixing the head of the partition which I have found to be very successful, is to drill a couple of $1/4$in holes in the ceiling lining on the centre line of the partition and then screw a couple of suitably sized screws into the top edge leaving about $3/8$ths projecting so

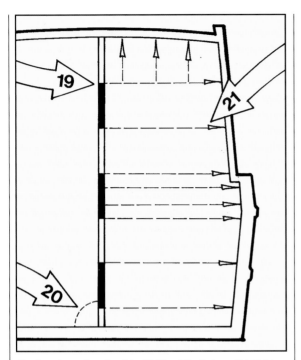

How to make a pattern for a lateral bulkhead. The first essential aid is a giant home-made (from ply off-cut) set square. The second is a measuring post located at the innermost point of the planned bulkhead. Use the set square to position the post vertical in fore & aft and sideways planes. The post, which should be jammed firmly against the top lining with polystyrene or similar soft waste, will then provide a datum for measurements that can be transferred immediately to the bulkhead material. The set square can be used again to check that the bulkhead is vertical before it is fastened in place

that these locate into the holes. If the partition is a good fit and the joint is well glued the result is a very firm fixing.

Stick with it

A word here on the subject of glues. I have always used Evode PVA woodworking adhesive (in the green bottle) for general woodworking jobs. This is very strong and quick setting but dries with a white film which will show through varnish if you don't wipe off all the excess. I therefore decided to switch to the waterproof variety (in the blue bottle) for this project. This is just as strong and has the additional advantage that it dries clear.

THE BATHROOM

With the boat lined out, and the partitions cut, I had a choice about which part to tackle next. I decided on the bathroom, partly because I wanted to make sure I could get it to fit in before my options were closed by other things around it and partly because I felt I needed the encouragement of seeing at least a small part of the boat completely finished.

Water heating

We decided to use a twin coil calorifier heated by the engine and the Alde gas boiler to supply the domestic hot water. The installation of the boiler is described in chapter 12. Using engine heat to warm a lagged calorifier is simple – but doesn't give constant hot water. The engine will usually heat twelve or so gallons in just over half-an-hour; and the lagging normally keeps water hot overnight. An

increasing number of marine calorifiers are fitted with house-type 230-volt immersion heaters so you could even heat your calorifier with power from a built-in generator. Wasteful though that might seem, it is probably less undesirable than regularly running the boat's main engine off-load just to heat water – which can cause long-term engine damage. However, since we had decided not to install 230-volt power, we did not have this option.

The simplest way to ensure constant hot water is to fit an instant gas water heater but none of the current models have a balanced flue and so are not permitted by the new BS 5482.

Water pump

The most popular pressure pump is the American-made Shurflo. In its most basic form, its electric motor drives a flexible impeller. A pressure switch mounted on the end of the pump sets the motor running when it senses a drop in water pressure caused by turning on a tap. It cuts the motor out when pressure climbs to a set level – so the system is always operating within a pressure range. If you fit an accumulator tank (an air-filled bottle) into the system, the pump will compress the air, providing a reserve of pressure before the pump cuts in when a tap is turned on. This reduces the machine-gun rattle of the pump's on-off

Pressure in the Shurflo pump can be adjusted by turning the screw under the end cover

cycle and should eliminate sudden pump bursts caused by dripping taps. The next stage of sophistication is a separate pressure switch – built-in ones do not always suit instant water heaters and/or may be fixed at unrealistically high pressures. The Square D is invariably the separate switch chosen for narrowboats. Its high-pressure cut-out and low pressure cut-in switches are both adjustable.

If a Shurflo goes wrong, you can obtain some spare parts but the urgent situation of a waterless system often persuades owners

The elements of a water pump system – the pump has a non-adjustable pressure switch but many owners prefer to fit the separate adjustable type (foreground) pressure switch

simply to buy a new pump. Some prepare for the worst by installing two pumps in parallel – one on stand-by. Jabsco's Water Puppy is an impeller pump with sturdy bronze body and quickly removable face-plate for cleaning. Pumps that work by diaphragm action rather than impeller are more durable because they are more able to withstand dry running. Jabsco's diaphragm pumps are the next stage up the quality (and price) range from Shurflo.

The installation

It's best with tightly planned areas, especially those containing bought in equipment, to try to assemble as much as possible without permanently fixing anything so that you can make adjustments for problems you hadn't anticipated. By this means I soon discovered that the space left for the water pump and pressure accumulator was very narrow. I tried various arrangements and eventually came up

with something that seemed to work – and fit. Then I realised that I had not included a non-return valve on the supply to the calorifier. This meant that a small amount of warm water could be drawn back into the cold supply when the cold taps were turned on. I devised another,

Rome's **Mansfield WC sitting on polypropylene holding tank. Pump-out and vent fittings are visible on left**

even more convoluted layout of pipework and equipment to overcome this. After consulting various 'authorities' on the subject I decided to use the first layout and see what happened, knowing that if I found that there was a problem I could still get at the pipework to modify it.

Our test trip showed that this would be necessary. By the end of a day's cruising the water was so hot that, to quote a friend "Yo cor 'old yer 'ond under it". But by the next morning, even without having a shower in the evening, the water was not much more than luke warm. This could be accounted for by insufficient lagging – I had opted for safer mineral wool – or the fact that horizontal calorifiers may be less efficient than vertical ones. I suspected, however, that the main reason was the fact that every time we drew off cold water a considerable amount of hot water was drawn back from the calorifier. So it was back once again to doing the job properly and adding a non-return valve. There must be a moral here somewhere.

The pump, a Shurflo model 2088, and accumulator were mounted on a water-proofed tray on rubber feet which serves to catch any minor spillages which might occur

when filling or emptying the system, and further isolates the pump vibration from the rest of the boat.

For emptying the system I find a Black & Decker in-line pump attachment very useful. These little devices

Shurflo pump and accumulator mounted on a leak-proof tray

cost about £8 or £9 and fit into the chuck of practically any drill, even cordless. With the 'in' pipe fitted to the drain-off cock and the 'out' pipe discharging into the bath or washbasin it empties the system in no time. It can also be used to empty the water directly from the water tank provided the filler pipe does not have any right-angled bends in it.

Useful water system accessories include pre-filters (to protect the pump from water-borne particles), and purifying filters. The latter can work by removing suspended solids and unpleasant taste – like that left by sterilising tablets. More sophisticated versions actually remove bacteria by using ultra-violet light. The filtering action can be so fine that water flow is reduced – requiring them to be fitted in a branch line to a special drinking water tap. This also increases the time between filter changes. Finally, it is important to make sure that there are sufficient drain-off cocks to drain the water on both sides of the non-return valve if fitted.

Bath

Drainage for the bath was fairly simple. My first thought was to use a sump pump in a small tank which is connected at low level to the outlet of the bath. This was the standard method of emptying baths and showers some years ago. Since then, the pump manufacturers stopped giving the pumps removable impeller covers making it much more difficult to clear the inevitable hair and fluff which eventually clogs them up. The recommended alternative

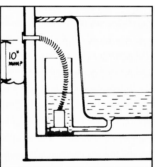

when I fitted out *Rome* was an in-line pump, not unlike the Shurflo but without the pressure switch, and about the same price. The cover plate over the impeller is quite easy to remove so that debris can be cleared. I was advised that these pumps, made by Johnson, must not be allowed to run dry so it is a good idea to use a horn type push switch to

Emptying the bath with a submersible pump ...

operate them. Fortunately they are quite fast emptying so your thumb is unlikely to go too numb while emptying the bath.

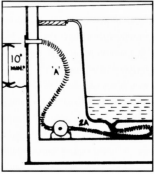

It is also a good idea to make sure that the pipe from the bath or shower outlet to the pump is about twice the length of the pipe from the pump to the skin fitting in the hull. This gives the water left in the pipe when you switch the pump off somewhere to go, and should prevent that annoying half-inch of water coming back through the plug hole.

... or an impeller pump. Note the pipe lengths

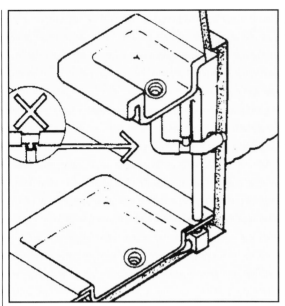

If the shower shares an outlet pipe with wash basin, it must join from above – to prevent basin waste running into the shower

Toilets

The subject of toilets is one which always seems to excite a great deal of interest amongst boaters. There are basically two types of toilet – those with fixed holding tanks and those with portable ones. Fixed tanks have to be pumped out at intervals, possibly as frequently as once a week, and this can cost about £10. Portable tank toilets are simply emptied at a sanitary station every two or three days and there is no charge.

The Baby Blakes hand pumped toilet

The most common fixed tank toilet is the dump-through which has a foot operated seal in the base of the bowl. When the pedal is pressed down, the seal moves aside and allows the contents of the bowl to drop into the tank below. The market leader is the Mansfield Traveller which costs from £170 to £220. Advantages are price, ease of installation, tolerance of abuse and economy of water (the quicker the holding tank fills up – the sooner you have to pay to have it emptied). On the downside are the need for that tank to be directly under the bowl and the fact that, when the pedal is depressed, foul air can enter the cabin.

To overcome the last problem you need a remote tank. The most basic of this type of toilet is hand pumped. These are fairly cheap to buy (£150 to £300 except for the Baby Blake which is a staggering £825) and some can be converted to electric operation. Their drawbacks

The Microphor compressor toilet

The Elsan Bristol basic toilet

are their rather complicated, hard-to-clean design and a tendency to use a lot of flushing water. Nevertheless, they seem to be becoming more popular of late.

Moving up, there are various types of electric toilets which give nearer to home loo performance – but at a price. The Microphor works by compressed air, the Vacuflush by vacuum and the Sanicompact, Superflush and Saninautico are macerator or centrifugal pump types. These will set you back anything from £650 to £1,600 – and they still call it spending a penny!

There are also several 'dry' biological toilets on the market. These use a starter pack and some heat to reduce sewage to a reusable compost. Not for the faint-hearted, they have a small but enthusiastic following.

The Thetford cassette toilet

Toilets with portable tanks go from the most basic bucket and chuck it, through the coyly named 'Porta Potti' types with their limited flushing facility, to cassette toilets which are a very acceptable alternative to a pump out. Prices here range from £70 to £400.

We had pump-outs on the last two boats and found them a great convenience – no more lavatorial puns I promise! I looked at some of the newer, more sophisticated models now available but decided on grounds of cost and fear of the unknown to stick to what we were familiar with – the Mansfield Traveller. The loo is one item of equipment you need to have total confidence in.

The latest Mansfields have been restyled with a plastic cowl around the base which improves the appearance enormously. They are available in white, bone (a light cream colour) and grey. The white and grey are exact matches to the colours of baths and vanitory basins made by other manufacturers and the bone is a near, but not quite exact match to champagne. Nevertheless we thought the white and grey looked just a bit cheerless so took a chance with bone/champagne. In some lights they look prefect, in others not – but we still prefer it.

Fitting the unit is simply a matter of positioning it on the tank, marking and cutting the hole, fixing the mounting ring to the tank and bolting the pan down to the ring. A couple of quick connections to the cold water supply and the pump-out skin fittings and it's done.

Holding tanks

The practice of providing integral loo tanks seems to be waning although one builder did once tell me that when he had to cut through one while lengthening a boat, he found that it was the best preserved (pickled?) bit of metal on the whole boat. Most people nowadays seem to use separate tanks made of stainless steel or polypropylene. Stainless steel is obviously very suitable but the thickness of metal required to prevent flexing makes them rather expensive. Polypropylene tanks are cheaper and if properly reinforced inside should not flex unduly. Midland Chandlers make a standard polypropylene tank which is very reasonably priced. The tank measures roughly 4ft x 2ft x 10in which allows them to make one out of one sheet (or two out of two sheets to be precise.) This economy means that a non-standard tank of only very slightly different dimensions could be a lot more expensive

I decided to position the pumpout fitting and vent in the roof so that they are easily accessible from both sides of the boat. Both are of hefty brass and therefore not cheap. They are however quite easy to fit once you have cut the holes for them with an electric jig saw. A bead of clear silicon rubber sealant around the edge of the holes prevents rainwater coming in. The flexible pipe, with spiral nylon reinforcement, is fitted over the ribbed spigots of these and the similar fittings in the top of the tank and paired jubilee clips are tightened round them. You will need to soften the end of the pipe with water which is actually boiling in order to get it over the fittings – hot water is not enough. It is essential, particularly with a polypropylene tank, to have a minimum 11/2in diameter vent to prevent the suction of the pumpout imploding it.

Fresh air

Our decision to have portholes meant that bathroom ventilation was somewhat limited. There are several solar powered extractor vents on the market which could be used to boost the airflow. These however have a cowl which does not match normal brass mushroom vents. Since I was keen to standardise the roof vents as much as possible I bought a small fan which, after a slight modification with a hacksaw, fits under the base of a standard

Small electric fan mounted under the mushroom vent in the bathroom

mushroom vent and runs on electricity from the main batteries. A small switch at high level turns it on and off and this, combined with a louvered door to the bathroom, gives sufficient ventilation.

Wall tiling

So much for the technicalities – what about the finishes? In our two previous boats I have used sheet vinyl flooring stuck to the walls. The relatively few joints can be sealed with clear silicone rubber sealant making a very waterproof lining. If a suitable pattern is chosen it can fool most people into thinking it is real tiling. But real tiling is what

the majority of smart private boats seem to use nowadays so we thought we would give it a try this time. The big question, after you have made your choice of pattern from the hundreds available, is what to use to stick them to the walls. Ordinary tile cement may seem to work for a while but movement from flexing of the plywood or vibration from the engine, not to mention the occasional sudden meeting with a lock gate, cause its (literal) downfall sooner or later.

Asking around I discovered various solutions to the problem from 'tile-on-wood' type tile cement to horizontal beads of Dow Corning gunned onto the wall and used to bed the tiles. This set me thinking about other adhesives I had used and I recalled that cork tile adhesive seems capable of sticking most things to most other things, so I tried it on an old tile and an offcut of plywood. I deliberately left the tile overhanging the ply by an inch but, even so, I couldn't get the two apart the next day. Being a rubber type adhesive it has a small amount of give and, remembering the largish areas to be covered, it is not too expensive either. I covered the wall with adhesive, using the notched spreader provided, and let this dry for a while. I then spread a thin coat of adhesive on the back of the tile and pressed it in place on the wall. Spacers are a good idea to stop the vertical tiles closing up. Inevitably, I got adhesive all over my hands but this came off quite easily with warm soapy water.

The large partition between the bathroom and the engine room could have caused a problem by flexing too much but this was overcome by building shelves in an egg-crate form on the engine room side which provide useful storage and also stiffen the partition. The tiles were grouted with standard grout except at the edges where they met other materials or at internal angles between

Rome's Bath/shower with ceramic tiled surround, and varnished cork tiles on the floor

two walls of tiling. Here I used white silicone rubber sealant. All the tile joints on the top of the loo tank were also pointed with sealant because of the greater possibility of flexing.

There was also some woodwork to get my teeth into, but this was all on a rather small scale compared with the galley, so I will go into it in more detail in the next section.

CHAPTER 11

THE GALLEY

Appliances :
Fridge, Cooker and Sink unit
Woodwork:
Carcassing
Worktops
Fancy woodwork
All systems go

The next area I tackled was the galley. This was the other rather tight area and I hoped that when it was all installed I would be able to relax a bit. I had allowed only 5ft of boat length for the galley which, even with the more efficient centre corridor plan was a bit on the small side. However, since the only way to increase this was to take space from the saloon, which I was not prepared to do, my solution was to think laterally – or in this case vertically. Nearly all kitchens in houses have wall

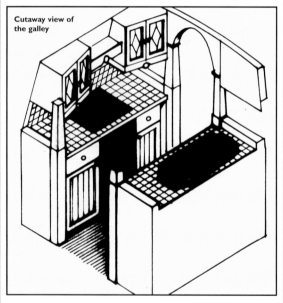

Cutaway view of the galley

units as well as floor units and these contribute to the overall built-in effect as well as providing useful storage space. Narrowboats, especially those with U-shaped galleys seem to be making increasing use of suspended storage cupboards as part of the dividing screen between the galley and saloon. This looked like the answer to my problem.

The only snag was that I also had a hankering after the triple-arched dividing screen which I had used on *George* This had provided just the right amount of separation between the two areas and also picked up the theme of cir-

Rome's arched galley, looking forward

cles started by the portholes. In a boat actually called *Rome* it seemed even more appropriate to have Roman arches. I pondered the problem for some time and was near to abandoning either the arches or the cupboards on several occasions. Eventually I arrived at a solution which accommodated both so I thought I would try it.

Before we get too deeply involved in this, let's have a look at the technical side of the galley. Having denied myself a 230-volt supply I was spared the problem of trying to fit in a microwave, washing machine, spin drier, freezer, toaster, food processor and all the other paraphernalia of modern life which is finding its way onto boats these days. What I did have to find room for was a fridge, a cooker and a sink unit.

APPLIANCES

Fridge

Although designed for caravans, the convection-driven Electrolux gas fridge was almost universal in narrowboats for many years. The manufacturer never approved their use in boats but others, like Sibir and Gaz were happy for their products to be used and vented into the cabin. However, as mentioned in Chapter 2, all gas fridges must now have a balanced flue in order to comply with BS 5482

Pt 3. Since none of these models is supplied with a balanced flue at the present time, they cannot be installed in a new boat.

I have always avoided the gas fridge controversy and installed Engel electric models in previous fit-outs. These are fairly quiet and economical to run but, even so, we ended up switching them off at night to stop them keeping me awake and to conserve power. Engel introduced some even more economical models but a new manufacturer, Batts, appeared on the scene offering extremely quiet models with very low stated energy requirements. These are mostly domestic fridges with 12-volt compressor transplants so they provide around 4 cu ft of storage capacity. The stated 1 to 2 amps an hour consumption is an average once the fridge is down to temperature but, we thought, if it is as quiet as they claim and we don't have to switch it off at night we should achieve this for most of the time so Batts it was. Unfortunately, since fitting out *Rome*, Batts has ceased trading but similar fridges are now made by Ranger, Shoreline Refrigeration and Brisk – addresses at the end.

Installation is fairly simple. A recess for the case – making sure there is sufficient air space to ventilate the fins at the back – and a supply of electricity from the required thickness of cable – in our case 6mm. After trying the fridge, I have only one word for it – brilliant. On one occasion, we set off with less than fully charged batteries on a short trip to a rally. This scenario would previously have spelled disaster, even if we had switched the fridge off at night. In the event the fridge kept going, virtually silently, for the entire trip with only occasional bouts of engine running while stationary, and kept our frozen food really frozen.

Cooker

The narrowboaters' favourite gas cooker has been the Vanette for over a decade. Its position was strengthened when the manufacturer introduced a built-in version, with separate hob and oven/grill – at a considerably lower price than other build-ins. The hob is available with igniters that can be wired in to the cabin battery system; and, looking ahead to European legislation, it is now offered with flame-failure devices. The original free-standing model is still in production.

Although nominally a 'full-size' cooker and usually with four hob burners, the Vanette is not large enough for all tastes. You could buy a domestic cooker with an eye level grill but bear in mind that the height of the grill conflicts with cabin side tumblehome – so unless this type of cooker sits facing forward or aft against a bulkhead, it will not fit in compactly.

For smaller narrowboats, Flavel's Vanessa cooker – two burners, grill, small oven – may suffice. A few more up-market looking cookers of this size, such as the Spinflo Cara, have also appeared on the scene. If you allow the same space as for a larger cooker but perch the Vanessa on a shelf, you (or the next owner) can always change to a free-stander later on.

Combination tops – about 3ft 6in long, with sink, drainer and two burners set in, and grill & oven underneath – are even more compact. To reduce the galley's impact on a small cabin, the combination top can be covered by a hinged lid. Optimus' built-in cookers have lost much of their previous popularity because they

Two combined sink/hobs, useful in a smaller galley

are not much bigger than a Vanette, but more expensive than a Vanette.

Gas-free cooking

A properly installed and maintained gas system should be perfectly safe but more and more boaters are finding additional peace of mind by eliminating gas altogether. Gas is a very versatile fuel. Finding an alternative way to heat the boat or keep your food fresh is not too difficult. Cooking without gas is more of a problem but not impossible.

If you install a 7kVA generator or one of Beta's new PropGen packages, you could cook on electricity. A less ambitious option would be to run a microwave off an inverter or small generator and back this up with a solid fuel stove.

Flavel Vanessa cooker suitable for smaller galleys

Dickinson diesel cookers could allow gas-free boating – although a gas cooker is, as yet, more convenient to use

Oil stoves can be run on diesel – the same fuel as the engine – or paraffin, also known as kerosene, which has to be stored separately. Diesel stoves produce heat by drip feeding oil into a burner pot where it is vapourised and burned. It therefore has the advantage that it requires no electricity but takes some time to get up to temperature. This time can be reduced by leaving the stove ticking over instead of turning it off between uses but, unless the galley is well ventilated, this can turn the cabin into a sauna in summer. Examples of this type of stove are the Dickinson and Esse.

For pure paraffin stoves, the fuel is pressurised by a small hand pump incorporated into the tank. The stoves are lit with a pre heating fuel – usually methylated spirit – to get the burner up to temperature before the paraffin is introduced. As with diesel stoves, paraffin stoves take a little time to get hot and are not as controllable as a gas cooker. The main producer of this type is Chillington Marine who make the Taylors.

To overcome some of the disadvantages of diesel and paraffin stoves, a Finnish company, Wallas, has produced a stove which uses pumped fuel and air making it behave more like a gas cooker. Its combustion is so complete that maintenance is reduced and the exhaust can be emitted through a small pipe in the cabin side if required.

The Esse Doric solid fuel range

Finally, there are solid fuel stoves. These range from the Epping or Premier, found in many a traditional back cabin, to the galley centrepiece Esse Doric. Both place greater limitations on the user but many are as happy to accept these as their land-based, Aga-using cousins are.

In our case

At risk of adding to the list of 'famous last words', I have never been too worried about having gas on board for the advantages it gives. In any case, the distaff side had decided it definitely had to be a split hob and oven on this boat. Valor, now trading rather confusingly as Stoves, brought out a split version of their popular Vanette. So far so good. The problem is that the hob, instead of being modelled on the top half of the Vanette, had nasty chrome pan supports which would look more at home on something coupled up to a canister of Camping Gaz. Added to which I was informed that it was too small for the waterborne feasts being planned (perhaps things weren't so bad after all).

A couple of phone calls to Stoves suggested that they might be about to bring out a better looking hob but it transpired that this was not so and we were back to square one. The problem with the other bottle gas hobs

Built in oven and grill

and ovens on the market is that most have expensive gadgets like timers and ignition devices which require a 230-volt supply. After a lot of research we discovered that the dark brown New World hob which still has battery ignition and looks like a real hob, is an exact colour match to the dark brown Stoves oven. It has to be said that the hob was also about twice the cost of the Stoves model, but what price peace and harmony? Stoves has since brought out the 7000 series ovens which have much larger grill compartments without seeming to reduce the oven size.

Sink unit

The choice of sink units is very wide and can also lead to protracted 'debates'. We were quite taken with the brass bowls and drainers now in the shops but even the salesman reckoned they would be difficult to keep clean. Because of the tight planning we needed a compact design and were fortunate to find a two and a half bowl unit only 37in long and at a very reasonable price in MFI. It has a pop-up waste which keeps me amused for hours and MFI supplied a very good drainage kit just as reasonably priced which contains all the necessary traps and overflows. Don't waste time looking for this particular one though – they discontinued it shortly after we bought ours.

Since the skin fitting in the hull is just below the magic 10in above water level demanded by the Boat Standards it was important to see that all the pipe connections, up to and including the waste outlet in the sink, were good and watertight. To this end, I used a Jubilee clipped hose pipe from the skin fitting to the trap outlet and made sure that all the connections in the branches and traps under the sink were well tightened. Another solution is to ask the builder to weld an externally threaded $1\frac{1}{4}$ in BSP pipe stub to the inside of the hull so that you can connect the plastic plumbing directly to it. This means that the piping is not reduced to a smaller diameter at the skin fitting and consequently the basins empty much more quickly.

THE WOODWORK

So much for the nuts and bolts, now for the part which I find more enjoyable – the woodwork. This was the first opportunity I had to really try out the router and the Triton Workcentre and, while I don't imagine that you will want to copy exactly what I did, I hope that the description of the techniques involved will show what is possible and perhaps provide some food for thought.

Carcassing

The first job was to make the floor units. These were very odd sizes so it was not possible to use off-the-peg fittings as I have done in the past. I did, however, use melamine-faced chipboard for this, and only this, part of the job, in spite of the accepted wisdom on the subject. If you ventilate the boat properly there is no reason why the atmosphere should get so humid as to adversely affect the chipboard. The only argument then is what happens if (heaven forbid) the boat sinks; to which my reply is that, if this did happen, the first thing I would replace, whatever it was made of, would be the galley.

Having made this momentous decision, the rest was fairly straightforward. I cheated slightly and got the DIY store to

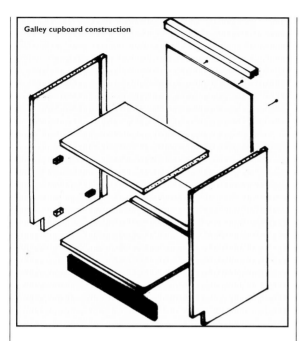

Galley cupboard construction

cut the board to length for the unit sides and shelves. OK I could have done it myself but they offered – and it was free. It was then simply a matter of cutting a groove near the back of each piece for the backboard and assembling the pieces using plastic block connectors, as I had not discovered the Kreg Minijig at this stage. I cut the first couple of grooves with a 'flute' bit in the router but the resin in the board soon blunted it. Then I tried setting the saw blade to a height corresponding to the depth of the groove and making two or three close parallel cuts to form the required width. I found this to be a much better method of forming grooves or rebates in any material. There were three units, one each side of the oven and one under the sink. These were pushed into place and the various bits of equipment added so that adjustments could be made to accommodate the wiring and pipework.

Worktops

After the units came the worktops which I had decided to tile. A firm, stable base is needed for this so the 18mm plywood I used for the flooring seemed the best answer. Both tops had a largish hole in them, one for the sink and the other for the hob so, rather than use large sheets of ply I made them up from $1\frac{1}{2}$ in x $\frac{3}{4}$ in battens with 18mm ply infills. This gave just as stable a base but meant that I could use off-cuts of ply instead of breaking into a new sheet. With these cut and loosely fitted the next thing to think about was the facing materials.

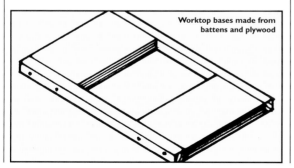

Worktop bases made from battens and plywood

Materials

My first thought was to use a combination of oak and mahogany for the interior generally; oak for the background and mahogany for the details. I started off buying some 4in x $\frac{1}{2}$ in planed oak – which was really for the cabin side framing – and some 2in x 1in sawn oak which I intended to convert to whatever size I needed using the Triton and then plane. I then had a number of changes of heart. Because I enjoyed using the oak so much and could not decided which bits to do in oak and which to do in mahogany I simplified the whole thing by ditching the mahogany – Friends of the Earth please note. Then I realised that I would have great difficulty fixing the 4in x $\frac{1}{2}$ in sections flat to the cabin sides satisfactorily and so tried strips of 4in wide 9mm oak-faced ply instead. These were much easier to fix and, with the right moulding to hide the edge, several visitors thought it was solid oak. This meant that I had about a hundred feet of surplus planed oak – a possibly expensive mistake.

It was, however, one of the best mistakes I had made as I discovered that I could cut it down with the Triton to make excellent door stops, edge trims, shelves, fascias – you name it. It was so useful I actually ended up ordering some more when the first batch was used up. Incidentally, if you have never worked in oak before you have a treat in store. The smell as it is being cut or planed is reminiscent of single malt whisky, but do remember to wear a mask if you are creating dust.

As you see from the sketches, the plan was to have two triple arched screens, one at each end of the units, with angled wall cupboards fitted into the corners where the screens met the cabin sides. This left the middle third of each side, where the sink and hob and the two portholes occurred, free of cupboards. A high level shelf just above the portholes linking the cupboards provided useful additional storage as well as visual continuity.

Arches

It may seem strange to start at the top and work down but the first parts of this scheme to go in were the arches.

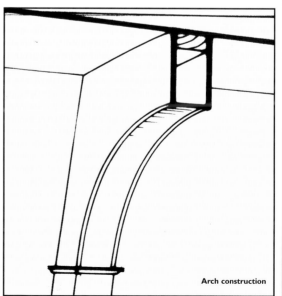

Arch construction

These were cut carefully from sheets of 9mm oak-faced ply, two for each arch, and fixed either side of a batten which had been screwed to the ceiling. For these cuts I used a power jigsaw with a narrow fret blade. Next came the more difficult job of filling in the curved undersides of the arches between the ply sides. DIY stores have now switched on to oak and sell sheets of iron-on veneer which I could have used. This veneer, however, is formed from thin strips of wood glued together before being sliced through at right angles. The resulting appearance resembles the edge of a piece of plywood which is exactly what I was trying to cover up! A bit more head scratching and I devised a plan to clamp a piece of the 9mm oak-faced ply to a thicker batten so that it could be passed safely over the circular saw to turn it into 2mm ply. This was a delicate and dusty operation but it worked and I now had an exact match of plywood in a thickness I could bend. I have subsequently achieved the same result, much more easily, by passing the plywood through a planer thicknesser.

Inevitably some pieces took the bend better than others but with patience I managed to fill in all the arches. The strips were held in place with hundreds of pieces of masking tape while the glue dried. I had hoped to leave the edges of the arches plain but soon realised that they needed an edge trim to tidy up the joint between the face and the veneer strips. Problem – where do you get thin oak mouldings to match the rest of your oak. Answer – make them yourself. I rounded the edge of a 4in x $^1/_2$in oak plank and then cut off the half round section on the saw table. The square edge of the plank was rounded again and the whole process repeated until I had enough strips to go round all the edges. They had just enough spring in them to go round the smaller arches and were glued and taped in place as before.

Columns

Next came the columns. On *George* these were round in section but, since I could see problems in getting the cupboards to marry up to round columns, I opted for square section ones this time. I decided on 4in x 4in oak bases up to just above worktop height and a slightly smaller section for the column from here to the underside of the arches. To provide some interesting detail I thought I would rout a series of flutes into the faces of the columns. This would have been fairly easy to achieve by passing the columns over a $^1/_4$in semi-circular router cutter guided by the fence on the Triton. The flutes would all be parallel and by adding a couple of temporary stops they would all start and finish on the same line. Easy – until I decided that if

the columns were the same thickness all the way up they would look rather clumsy and top heavy.

Classical columns have a gentle taper from about a third of the way up from the base which makes them more pleasing to the eye and which the Greeks, who had a word for everything, called entasis. The taper was not too difficult. The outline was drawn on opposite sides of the column and the other two faces were planed down to these lines. The process was then repeated starting with the faces just completed and the other faces planed. Having done this I realised that the flutes would have to converge slightly to correspond so I had to abandon the Triton method.

Thumbing through the router instructions (always the last resort) I noticed that there is a collar which fits over the spindle and allows you to use the router in a template to produce, in the case of the illustration, the outline of a jolly whale. This was not exactly the shape I had in mind but the principle would apply equally well to straight lines on a column face. I quickly put together four pieces of 6mm ply to form a slot of the desired length and the width of the collar and G-cramped this to a piece of scrap wood. After a bit of practice I was reasonably proficient and was ready to try it on the real thing.

Everything was going well until I inadvertently cramped the template diagonally from the top of one slot to the bottom of the adjacent one and routed it. After the air had returned to its normal colour I tried filling in the diagonal one with some of my homemade half round beading, sanding it level and then cutting the routs on the correct lines – amazingly it worked and I was saved the expense of a new column. The capitals between the columns and the arches were made from 4in x 4in x $^1/_2$in pieces of oak with mouldings routed onto the four edges. This has to be done very carefully and remembering to do the with-the-grain routs first to avoid splitting the grain at the end of the cross grain passes.

Pelmets

Encouraged by this I decided to apply the router to the downstands at the bases of the wall units. One thing I seriously dislike is lighting in the middle of a ceiling throwing a boring, even light over everything. In a galley it is even more undesirable as it means that you are usually working in your own shadow. I had therefore decided to light the galley with small fluorescent strip lights fixed under the wall units, hidden from view by timber downstands or pelmets. I played around with various shapes for

Shaping the columns

Pelmet detail in *Rome's* galley – with circle motif repeated under suspended cupboard. Also in shot: fluted column supporting arch

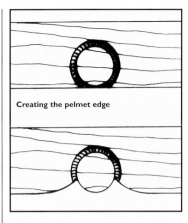

Creating the pelmet edge

the outline of these, making sure that I did not remove too much wood and reveal the light fitting behind.

Eventually I arrived at a shape with a central circle (picking up the arch/porthole theme), the side pieces being cut away to leave the lower third of the circle in silhouette. This time I made a template with a hole just larger than the circle to allow for the thickness of the collar and clamped this to the middle of a downstand, lining up with the bottom edge. Running the router around this without wandering into the middle was not easy but I managed it with a bit of practice on some scrap wood. You soon find that, if you don't keep the router moving, you are likely to scorch the wood. This also happens as the cutter becomes blunt. You can try to sand or scrape off the scorch mark – a bit like scraping burnt toast. Alternatively you can lower the cutter very slightly in the router and give it one last quick whisk round to clean up the groove. When all the routs were complete I cut away the wood either side with a jigsaw and then cleaned up the whole piece with glasspaper.

Tiling

With the basic structure of the galley in place it was time to fix the tiling and fittings. In such a small space, a jazzy tiling pattern didn't seem right so we settled on a fairly neutral oatmeal colour. Looking round the tiling shops I was amazed at the price of worktop tiles. In one shop, the cost of tiling our modest area was about £100. Once again MFI came up trumps and we got the same quantity of a very similar tile for £58. For fixing these I put my faith once again in cork adhesive. The tiles come in 9-tile (3 X 3) panels held together by perforated paper. This means that the majority of the tiles are pre-spaced and all you have to do is make sure that the edges of the panels, and any odd tiles, are similarly spaced. The next question was what to use for grout. We wanted a contrasting dark brown colour and this is available in the special epoxy grout which is recommended for this job. However, when I learned that it comes in a two-part pack, has to be used in a fairly short time and, on the salesman's own admission, was not easy to apply, panic set in.

What I eventually used was waterproof shower grout, reasoning that the galley would not receive anything like the use that a domestic kitchen gets and, if it was waterproof, it should be OK. Even using this was not that easy. If I wiped off the surplus on top of the tile before it dried I disturbed the joint and if I waited until the joint had dried the surplus was nigh on impossible to shift. The only consolation was that if the grout was that difficult to remove I shouldn't have any problems with it once it was finished. I managed to find a fairly good matching silicon sealant to go round the edges of the worktops and walls and at last

the job was done. Just in time to be too late for me, but not for you, BAL has since brought out Easy-Poxy. As its rather unfortunate name suggests, this is an epoxy grout which is easy to apply. Having tried it, I have to agree that it is much easier to use.

Doors and drawers

Rome's galley awaiting a decision about the doors

At this point in the proceedings I left the galley and got on with the boatman's cabin and then the outside painting while I thought how to finish off the galley. The main question was whether I made the doors and drawer fronts myself or took the coward's way and got them made professionally. My first thoughts were the latter path but the old credibility argument persuaded me in the end to have a go myself – the moths in my wallet readily agreed.

Frames

Although the manufacturers of the Triton reckon that mortise and tenon joints are, to put it in their (Australian) words 'a breeze', I did not fancy putting this to the test just yet. I therefore opted for the much simpler half-lap joints. The only complication was that I wanted a rebate on the inside edge of the frames for the panels to sit in and a moulded section on the outside for appearance. I sketched around on a piece of paper for a while and then tried out my method on a piece of scrap wood until I felt confident enough to try it on the real thing. To give myself a good start I ordered some $2\frac{1}{2}$ in x $\frac{1}{4}$ in ready-planed oak for the frames.

I started with the wall unit doors as these were small and any mishap would not waste too much wood. The overall

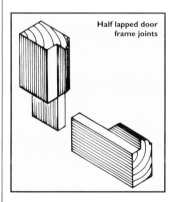

Half lapped door frame joints

width of the section was first reduced down to about 2in to give a reasonable area in the middle for the panels. Next, I cut a rebate on one edge, using the saw method described above, and routed a moulding on the adjacent edge. The oak was then cut into lengths slightly greater than the heights and widths of the frames.

The basic technique for cutting the joint is to set the table saw blade height to exactly half the thickness of the wood and set the side fence to the required distance to produce the length of lap you need. This distance may be different on the horizontal and vertical pieces if the depth of the rebate is not the same as the depth of the decorative moulding on the front. The end of the wood is then passed over the blade at right angles, advancing a blade width at a time, until it meets the stop. The Triton has a useful sliding stop which ensures that the wood remains at right

Forming a half lap joint using the Triton

angles to the blade. To avoid breaking out the grain on the back edge it is better to make the first pass with the wood resting against the stop and then go back and work in towards this cut from the other end. When all the passes are complete it is simply a matter of smoothing off the surface with a sharp chisel. For aesthetic reasons the vertical pieces should overlap the horizontals when viewed from the outside.

Then comes the trickier part where the moulded parts are cut back and mitred to allow one piece to fit in with the next. I started off doing this by hand but eventually realised that most of this part of the job could be done on the Triton with much greater speed and accuracy. A much simpler way of achieving almost the same result is to leave the frame

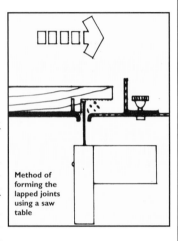

Method of forming the lapped joints using a saw table

edges square and glue in some off-the-peg moulding where they meet the panel or glazing. When all the joints had been fitted and cleaned up – a long and rather tedious job – the frames were glued up. For the small frames I relied on masking tape to hold the joints together while the glue set but the larger floor unit doors were held in the Workmate and G-cramps.

Panel treatment
The panels in the larger doors were to be 9mm oak faced ply but when I tried a piece in the completed frame it looked rather 'utility'. Raised and fielded panels of solid oak would have looked better but I did not have the equip-

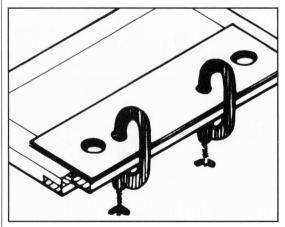

Using a template to position hinge holes

ment to make these. I considered making up some solid oak T&G boards but first tried cutting V grooves at about 3in centres on the oak-faced ply using the router. Fortunately the ply I was using did not have a very pronounced figure so the effect was very realistic and, by making the spacing of the cuts regular rather than random, I avoided the panels looking like 'wallboard'.

To fix these doors I used the offset hinges used by kitchen unit manufacturers. They require two large diameter shallow holes to be drilled fairly close to the edge of the back of each door. For these you use a special drill bit which has to have a very small pilot point and so tends to wander. You could mount the drill in a stand to overcome this but the bit cuts more easily if the drill is rocked gently from side to side a couple of degrees from the vertical. I made up a simple jig consisting of a piece of 12mm ply about 20in x 4in with two holes cut right through it, using the special bit, at the centres needed for the hinges. A thin strip of wood was then screwed to the face of the ply about $1/8$in from the edge of both holes. This enabled me to position the jig accurately on the back of the door and then clamp both securely to the Workmate ready for drilling. The holes in the ply guided the bit and made sure that it did not wander off course. I drilled about $3/16$in into the door through each hole and then removed the jig so that I could gauge the depth more precisely while drilling out the rest of the holes.

Leaded lights
By this time, I had become used to the wall units having no doors and was a bit concerned that when I did fit them they might make the galley feel rather claustrophobic. I hoped that this could be avoided by having glazed doors. Visions of glazed china cabinets, possibly with leaded

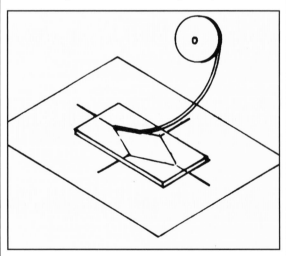

Method of making leaded panels

lights started to materialise in my mind – then I thought of what would happen if we hit the proverbial lock gate. Clearly china would be a lot safer stored at lower level and the wall units used for lighter, less breakable but also less picturesque items. This dilemma was solved one night sitting in our newly refurbished local (the source of many an inspiration) where the designer had used leaded glass screens with slightly obscured glass.

The next scene was down at the glass merchant ordering eight pieces of Stippolite glass and a reel of lead tape. The tape is much easier to put on than I had imagined. First the glass has to be carefully cleaned to make sure that no grease, or cleaning agent deposit is left on the surface. The trick is then to draw out the required pattern on a piece of paper and place this under the glass, which is smoothest side uppermost. The tape is then cut with scissors or a sharp knife, the backing paper removed and the tape stuck in place over the previously drawn lines. The only problem was to decide how to handle the junctions where three pieces met but after a couple of trial runs the best method soon became apparent.

Drawer fronts

My original plan was to make the drawer fronts in the same way as the doors but the thought of sixteen more joints to fit made me reconsider. I decided instead to make up the fronts from three pieces of $3/_4$in oak half-lapped together along their edges and with two short lengths of oak half-lapped at right angles at each end. The edges of the middle piece were chamfered all round to give a panel

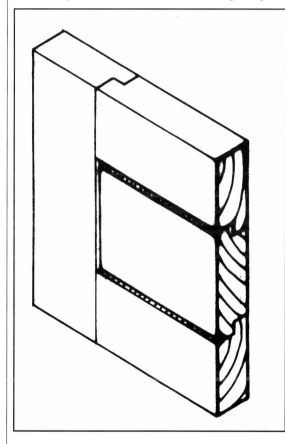

Drawer front construction

effect against the surrounding pieces. Apart from being quicker and easier to put together, the fronts have a more solid feel and present a flush face to the inside of the drawer. For the drawers themselves I chickened out and bought DIY plastic drawer kits which matched the 'off-the-peg' look of the interiors of the floor units. All that remained

Galley door and drawer

was to varnish the wood and fit the brass pull handles but I decided to leave this until I had completed the rest of the interior so that it could all be done in one operation.

ALL SYSTEMS GO

I could now fix the sink and hob units permanently and try out the water system. It is always a slightly nervous moment when you switch on the pump for the first time in earnest but it drew the water down the pipe from the tank

Adjacent side doors. Steps conceal a wine rack

very quickly and soon started pushing it round the system. The only leaks were from the brass fittings – mainly where I had forgotten to fit the fibre washers - so these were soon sorted out. So another landmark had been reached as we could actually draw water from the boat's own supply.

CHAPTER 12

THE BEDROOM AND SALOON

Dinette woodwork
Saloon design and woodwork
Fitting the stove
Alernative approaches
Bed details
Dinette details

Keeping warm

The bedroom and saloon on *Rome* contain the two means of heating the boat so, before we get too involved in the detail, let us have a look at heating systems in general. There are three types of fuel for central heating systems – gas, oil and solid fuel.

'Canal' version of the Alde balanced flue – it still looks like a pagoda

The gas fired Alde is a slim Swedish design, initially introduced for caravan installation although it has a well-proven history of coping with the larger space of narrowboats. The first Aldes to be fitted in narrowboats drew their combustion air from the cabin at low level or from the space under the floor. In recent years, the balanced flue version has been developed and this is the only type which complies with BS 5482 Pt 3. It draws its air through a special roof terminal which also serves as the exhaust and looks rather like a Chinese pagoda. This is probably robust enough for private use although many hire bases construct a steel 'roll-over' bar to protect it on their boats. A 'canal' version is available, finished in matt black and polished brass – it still looks like a pagoda.

The only real gas alternative was the British-built Ellis 6.7kW boiler, which had an even longer provenance in narrowboats – particularly in hire fleets where its simple, rugged design was appreciated. Unfortunately, the difficulties and cost of complying with new European legislation caused the manufacturer to stop production, although spares are still available for existing models.

Gas now faces strong competition from diesel-fired central heating. This uses the same fuel as the engine which is inherently safer than gas. There

Eberspacher forced air diesel boiler

are two basic types of diesel heater – forced air and gravity feed. The first is represented by Eberspacher, Mikuni and Webasto. Eberspacher is most prominent since a UK supplier reduced the price of its systems to narrowboat-viable levels in 1991. The heater units are so compact that they fit easily into an engine compartment. They require 12-volt power to blow air over a diesel injector. The ignited mixture then heats a water matrix before exhausting overboard. The systems are highly controllable – by timer and thermostat – and are built in several output sizes.

Typical current consumption is 2.25 amps in central heating (rather than just water heating) mode – about the same as an electric fridge. They are also fairly noisy, particularly to people on the towpath or adjacent boats, but the exhaust can be fitted with a silencer. All three manufacturers also offer diesel-fired warm-air systems which are better suited to smaller craft.

Gravity feed heaters are much simpler. A regulator controls the flow of diesel to a burner bowl where it vapourises and is burned. Ignition is manual, initially with meths, but the effort required is less than for lighting a solid fuel stove and, once lit, the heater can tick over for weeks without mess or maintenance. Gravity feed is less expensive than the forced air type and

Kabola E type boiler

needs no electric power. Numerous makes are sold on the Continent; two are well known here – Refleks, a sturdy fishing boat heater, and Kabola, which may appeal as better looking. Some Kabolas can be hidden away like gas boilers while others have a casing which resembles a solid fuel stove, enabling them to be installed in the saloon fireplace. Ceramic coal versions are now available to complete the illusion.

Kabola Old English natural draught boiler

Most solid fuel stoves can be fitted with a back boiler which will provide enough heat for a central heating system. In order to reduce power consumption and minimise noise it is preferable to have a gravity system – where the water moves round the system by convection – rather than a pumped one. Unlike the gas and diesel systems, it is not possible to install a thermostat in a solid fuel system but, with practice, they are not too difficult to control.

Space heaters

For boats of less than 40ft, a single space heater is probably sufficient. The cheapest narrowboat heater has been the gas catalytic type but this is flued into the cabin and so does not comply with BS 5482 Pt 3. The only space heaters which appear to comply at the time of writing are the Truma Combi and the Carver Whispair P4.

The other simple space heater is the solid fuel stove itself. Lazing at the end of the day before the quiet glow of a solid fuel stove is, for many, an essential part of narrow-

The Premier back cabin stove

boating. The simple Tor Gem (currently out of production) was the popular choice before the arrival, in the eighties, of the Squirrel stove. This is available with vitreous (ie, coloured and shiny) or matt black finish. It adjusts for solid fuel or wood burning and is highly controllable. Even so, if your boat is medium to small, you might do better with the smaller Heron or Carabo stoves.

THE BEDROOM

One reason for tackling the bathroom and galley first was that it meant that there was still plenty of room left in the boat for the Workmate, the tools and all the materials needed. I set myself up in what was to be the bedroom area as this was conveniently in-between the two. With these areas now more or less complete it was time to move myself into the saloon area and start the bedroom furniture.

Gas boiler

First to go in was the wardrobe. This would have been a simple job but for my plan to incorporate the Alde central heating boiler into it. I had never fitted one of these before and so had to resort frequently to the well illustrated instruction manual. At the time when I fitted out *Rome*, it was common practice to draw combustion air from under the floor. Provided there is sufficient space between the ballast and the underside of the floorboards and there is a good supply of fresh air from the outside, this works well and creates air movement in the bilges. I used this method but, as mentioned above, only the balanced flue version should be used from now on.

The manual shows a piece of metal trunking near the base which draws air from below the floor and introduces it into the casing near to the combustion area. My supplier said that this was not necessary in a boat and one reason for his keen price was that he did not include this part. I understand that the theory is that the air is warmed and carries on up the casing, leaves via slots near the top of the front plate which warms the surrounding area. If you omit the trunking and leave the knock out panel in the side of the casing in place, more of the boiler's heat is directed to the water which then heats the calorifier and radiators. Since I was planning to have louvre doors on the wardrobe I decided to knock out the panel and put a brass grille over it so that air would be drawn through the wardrobe instead.

Exhaust

At the top end is the exhaust pipe which passes through the roof and has a rain cowl over it. Alde supplied a cowl but this was a fairly flimsy affair, liable to be crushed under a low bridge causing a potentially fatal build up of exhaust gases in the cabin. I therefore discarded this in favour of a special (but Alde-approved) brass mushroom vent which allows a passage of air even when screwed fully down. The installation kit includes a neat trim to seal round the exhaust pipe and hide the edge of the hole in the ceiling. Unfortunately this only allowed for a total lining thickness of about $\frac{3}{4}$ in so I had to cut a clean hole in the ceiling below the trim – but this can't be seen when the installation is complete.

The gas connection was straightforward, following the instructions in the manual although, for the reasons given in Chapter 2, it is now advisable to have this done by a CORGI fitter. The electrical connection would have been just as easy except that the wiring diagram in the instruction manual did not match the diagram stuck inside the thermostat. After the confusion was cleared up, connectors were crimped to the five wires and the nylon terminal block used to locate these into the top of the unit. I had a job satisfying the requirements for the location of the thermostat and it ended up on the side of the wardrobe. It is probably too near to the boiler or the porthole even now but I am sure that I can turn it up or down to compensate. The flow and return pipes were connected to the pipework already installed at lining-out stage

Woodwork

All that remained was to build the wardrobe around it. I have seen Aldes installed to one side of a wardrobe allowing the clothes to come into contact with the casing. This is probably acceptable but to make sure I built a ply partition round the sides and back – being careful to leave a $\frac{1}{4}$ in gap all round. The sides of the wardrobe are 12mm ply with the framing and moulding treatment and the doors are the bought-in ramin louvre type. Yes, I did feel guilty about taking the easy way out but I justified this with the thought that I did not have the time to make them myself and they seemed to fit in reasonably well with the over all decor. Also, in a boat with fixed portholes, louvre doors tend to promote a good through flow of air. I did intend to replace them at a later date but, after five years, they are still in service.

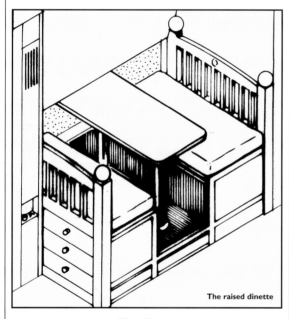

The raised dinette

The dinette

Dinettes were very popular on hire boats a few years back and we had one on the Burland cruiser which we owned before *Bess*. The space needed for a double bed is exactly the same as that required for a four person dining table with bench seats either side so the two can be combined quite happily. Looking round boats at waterways festivals and boat shows, it seems that I am not the only one who has rediscovered the virtues of this layout. Of course I couldn't just design a plain, straightforward one; mine has half the calorifier and half the loo tank under one bench seat and a finrad built into the front step. Evelyn was heard to remark that she would not be able to sleep a wink on the thing for fear of being drowned, blown up or dropped into something extremely unpleasant. I ignored this and carried on.

The half built dinette showing the calorifier, holding tank and pipe runs

Setting out

The first job was to set it out on the floor and walls. By keeping the casing to the calorifier and loo tank as tight as possible I was able to achieve a reasonable width of table and a not too deep bench seat. The floor level between the bench seats of the dinette is usually raised 6in or so which allows a better view out of the windows. This consideration did not really apply in our case as we have portholes but I decided that I would do it anyway as it would enable me to install the finrad in the step and would give more storage space under the benches. I made the raised floor 8in above the general level and the top of the fixed bench 14in above the raised floor. This meant that the backrest height fitted in nicely at about gunwale level.

Style

Next came the question of style. I toyed with the idea of continuing the arch theme into a four poster design but gave this up fearing that it would lengthen the already narrow corridor down the side of the boat and would not really look right in dinette mode. What I needed was something which suited both uses. Sketching around I eventually came up with the idea of having 4in square oak posts about 3ft 6in high at the four corners with arched bedhead cum backrests spanning between the posts at either end as shown in the sketch.

Turned oak newel cap on corner of dinette

The construction followed the principles used in the galley except that I did manage a few mortise & tenon joints into the corner posts. The tenons were formed with the circular saw in a similar way to the half housing joints and the mortises were roughly drilled out with a drill and squared up with a chisel. The 'rungs' of the bedhead were fixed by the same screwhead-into-hole technique as the tops of the partitions. The trick was in making all the rungs the same length and then making the cross members equal lengths so that when the whole assembly was cramped together (a good trick in itself) everything was square. To finish off the posts I asked a local joinery firm to produce some turned oak newel caps in the form of acorns – naturally.

Drawers

In order to increase the amount of easily accessible clothes storage space, I fitted three drawers into half of the forward bench so that they faced towards the wardrobe.

These were made in exactly the same way as the galley drawers and, since they are visible from the galley, provide a good visual link between the two spaces. The table top/bed insert is made from veneered ply edged with solid oak trim and supported on Desmo legs with the sockets let into the raised floor. I also made an angled shelf in the corner opposite the wardrobe, partly to act as a dressing table and partly to hide the solid fuel radiator bleed valve.

Drawers and discreet skirting radiator in base

Finrad

The 8in step was not quite enough to accommodate the standard finrad cover plate but I did not want to make it any higher as headroom would have become rather limited. I thought first of making up thin plywood covers but these would probably have twisted in the heat and would have been difficult to fix. Then I tried trimming the metal cover plate down to the required height with a hacksaw and Aralditing the offcut to the back of it so that it would still hook onto the similarly reduced brackets. With the sawn edge filed to a straight line and the cover painted to tone with the surrounding woodwork, you would never know the difference.

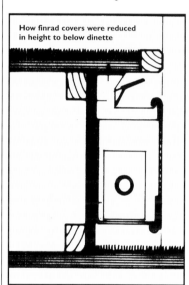

How finrad covers were reduced in height to below dinette

Atmospheric dinette/double bed in *Rome*'s centre cabin. In dinette mode . . .

. . . and as a double bed.

THE SALOON

If you are the sort of person who sees problems as challenges then the saloon is an area you will probably enjoy. It is arguably the most difficult area to plan as there are few 'obvious' solutions and many possible ones to mull over and come to a decision on. Since the woodworking methods are basically similar to those employed in the galley I will restrict myself to thoughts on design and layout, plus a few essential technicalities.

The stove

Let's start with this popular feature found in most narrowboats nowadays. I recall a boatbuilder and advocate of solid fuel stoves saying once that they heated up an area 20ft all round them. Evelyn spoiled his day by asking him why, if this was the case, he always placed them against the front bulkhead where half the area round them consisted of the front deck. The only good reason I have ever heard for doing this is that the bulkhead stops the stove being hurled forward if the boat gets suddenly drawn forwards in a lock and hits the far end. On *George* I positioned it at 45° against the screen between the saloon and galley, made sure its feet were well fixed to the floor and hoped for the best – it was fine. This arrangement also meant that the chimney did not spoil the line of the front of the cabin. It all worked so well that we decided to do exactly the same on *Rome*. The only changes were the type of stove – we chose a Little Wenlock (British) instead of the Squirrel (Swedish) – and the treatment of the surround.

It is a good idea to position the stove on the port side of the boat if possible as this will mean that the chimney is on the side of the boat away from the bank when meeting traffic coming towards you. In this position, it is less likely to be knocked off by trees or tunnel linings and therefore saves you dashing forward to remove it so frequently when danger looms.

Fireplace

Stoves usually have a tiled area around them to provide an easily cleaned surface and to protect the hull lining from excessive heat. On *George* I took this idea a stage further and used 1in thick 'bricks' stuck to the wall and pointed with mortar to look like the real thing. I stuck them with Tile-on-Wood adhesive and used ordinary sand and cement mortar. Somewhat to my surprise, they remained in place perfectly all the time we owned the boat. For the hearth I used quarry tiles which seemed to go well with the black cast iron and red bricks. My newly acquired routing capability encouraged me to try something more ambitious on *Rome*.

Adam style fireplace sets off the Little Wenlock stove

Our fireplace at home is in 'Builder's Merchant

Coalbrookdale Little Wenlock stove with Adam-style fireplace, in aft corner of saloon. Note how mirror in top of arch disguises cupboard on other side

Adam' style and the more I looked at it, the more I thought I could do something similar. One major difference between the two was that the boat fireplace had to be built into a corner. This was not such a bad thing as I had decided that the area immediately around the stove should be covered by those very ornate Victorian tiles now available and which are often set at 45° to the fire. The woodwork seemed to fit round the tiles quite well with the centre section following the angle of the stove and the two outer 'wings' parallel with the bulkhead and hull side. The whole job took about 30ft of planed 3in x 1in oak. For the hearth I used quarry tiles with an oak edge trim once again.

Stove pipe

On our previous boat we used a stainless steel pipe which tapered from about 5in diameter at the base to about 3 $^1/_2$in half way up and then continued at this diameter. Being made of thin metal it warmed up very quickly but the taper, coupled with its tendency to cool down just as quickly meant that at times the pipe did not 'draw' very well. This time we used one of Midland Chandler's cast iron drain pipes which, it seemed, would overcome all these problems but would need cutting to the correct length and angle. MC advised using an old piece of plastic drain pipe of similar diameter to make a template before cutting the real thing. This sounded like a good idea but I did not have any pipe and did not feel like buying a piece just for this. I therefore cut a piece of plywood with the same width as the pipe diameter and used this to make a two-dimensional template.

Carefully cutting the flue pipe to the correct angle

For cutting the cast iron pipe I hired a 9in angle grinder. This had a tremendous kick-back when started but made short work of the pipe. I was pleasantly surprised how easy it was to follow my pencil marking and produce a clean cut even though I had to work in from both sides. I have since bought a 7in Black & Decker industrial angle grinder and find that this copes just as well. The collar on the Wenlock is quite big so I left as much of the socket as possible on the base of the pipe to reduce the amount of fire cement needed to fill the gap. The space between the top of the pipe and the chimney collar was filled with heat resisting mastic putty, flaunched at the top to direct gooey substances down the inside, rather than the outside of the pipe. If you are planning to use a double skin chimney, make sure you finish the top of the pipe about an inch lower than the top of the chimney collar so that the inner liner does not cut into the mastic.

Chimneys, unlined (left) and lined

Final connections

Then it was just a case of connecting the radiator and fitting the feed and expansion tank so that I could have my first fire. The final connections to the rad were made with car heater hose and jubilee clips which allow the copper pipes to expand without a lot of clicking and creaking. This may sound a bit Heath Robinson but if the screws on the clips are positioned to face the hull lining and all the pipework painted in one colour, they soon blend in with the background.

Flexible connection in central heating pipe allows for expansion

The best place for the feed and expansion tank was on the wall in the engine room so it had to look right if it was not to spoil the rest of the space. Finding a suitable tank was more difficult than I anticipated and I had to get one specially made. It needs to be about 1ft square by about 2in from front to back. The chap who welded it up entered into the spirit by providing a nice brass cap and, with the main body painted dark green and the copper down pipe polished, it looks a treat.

All that was left was to fill up the system and try it out.

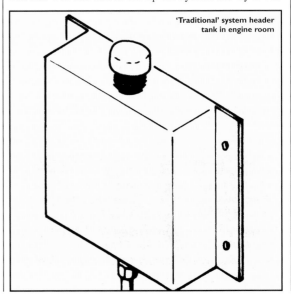

'Traditional' system header tank in engine room

The whole system takes about three gallons so I bought a gallon of antifreeze to go in it which not only stops the water freezing but also inhibits corrosion. I filled it with pure water initially and was very glad that I did. The drain cock on the radiator leaked a bit but this was soon dealt with. After we lit the fire we noticed a pool of water on the hearth which we discovered was coming from the two holes provided as alternative connection points and for which blanking plugs are supplied. I had bedded these in sealing compound but either I had not used enough or it had been squeezed out when I screwed the plug in. So it was yet another draining down operation and I did what I should have done in the first place and wrapped the threads in PTFE tape, being careful to wind it in the right direction so that it was not unwound as the plug was screwed in. It took a considerable amount of tape to make a seal but after a couple of attempts the drips ceased.

Furniture

I suppose I could have opted out of this problem altogether, nipped down to MFI again and bought a three piece suite. The problem with this is that, unless you manage to find a very compactly designed one, they fill the entire

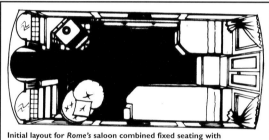

Initial layout for *Rome's* saloon combined fixed seating with a swivel easy chair

area and the knees of the people on the settee are almost touching the opposite wall. I must say in fairness that I have seen some nice layouts which used just two armchairs or a combination of built-in and loose seating. As we hoped that we would be entertaining our friends on the boat but would not want to give up the only two comfortable seats, we opted for the latter. I tried a few layouts

Boxes can be changed from seat to low table by flipping top over

on paper first and we agreed on a single fixed seat to one side of the front doors with a two seater version on the other. This would leave enough space for a loose, possibly swivel chair at the other end, opposite the stove. The only The fixed seats have cupboards built into the backrests and

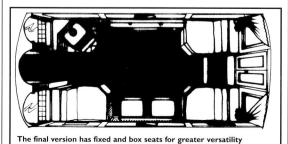

The final version has fixed and box seats for greater versatility

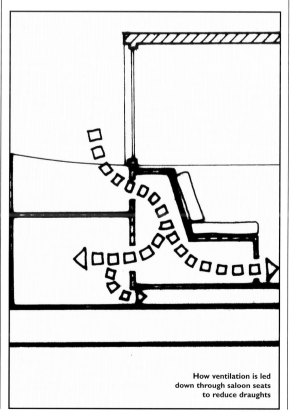

Rome's saloon with built-in seats and movable boxes

snag with this was that the radiator would not be centred under the porthole where what is left of my tidy, architectural mind said it should be.

This thought persuaded us to try a few more layouts and we finally decided on single fixed seats in the three vacant corners of the saloon and two purpose made loose boxes which can be used as occasional seating, tables or storage units. This leaves a decent sized area in the middle of the saloon which makes it feel more spacious. To enable us to eat in the saloon I positioned three Desmo leg sockets in the floor. I find this system very neat and versatile as the holes can be used singly or in pairs to support small tables in different locations or a larger table over the whole area. If you are keen on golf you can even practice your putting shots on wet days!

How ventilation is led down through saloon seats to reduce draughts

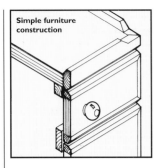
Simple furniture construction

he front ones help to direct air from the grilles in the front bulkhead down to low level in the cabin. The rear seat has a car radio/cassette player installed out of sight in the backrest cupboard with the speakers mounted, one each side, under the galley wall units. This seat also houses a 12-volt socket and TV aerial socket from the Omnimax mounted on the roof – although I somehow doubt whether we shall have much time for TV watching. The only other piece of furniture is a range of bookshelves along the wall between the stove and the front seat.

ALTERNATIVE APPROACHES

That completes the 'modern' part of the boat so, before we start on the traditional engine room and back cabin, now is a good time to consider some other ways that you could tackle the design and construction of the furniture and fittings.

Construction first – some of the methods I used may seem a bit ambitious although most were self-taught by building up from simple projects to slightly more complicated ones over a period of years. If you are newer to the game, you may prefer to use a more basic approach – remembering that you can always refit parts of the boat at a later date when you feel you can improve on them.

It has been suggested that if you can build a sturdy box that looks half decent, you can fit-out a basic narrowboat. Consider a typical traditional-style boat with engine room, aft bedroom, toilet/shower room, forward galley/saloon. After fitting bulkheads, the absolute bare minimum of furniture you need to make is double bed, wardrobe and galley. From this level, fitting-out can be as elaborate as you want to make it. Additional furniture might include engine box, dressing table/drawers, bedroom shelves/suspended cupboards, base for wash basin in toilet, dividing shelves between galley and saloon/more suspended cupboards, dinette and a variety of saloon storage units but most of these items are essentially boxes. If your woodwork skills are wanting, a simple, discreet but careful style might be the answer – particularly when combined with lively soft furnishings.

You could decide to use a single unobtrusive timber (preferably a light one – like oak or ash) for all linings and furniture so that it is deliberately subordinated to more lively soft upholstery, curtains, carpets and cabin fittings. As a part of your 'careful joinery' policy, you might decide that no raw edge of timber panel should be visible. Most timber merchants will saw oak/ash into 9mm x 12mm, 15mm or 18mm strips (depending on the thickness of panels to be capped). DIY stores all have a large selection of mouldings in pine, red hardwood and, sometimes, oak. These can give joinery a more finished look although they are not cheap.

When gluing and pinning, punch in all pins and conceal with carefully matched filler – you may have to mix two colours. If your mitring might've been better, the matching filler will perform an effective rescue. Matching timber knobs and handles, rather than ornate brass, will maintain the joinery's quiet character.

Doors are not the easiest things to make and they have a nasty habit of warping. The DIY stores can help here by supplying both cupboard and room doors in a variety of sizes and styles. What they cannot supply is those awkwardly shaped doors which you need for closing off a side corridor. If you don't feel up to the task, your only options are a friendly local joinery firm or a curtain. Curtains could also be used to screen the contents of low level cupboards and under-bed storage areas. You can make better use of these difficult-to-reach spaces by building a 'truck-

Detail I

le drawer' which is really a simple box on castors or fridge runners. These can be designed to fit into your car boot and pre-loaded with clothes at home.

Bed details

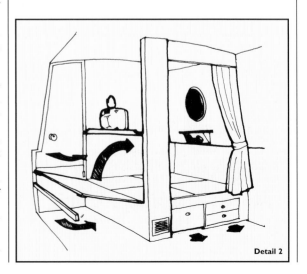
Detail 2

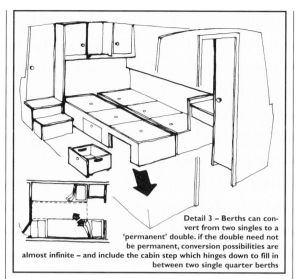

Detail 3 – Berths can convert from two singles to a 'permanent' double. if the double need not be permanent, conversion possibilities are almost infinite – and include the cabin step which hinges down to fill in between two single quarter berths

Moving on to design – detail 1 shows a permanent double bed with truckle drawers. Note the slots on the drawer sides for carrying to and from the boat. The detail also shows top loading panels. These can be drilled with (say 1in diameter) holes to ventilate the mattress, although ply thickness may have to be increased to allow for consequent weakening of the ply. Many double beds have a shelf or cupboard over the head. Detail 1 shows a combination of both with centre housing to conceal the gubbins of reading lights. At the bed foot, there are conventional drawers with side slide rails.

Even DIY narrowboats can cost £500 to £700 per foot (1998) so turning the permanent double bed (which is dead space during the day anyway) round to lie across the boat could save you a considerable sum or give more space in the saloon. This assumes a conventional shell section that allows decent head and foot room for a 6ft 3in long body under the side decks. Detail 2 shows that access past the bed to the engine room (or wherever) is possible by hinging the bed foot. This should not reduce the bed's 'permanent' status in this era of duvets and fitted sheets. The flap could be held vertical by sliding a bolt into the bulkhead – but is given more substance here by a column and TV shelf. As shown, the column could be a duct, bringing low-level cabin ventilation down from the cabin top – rather than draughtily through a bulkhead door. The door does have to be split to maintain an escape route when the bed is down. You could use a number of devices to give the cabin character, probably (as this is a cross-bed) on a boatman's cabin theme. Hanging drapes along the side is just a start.

If the aft cabin can be 8ft long, the arrangement in Detail 3 allows the alternative of a permanent double or two singles. One single unit is a movable box. It is shown here with truckle drawers, so the unit needs apertures on both sides to house the drawers in either mode. As shown – with aft door opening inwards, the cabin needs to be at least 9ft 6in long. The shorter length is possible if the door opens outwards or (more difficult) if hinged on its outboard edge.

In *Rome's* boatman's cabin, I have tried to recreate the

details of working craft. You may decide that you need something which is like a boatman's cabin – but isn't. It could be one that provides a day cabin settee sociably close to the steerer, while converting to a guest cabin by night. As the dinette is raised it provides space for the prop shaft to run below – while the walkway to one side allows full headroom. You could even combine this cabin with the trad/semi trad sliding roof shown in Chapter One so that the space becomes a sun lounge.

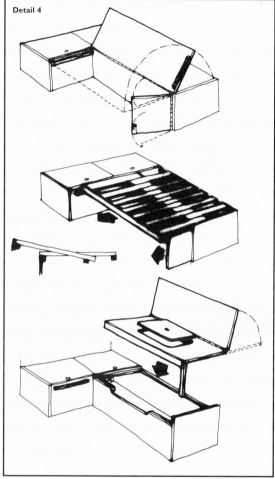

Detail 4

Dinette details

Of all dinettes the L-shaped version seems the most popular – but not the easiest to convert to a double bed. The table on *Rome* sits between two settees and just drops down to convert to a bed – an L-shape needs additional support on its fourth corner. A flap can hinge or slide out (top two arrangements in Detail 4) for the table to sit on, or the fill-in panel can hinge over to store under the settee's upholstery. The extension can be slatted to slide back in – and to ventilate the upholstery's underside.

The rising star among dinette conversions is the bottom arrangement. The settee top panel is attached to a back rest panel by a piano hinge. When drawn out, it drags the back panel after it, to make a conversion in seconds. As shown, the fourth corner is supported by a permanent leg. In bed mode, the main pull-out panel (as against the backrest

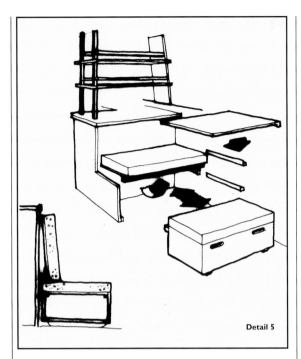

Detail 5

panel) should still be supported by the lip of the settee to avoid straining the hinge. Although the panel & backrest assembly can fit fairly loosely, the main panel should have a lip on its underside to prevent it pulling out too far.

A drop-down table, borrowed from a boatman's cabin, is ideal for quick meals

Unlike the other two arrangements shown, this one can allow top access into the settee storage space.

Detail 5 shows a settle – a settee that backs conveniently on to the 4ft bar of a galley. The settle has a suitably cottage character, and with demountable table, provides a space-effective (4ft x 4ft) eating place. Put two folding chairs on the other side of the table and you can have a dinner party. But this is a flexi-settle. The base is a freestanding box that can slide out to make the two extra dining places – while the backrest drops down to replace the settle seat. At the end of the evening, the table can drop down between box and settle to make a 6ft x 4ft double berth.

If you would like to give the saloon a definite character, the evocative feature exploited by several boatbuilders is the table cupboard, borrowed from a boatman's cabin. This might be fitted almost flush to the cabin side so that it drops down to make a four-place dining table, with diners seated on pine stools or folding chairs. Disadvantage: it is not possible to position a window directly over the table for diners to see out. The theme might be picked up by shelves recessed behind an arch – the advantage here is that the circular profile does not have to be trimmed. Pick out the raw ply edge instead in red (smear the edge with woodworking glue and allow to dry before sanding to help achieve a smooth finish); and paint the recessed shelves in traditional green. The face of the unit remains, like the interior generally, in light oak or ash veneer.

You can buy, or have made, small folding gate leg tables. One particular proprietary table (often seen in mail order catalogues) has a store for folding chairs within its centre frame. The simple and popular way to support a demountable table is the Desmo leg – a sturdy aluminium tube tapered at both ends to fit aluminium sockets on the underside of the table and on the floor. A single leg supports a small table and even allows it to swivel. This can be useful where a dinette straddles the forward doorway so that the table, when erected, bars passage. If the Desmo leg is mounted slightly off-centre it allows the table to swivel 180 degrees, creating just enough space to squeeze through.

CHAPTER 13

THE BOATMAN'S CABIN

References
The essential elements
Engine room
Tips

The boatman's cabin

This was the first boatman's cabin that I had attempted, and I was slightly daunted by someone who had just done one saying that it was the worst part of the job – "you can't stand up straight and there's hardly a right

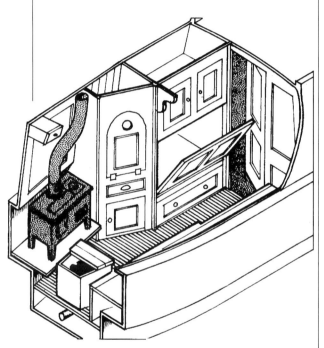

Three dimensional layout of a typical boatman's cabin

angle in the whole thing". No doubt he was right about this but I must say I quite enjoyed it, partly because I was no longer working in hardwood and any little mishaps could be filled and eventually painted.

References

The basic layout of the cabin follows certain rules which have to be adapted to suit the shape of the rear of the boat in question. The first thing to do is to acquaint yourself with this basic layout from as many sources as possible. The best of these is a genuine boatman's cabin in a genuine working boat of which, thankfully, there are still a fair number about including those at the museums at Ellesmere Port and Gloucester. Some modern boats also have them but these have been interpreted by their modern builders (like me) and so should not be relied upon without checking against original sources. One thing you will

notice is that the standard of joinery on the genuine article has a certain panache, not to say roughness, about it. This should not be taken as an excuse to knock the whole thing together from orange boxes but it might make you think twice about producing anything too 'twee'.

Books and magazine articles are useful, 'Soap 'oles, Bed 'oles and Bugs' by Tony Lewery (October 1989 *Waterways World*) being particularly good. John M Hill's book *From Stem to Stern*, although it is principally concerned with painting, also has some useful information on layout and details. Probably because boat people were understandably reluctant to allow strangers into their domain, photographs in books are fairly rare and the detail is often covered by drapes and ornaments. Tom Chaplin's book *Narrowboats* contains plans, and *Flowers Afloat* by Tony Lewery has some useful photographs and details.

The normal length for a boatman's cabin in a motor boat (ie, as against a horse-drawn narrowboat) was 8ft. This can be squeezed to just over 7ft 6in if you are tight for space and can be stretched to about 10ft. Beyond these sizes they start to look a bit odd and not like the thing you are trying to recreate. I had originally allowed only 7ft 6in but when we decided on the smaller engine I reduced the engine room and gave the boatman's cabin another 3in. The first things to be set out were the widths of the stove space, the table cupboard and the bed cupboard along the port side. The first was determined by the need to allow a safe amount of space around the stove, particularly at the firebox end, and remembering to allow an extra 3in against the back bulkhead for the soap 'ole and windlass 'ole. The width of the bed cupboard depends on whether it is to be a double or a single bed. In our case it was to be a single but I realised that, because of the width of the boat at this point and the height of the gunwales above each end, any occupant over 5ft 9in would probably have to sleep diagonally; so I allowed about 3ft This left just under 3ft for the table cupboard.

Bull's eye

Then I noticed that the line between the cross bed and table cupboards, where the roof beam is situated, went straight through the bull's eye in the roof. These devices were originally made specially for the job but modern ones are made primarily for lamps and so focus the sun's rays onto the inside of cabin creating a fire risk. Nevertheless they are a nice original feature and provide a remarkable amount of light to an otherwise dark space. We were assured that the fire problem could be overcome by painting a spot on the middle of the lens or by grinding the

Roof beam positioned to miss the bull's eye in the ceiling

top to a small flat section, so we asked the yard to fit one. It had been positioned to be clear of the slide in fully open position and was thus a bit forward of its normal location over the table cupboard. The beam was an essential part of the cabin so something had to move. I opted for increasing the size of the cross bed just enough to clear the bull's eye and making a corresponding reduction in the table cupboard.

Bed cupboard dimensions

Next to be determined were the depths of the fittings across the boat. This is where you really have to start

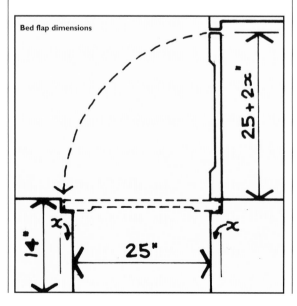

thinking three dimensionally because the width of the corridor determines the height of the bed flap, which in turn determines the amount of space above the port end of the bed. According to the very useful working drawing in Tony Lewery's article, this dimension seems to have been about 2ft 4 $\frac{1}{2}$ in which seems a bit wide for a corridor. I considered allowing the flap to overlap the side bed which supports it in the down position by more than the normal inch, but this would have produced a rather complicated detail in order to get the flap and the side bed at one level, so I pushed and shoved a bit more and came up with a compromise height/width of 2ft 1in.

The height of the side bed itself, which is also the level of the lower edge of the flap of the cross bed drop, depends on the height of the gunnel above cabin floor level and the amount of overall headroom. In both cases mine were on the low side so I set it at 1ft 2in, compared with 1ft 6in on the working drawing. This gave just enough room under the gunnel for outstretched feet and allowed me to incorporate the finrad with its casing in the front face of the side bed.

Accessibility

As with the rest of the boat, the floor had been laid so that any section which did not have a built-in fitting over it was removable. This is particularly important in the case of the boatman's cabin because it not only allows access for inspection, maintenance and ballast adjustment, but also for greasing and possible removal of the prop shaft.

The first things to go in were the two partitions forming the sides of the table and bed cupboards. These were fortunately fairly easy to manhandle around but were quite complex in shape in order to fit the tapering side of the hull and cabin side. I was starting to see what my prophet of doom had meant. By cutting slightly oversize and accepting a lot of planing I eventually got them to fit.

THE BOATMAN'S CABIN'S ELEMENTS

Table cupboard: After the stove, the table cupboard is the focal point of the cabin. Its essential features are: a drop-down table with rounded top, which doubles as a door, a cutlery drawer underneath and a small cupboard at floor level.

The table has no supporting leg but is kept horizontal by its extended top surface which is held down by the shelf immediately above it. It is fairly chunky in section – I made it from two thicknesses of 12mm with one thickness of 18mm plywood sandwiched between. This enabled me to cut the outer layer from the same piece of ply as the surround to ensure a precise fit. The 18mm piece was then cut the

Rome's boatman's cabin, from aft doorway, with lace plates and final decoration

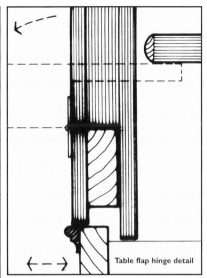

same size and the other 12mm piece similar at the top but extending about 2 ½ in at the bottom. If you make the overhang too big it fouls the drawer. Before the three pieces were glued and screwed together I cut a rectangular hole in the centre of the outer sheet

Table flap hinge detail

and a three inch diameter hole above it. The first would eventually have mouldings applied to the edges which would create the panel construction effect. The second would have a small mirror mounted behind it to provide another bit of interesting detail. Because of the thickness

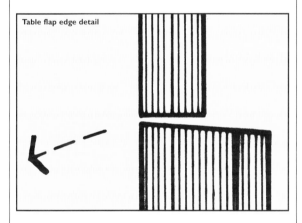

Table flap edge detail

of the door, the top edge has to have a slight slope all round to prevent the inner edge jamming on the surround when it is opened.

Determining the level of the bottom of the flap, where the hinges are, is a bit like the bed flap exercise, except this time you have to make sure that the top of the table in the down position is a convenient eating height in relation to whatever height you made the side bed. On the subject of hinges, we followed illustrations of originals that show them mounted in the face of the door and frame – not, as is normal these days, on the edge and in the rebate.

Partly in order to save wood and partly to enable me to plane the inside edges of the openings I decided to make up the lower part of the cupboard front from 4in wide strips of 12mm ply rather than cutting all the doors and drawers out of one piece. This worked well but I had to be especially careful to reinforce the edge that the flap was hinged to otherwise it might not be able to support the considerable weight and leverage.

Once made up, the flap was hung in position and swung down to a couple of degrees above horizontal (to allow for droop) where it was propped temporarily from the floor. This enabled me to position the shelf which holds down the bottom edge of the flap. A good stout shelf is required to resist the leverage force and it is advisable to fix battens above as well as below the edges to stop it being forced upwards.

The cutlery drawer does not run on slides like a modern drawer but is simply a box which sits on a shelf that is level with the bottom edge of the opening. I am still not sure whether the front of the drawer is supposed to be at

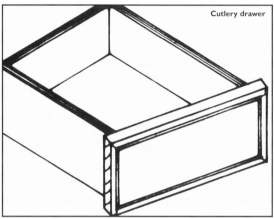

Cutlery drawer

an angle to the rest or whether the whole drawer is rectangular and pulls out at right angles to the front of the cupboard. I suspect it may depend on the angle you have made the cupboard front. I followed the drawing in John Hill's book and angled the front of the drawer which works quite well. The front face has mouldings fixed around the perimeter and these should finish just proud of the face of the cupboard when the drawer is closed. The bottom cupboard has a ply framed and moulded door. The amount of space you have inside varies enormously depending on the shape of the swim.

Bed cupboard: Construction of this part was on similar lines to the table cupboard. It is a good idea to build up the head of the bed, opposite, at the same time, even if only temporarily, to ensure that the flap is as good a fit in the down position as it is in the up. I fixed the bottom shelf which forms the foot of the bed, then the head, and then fitted the flap in between the two and recessed the hinges into the flap and the timbers supporting the front edge of the shelf. The flap itself was made of 18mm ply with 9mm framing round the edge so it can span the corridor width without flexing. Having planed the edge of the flap to fit snugly into the rebates in the shelf support and the head, I swung it up to the vertical position and

Bed'ole. Flap drops down to form thwartships double bed

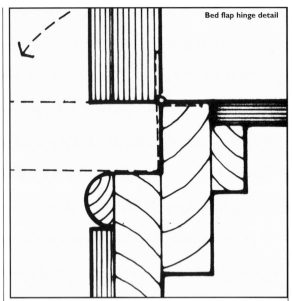

Bed flap hinge detail

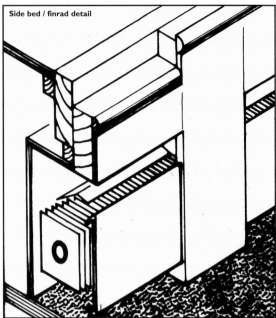

Side bed / finrad detail

wedged it in place against the sides. I was then able to position the timber which acts as the top of the frame and supports the front edge of the cupboard shelf above.

Side bed: This would have been a fairly easy job had I not decided to incorporate a length of finrad into the front face. The supply pipes for this had been laid at the basic

Skirting radiator under side bed, with fascia disguised by scumbled finish

services stage and so I first had to find the ends, coiled up over the fuel tank, and then pray that I had allowed enough length for them to reach each end of the bed. They did. As this was the highest part of this side of the circuit, I incorporated a drain-off cock to act as an air bleed valve.

I had bought a 6ft length of finrad for the boatman's cabin. This came with an enamelled front cover and deflector plate allowing the heater's output to be altered. Since I had made up my own casing for the bathroom finrad I had a spare four foot length which I was able to use in conjunction with the six foot length to make a continuous front to the bed.

The bed top was 12mm ply divided, supported at the half way point and with finger holes for lifting to get at the storage space below. The front edge has to have a small step in it over about half its length to receive the bed flap.

End cupboard: This cupboard, with a shelf below, fits into the corner between the cabin side and the rear bulkhead, opposite the range. Judging from photographs it seemed to take various forms and, because it had a round topped door, I decided to base mine on *Sweden* (from another Tony Lewery article in August 1989 *Waterways World).* Our shell builder had provided a steel side which also supported one end of the rear step so I had only to clad this and fit the shelves and cupboard front.

Allens had also provided a remote restart for the engine fitted into a small panel above the cupboard. I decided to dispense with the panel and incorporate the switch, along with the horn button and headlight switch, into the top of the front face of the cupboard. Here they would be within easy reach of the steerer but almost out of sight. I had also fitted a remote stop for the engine close to hand on the other side of the step.

Rear doors: *Rome's* rear doors (and the side ones) are made of sheet steel and fitted at the construction stage. This meant that the inside faces simply needed to be faced with ply onto which chamfered pads and strips of ply had been fixed to imitate traditional construction. The backing sheets and chamfered pads were 18mm, while the strips were 9mm thick. After the fronts and backs had been primed, the panels were screwed to the steel doors. I have seen boats with up to a dozen potentially rust-creating screws per door used to fix these panels. I used four screws and coated

Rear doors, soap 'ole and windlass 'ole

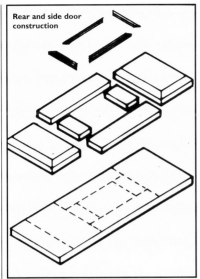

Rear and side door construction

the steel doors with cork adhesive before positioning the panels and they seem very solid. The holes in the steel doors were countersunk and the screw heads covered with Plastic Padding. You can now avoid holes altogether by sticking the door panels with Gripfill or a similar gun applied adhesive.

Soap 'ole, windlass 'ole, etc: Descriptions of boatman's cabins sometimes refer to these being semi circular openings which should have appealed to my current circle fixation. One thing that put me off was the fact that I would have had to leave the edges plain and unadorned with mouldings. What about the router? This might have been possible but when you rout into an internal corner the outer edge of the moulding is rounded rather than square and this gives the game away. Another reason was that I

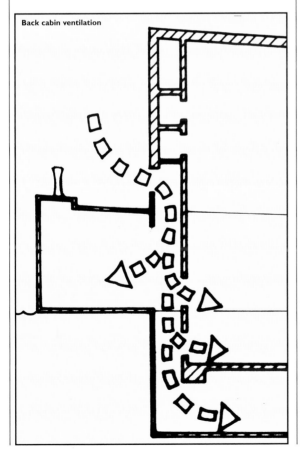

Back cabin ventilation

rather fancied the picture framed openings also seen on the *Sweden* photograph.

One important requirement of BW's Safety Standards is for low level ventilation (see Chapter 2). I checked with my friendly surveyor and found that I would need a 9in x 6in vent in the back bulkhead and this was installed about 3in above deck level. On the inside, I formed the sides of a duct around the top and sides of the opening so that, when the bulkhead was fitted, air would be deflected downwards and enter the cabin through louvres at low level, one by the stove and one behind the coal box. Another benefit of this arrangement was that, by stopping off the floorboard before it meets the end of the swim the under floor space is ventilated as well.

At the top of the bulkhead is the ticket drawer. Like the cutlery drawer this is simply a box which slides in and out of a housing fixed to the roof and cabin side. The rake of the front will depend on the shape of the cabin and your personal preference. I raked mine in fairly well at the bottom so that we would not hook ourselves on the knob when going through the quite narrow rear doors. If, as with the cutlery drawer, the shelf is wider than the drawer, it is a good idea to fix small sections of wood to the shelf to guide the drawer in and out in a straight line.

Stove: I bought the range – a 'Classic' (which has now reverted to its original name 'Epping') – before the shell was complete and got the yard to fit it. When I saw what was involved, I was glad that I did. The stove sits on a steel shelf supported on two steel angles welded to the top of the swim. The feet are bolted to the shelf to keep the stove firmly in place. Because of the relative positions of the smoke outlet in the stove and the chimney collar in the roof, the middle pipe which connects them has two considerable cranks in it. Allens supplied this pipe and I was amazed when I first saw it. It is made from a single length of 4in mild steel pipe with radiused bends which look as though they have been formed in a giant pipe bender – and, come to think about it, probably were. Anyway I can confirm that it works very well and is a great talking point.

Coal box: There are one or two loose items usually found in a boatman's cabin, the most important being the combined step and coal box. This is really just a wooden box with the top partly covered by a thick step, traditionally of ash, but as with everything else in the cabin, its shape has been developed over the years into something uniquely 'boaty'. It resides under the main step from the rear deck and has to taper from front to back so that its sides are parallel to the swim plates on either side. In boats which have inclined swim sections, the box can also taper from top to bottom to fit in the space.

I made up the basic carcase using 12mm ply which, when glued and pinned

Ash-topped coal box and steerer's step. Hinged access lid into coal box is just balanced open

together, was remarkably strong even without framing. I was keen not to use any framing as I wanted to line the inside with 1.5mm aluminium sheet so that the coal and shovel did not wear out the inside too quickly.

For the main step and the coal box step I bought some 1 1/4in x 6in ash, planed one side only to retain maximum thickness. The main step is about 11in from front to back so I rebated two pieces together edge to edge, and glued and cramped them. The coal box should have had just one 6in width so as to allow enough space behind it to get the coal in and out. This looked a bit narrow and I could foresee accidents as we missed our footing; so I departed from tradition and cut a second piece which I hinged to the first so making a 12in step which reduced to a 6in one when we wanted coal. The new hardwood looked superb and it seemed a dreadful thought that one day we would be tramping over it in muddy boots. I resolved to try to follow the tradition of keeping it scrubbed white.

The other loose items – the plank which fits in between the bed cupboard and side bed to form a temporary seat, and the stool I decided to leave until the rest of the boat was complete.

Framing the cabin sides

The thickness of the framing depends on the particular section of moulding you are intending to use so it is best to decide this first. The moulding can be done very effectively, if laboriously by using two semi-circular sections of different sizes fixed side by side. Not being this much of a masochist I opted for a single 9mm x 22mm broken ogee moulding. This looked best with a 9mm thick frame so I ripped a sheet of 9mm ply into 4in wide strips with the

Triton, planed the edges and got cracking. After cutting and trimming to size the strips were pinned and glued in place using Evode wood adhesive. Any wide joints could be filled with a proprietary filler as the whole cabin was eventually to be painted and grained. The mouldings were cut on a mitre block where possible, and by eye when not, and then stuck in place. Once again masking tape proved very useful for holding the mouldings in place while the adhesive dried. The only piece of framing not in 9mm ply was the piece immediately behind the stove which I judged would get too hot for its own good. This was done using a strip of Masterboard packed out level with the ply framing above.

ENGINE ROOM

This was treated in the same way as the boatman's cabin with framing and mouldings. Most illustrations of working boats show the door between the boatman's cabin and engine room swinging into the boatman's cabin. This was generally done because the gearbox prevented it from swinging the other way. It is probably better not to enquire how the occupants relieved themselves at night if the bed drop stopped the door from opening and the bucket was, as is usually reported, in the engine room. The gearbox on *Rome* was reasonably far forward so, to overcome this problem and to ensure that occupants of the boatman's cabin had a second means of escape at night, I decided to swing the door into the engine room. This also meant that it could be held open in a position which was less in the way during the daytime.

Both this door and the rather odd-shaped one between the engine room and the corridor were made from sheets of

Panel framing details

Shelves built in to the front bulkhead in the engine room provide stiffness

9mm ply with strips of 9mm ply and mouldings fixed to either side, similar to the panelled walls. Care is needed to keep the whole assembly flat while the glue is drying and the edges have to be filled or lipped to stop the end grain showing through. The result is a very solid, realistic looking framed door which will accept hinges, latches and knobs quite happily.

The large partition between the engine room and the bathroom was asking for some shelves to store the many useful items which find their way into the engine room. I had already ear-marked part of this space for the fuse cupboard so it seemed sensible, rather than fixing a number of shelves randomly, to incorporate them all into a series of openings in a double wall, rather like enlarged windlass 'oles. This not only tidied up the arrangement but, as already mentioned, stiffened up the bathroom partition so that the tiles were less likely to be vibrated loose.

Lighting
Until the advent of Grand Union Canal Carrying Company's motor boats in the 1930s, the only light traditionally found in the boatman's cabin was an oil lamp. This swung precariously on a cantilevered bracket fixed to the side of the table cupboard. Reproductions of these lights are available and we decided after much debate to go for the electric rather than oil version on grounds of safety and convenience. The switch for this was located on the framing between the rear doors and the windlass 'ole so that it is easily reached when entering the boat at night. For additional light that could be switched on and off from the bedside I positioned another wall light point on the partition between the boatman's cabin and engine room.

Other lighting was more utilitarian. I installed a fluorescent light under the counter so that I could see what I was doing when reaching down into the weed hatch. To give more light and to protect the inside of the hull I also gave this area two coats of white 'Smoothrite'. Not a pleasant job but one well worth doing. In the engine room I put aside my usual dislike of central light fittings and fitted two opal and brass lights in the ceiling either end of the pigeon box. These would normally only be used singly but could, if needed, give enough light together to enable me to work on the engine at night.
The batteries sat on the base plate and were retained in place by a steel frame, fitted at construction stage. I made a plywood cover to go over the frame which would prevent dropped metal objects from touching the terminals but which still allowed ventilation all round the batteries.

TIPS

While not wishing to set myself up as an RBK*, I inevitably made a few discoveries – mostly from bitter experience – during the many hours I spent boatfitting so it seemed a good idea to pass some of these on.

Sawing: When sawing across the grain of plywood, one side of the board usually ends up clean edged while the other side is distinctly ragged. If you are using a hand saw it is the underside which comes off worse and, if you are using a jig saw, it is the top side. It is therefore a good idea to bear this in mind when cutting locker tops and the like

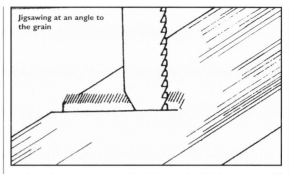

Jigsawing at an angle to the grain

and to plan your cuts so that the rough side is not seen. If both sides will be visible, you could try scoring both sides heavily with a Stanley knife or cutting the piece oversize and planing the edge down to the required size. Another way is to stick a strip of masking tape over the line of the cut on which ever side of the board you expect the rough edge to occur. Also, as Chris Lloyd pointed out in the first *Narrowboat Builder's Book*, when jigsawing at an angle to the grain the 'upstream' side of the cut will be rougher than the 'downstream' side.

Fine cuts: If you don't possess a dovetail saw and need to make some precise cuts try a fine hacksaw. I find both the junior and standard sizes useful, especially for cutting small sections of hardwood beading in a mitre block.

Planing: Although the grain of a length of wood may appear to be parallel to the edge they usually converge slightly towards one end or the other. To prevent the plane – either hand or electric – from digging in, always make sure that the grain rises as it goes away from you – not as it comes towards you. The real difficulty comes with curly grain which rises and falls. In this case the best thing is to plane it lightly with the electric plane set to minimum

The wrong and the right way to plane

Planing an edge

depth and power sand the whole surface to remove any remaining rough patches. If you want to plane the end grain of a piece of wood be careful not to overshoot the far end or the grain will split. This can be avoided by planing almost to the edge and then turning the piece round and planing in from the other end. If this is not possible, try cramping a piece of scrap wood tightly to the far end, level with the surface to be planed, and plane over both.

Right first time: There is always a temptation, particularly when starting a new part of the boat, to rush things to see how they will look. This is the best way to ensure that something will go wrong – you cut the wood too short or your chisel slips and you then have to spend twice the amount of time doing the job again or trying to conceal your mistake. I have been guilty of this on many occasions but I now make an effort to curb this tendency and remember the old saying 'more haste less speed'.

Right eventually: If you do discover that something been fixed out of line or out of vertical it is usually better not to make everything else fit around it but to grasp the nettle and redo it properly. Fudged mistakes have a nasty habit of coming back to haunt you with an even bigger problem later on.

Preplanning: At risk of repeating myself, try to think through what you want to do and anticipate where the problems are likely to be. The parts that gave me the most trouble were the ones where I tried to play it by ear as I went along. Making three dimensional drawings of whole areas or detailed parts is a very good way of ensuring that junctions are well managed and that clashes don't occur.

Practice makes perfect: Boat fitting involves acquiring many new skills. For the most part the learning curve will be quite steep as your confidence and ability grow. It therefore makes sense not to start off whatever you are doing, scumbling or tile grouting, in the most noticeable place. Begin in an out-of-the-way corner and wait until you have mastered the knack before tackling the rear doors or the galley worktops.

Long ones first: Quite a lot of the things you will need to cut accurately to fit will be in pairs or fours. In a perfect world, pieces destined for one side of the boat will be exactly the same size as pieces on the opposite side. In practice it rarely works this way and one will be slightly bigger or longer than the other. It therefore makes sense to cut the large piece first so that if you do under cut or over trim it there is a chance you can use it on the smaller side.

Jigs: When performing repetitive tasks, the time spent knocking up a quick jig will often repay you handsomely, both in speed and accuracy. You may recall I used one for routing the flutes on the columns and another for drilling the holes for the hinges on the galley doors (Chapter 11). I also used a T-square with notches cut in the blade to set out the yellow lines on the exterior paintwork. These are just a few examples of how useful a quickly-made jig can be.

Routed edges: Stopped mouldings are a good way of finishing the edges of dummy roof beams and the like but if they are convex and done with a router the ends are generally asymmetrical and don't look 'right'. You could try running the router over the edge again but starting from

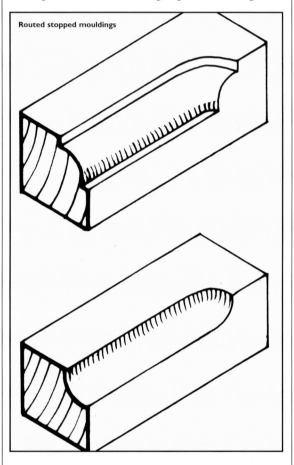

Routed stopped mouldings

the opposite end, or finishing off the ends by hand using a chisel, but both methods are fraught with disaster. You can avoid the problem altogether by using a half round concave moulding which will give you the same profile on both faces of the wood in one operation.

Pilot holes: When screw fixing into hardwood always drill a pilot hole rather than trying to pierce a hole with a bradawl. Brass screws in particular have a nasty habit of shearing off in the hole if it is not the correct size and depth. Also, when pinning and gluing hardwood a series of 1.5mm holes drilled in the outer piece will enable you to insert the pins so that they are ready to tap home and will stop them splitting the wood.

Door hanging: The obvious choice for hanging doors on a boat are brass hinges and brass screws. The trouble is that the screw heads tend to get chewed up while you're screwing them in and out trying to get the door to fit just right. For this reason I use Phillips-type steel screws (easier to use with a cordless screwdriver) of the same size for fitting the door and swap these for the brass ones when I am satisfied that it is OK.

Paint brushes: If you want to avoid washing brushes out between coats wrap the bristles and head tightly in Clingfilm. If it is a very warm dry day put a few drops of white spirit on the bristles first. The brush should stay pliable for two or three days. This will also enable you to take brushes home to clean them.

Never throw anything away: Not to be taken too literally or you won't be able to move but it is amazing how today's offcut can become just the bit you need for tomorrow's job. After I had cut the rebates to take the ply panels in the galley doors I was left with a pile of 6mm square oak strips. The only thing I could think to do with them at the time was to cut them up and sell them as chopsticks but I soon realised that they would make perfect beading strips to retain the glazing in the wall unit doors.

Cutting unbonded laminate: Use a discarded wood chisel, ground to give a sharp corner, to score the face (not the reverse side) of the laminate. Repeat several times, then bend and break the sheet along the line to ensure a clean edge. For curved cuts, place an off-cut of ply under the laminate to support it while cutting with a jigsaw.

Cutting apertures: When, for instance, cutting lift-out lids out of locker tops, you can try standing the electric jigsaw on its nose, then slowly swing the back of the machine down with the blade running. The blade should gradually cut through – but if you are not practised or careful it will stab large grooves either side of the intended line as it meets the surface for the first time. Start the cut along, rather than across, the grain to minimise the risk and any resultant mess. In fact it is probably easier to start the cut by drilling three or four close-spaced holes of about $^3/_{32}$in diameter. Waggling the drill gently along the line of holes will join them together, making a thinnish slot for the saw blade. Drill the holes where they are least likely to be seen – under hinge positions, for instance.

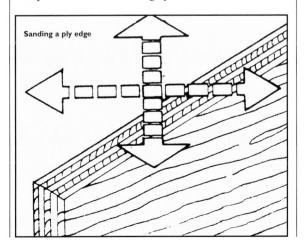

Sanding a ply edge

Sanding down, finishing off: Although sanding furniture down, prior to varnishing or painting, can be done by hand, an electric orbital sander is much preferable. Always sand with the grain of the wood – unless pencil marks resist erasure, in which case you can sand at an angle of 45º. The slight cross-grain component should not scratch the surface noticeably. After the marks have been removed, sand lightly along the grain. If sanding ply edges by hand, move slightly crosswise, rather than straight along the edge, to reduce the risk of picking up splinters. Better still, use a sanding block

* Right B——- Know-all

CHAPTER 14

FINISHING OFF INSIDE

Wall coverings
Scrumbling
Floors
Porthole trims and stoppers
Curtains
Upholstery

Finishing off inside

At last all the donkey work was complete and it only remained to add the finishing touches. Although this stage is very rewarding it is easy to underestimate the amount of time it all takes. In the main cabin the first thing to do was to protect all the exposed timber with varnish. I prefer not to have too shiny a surface and so use satin finish polyurethane varnish. There are a number of types on the market with various properties and which one you choose depends on your own preferences.

I have found that you can apply five or six coats of Ronseal, rubbing down between coats, and get a superb finish. Alternatively you can slap on a couple of coats of supermarket non-drip, rub it down and add a top coat of Ronseal and get a superb finish. Some boatfitters recommend using gloss varnish for the second coat to give better durability to the whole system. Whichever you choose, when it comes to varnishing the ceiling it is a good idea to use non-drip varnish as the thinner types can make an awful mess. For the boatmans cabin and engine room I used gloss varnish, partly because this area is likely to get harder wear but also because I wanted to give it a different, more old fashioned atmosphere.

Water based varnishes are now more common than they were when I fitted out *Rome*. Apart from the obvious advantage of being able to wash out your brushes with water and detergent, they produce far less vapour, which can be quite overpowering in a confined cabin.

Wall coverings

As I have already mentioned, we planned to cover the panels contained by the framing with a sheet material rather than use more veneered plywood. This approach has the advantage that a greater variety of patterns is available and the material can be changed without too much difficulty if we get tired of it or if it is damaged. For the panels up to gunwale height I used cork wall tiles. These blend pleasantly with the oak and are warm to the touch. They also help to prevent condensation at exceptionally humid times. Alternatively you could use a traditional anaglypta paper and scumble it to bring out the pattern (another pub trick).

The upper panels were much more difficult. I had a vague idea in my mind's eye but none of the hundreds of wallpaper pattern books that we ploughed through had any-

thing which matched up to it. We eventually found something quite different but which we could both agree on – and which had a matching fabric for the curtains. I gave the ply panels a coat of varnish to seal them and then set to with polycell, brush and pasteboard in the usual way. A visitor who arrived half way through this process thought Evelyn was joking when she said 'Graham is just wallpapering the boat' but we like the result and it is quite durable.

Scrumbling

If you frequent DIY stores you will probably have noticed that scumbling has recently been re-invented by the paint manufacturers who even produce videos telling you how to do it. Scumbling (or graining as it is sometimes called) with traditional materials is not quite as easy as the videos make it look but, with practice and a little care, a reasonable looking result is possible.

The basic system is a coat of primer followed by two or three coats of undercoat, the scumble coat itself which is combed to produce the grain effect, and then two or three coats of clear varnish. As you can imagine, with seven or eight coats in total, scumbling produces a very durable finish.

Knotted and combed scumble in the boatman's cabin

The undercoat and scumble can be bought from chandlers or from specialist paint suppliers. Both come in a variety of colours so that, when used in different combinations, a large number of wood types can be imitated. Narrowboats were generally scumbled in light or medium oak over a chrome buff undercoat but this can be changed to suit your personal taste and colour scheme. If you can't find an undercoat that gives exactly the desired effect, you can always ask the DIY store to mix one for you – provided it is a good quality paint.

The scumble will accentuate any slight imperfections in the undercoat so it is essential to prepare the surface well and fill any dents before you start. You should also make sure that the final brush strokes in the undercoats are in the same direction as the scumbling to avoid cross grain lines showing through. Try to think how the piece would appear if it was made of real wood and arrange your scumble pattern accordingly.

Now to the scumbling itself. Stir the contents of the tin until it is an even consistency, being sure to stir up all the 'mud' at the bottom, and then pour some into a small container. Most manufacturers state that the scumble can be thinned up to 50% with white spirit to make it run more easily. I am afraid that there is no substitute for experience here so its a case of trial and error. If you are working on large areas or if the weather conditions are particularly warm, a very small amount of linseed oil can be added to slow the drying time, but don't overdo it.

When applying the scumble the golden rule is 'a little goes a long way'. Dip the corner of the brush into the mixture and work it thinly and evenly over the undercoat, laying it off in the final direction of the grain. Be sure to push the brush into every nook and cranny so that all the undercoat is covered. If the brush which you have used is fairly coarse, the result will already show a resemblance to wood grain and this can be improved still further by drawing a dry brush over it. The result is brush-graining which can be used inside cupboards or the parts your comb can't reach.

Combing, knotting and other techniques add interest to larger, more visible areas. Combs can be made of rubber or steel. Rubber combs are usually triangular with differ-

Yellow undercoat with the scumble brushed on in the final direction of the grain

ent sized teeth on each edge. In spite of being made of a soft material, they tend to produce a harsher grain pattern. It is a good idea to buy two so that you can trim back the end teeth on one to make it easier to reach into corners. Steel combs are bought in sets and their springiness produces a softer effect.

Knotting rubber used with a rotating movement to put in the major figuring

Knotting rubbers have raised, concentric rings on their curved surface. The rubber is drawn across the scumble with a slight rotation so that the rings produce elongated arcs which resemble wood grain. If you rotate first one

Comb graining around the knotting completes the effect

way, then the other as you draw it across the piece, the result will be a symmetrical pattern with a knot at the centre or at each end. Don't get too carried away or you will produce what Chris Lloyd likened to 'a row of small bore rifle targets'. Watching the grain pattern appear before your eyes as you rotate the rubber first one way and then the other is rather like watching a photograph materialise in a developing tank. I prefer to do the knots first and work round them with the combs.

Combing and knotting produce a varied and interesting result but, if you are more ambitious, you can imitate all sorts of grain patterns with a rag stretched over your thumb nail or even an India rubber – it just takes practice.

It is a good idea to undercoat a scrap piece of wood to practise on if this is your first time. When you have built up your confidence, try starting on something small like a cupboard door. If you can remove it and place it flat on a bench, so much the better. The great advantage with scumbling is that, if you don't like what you have done and don't leave it too long, you can brush over the area and start again.

The problems come when you try larger areas like the whole of a boatman's cabin. These require planning with almost military precision to make sure that you don't let the first area of scumble get too dry before working on it and you don't smudge one already combed area when combing the next. Here it is even more important to get the consistency right. Too thin, and it runs together after you have combed it and then refuses to dry. Too stiff, and it dries in no time so that the comb makes no impression.

Once you have completed an area, a few light strokes with a dry brush when the scumble is almost dry will soften the harshness of comb graining and provide some subtle half-tones to knotting.

When all the combing and knotting is complete, leave it for at least two days before attempting to varnish it and then try an small corner first. It may look OK but it can be reactivated very easily if it is not thoroughly dry and there is nothing more annoying than ruining your hard work with your own hand. Genuine yacht varnish is suitable for the top coats or Ratcliffes produce a pale varnish especially for the job. Polyurethane varnish is too hard to live happily with the underlying coats and should not be used.

Not to be out-done by the re-inventers of scumbling, *Waterways World* can supply copies of Tony Lewery's video on the real thing which is entitled *Traditional Transformation*. It costs £14.99 plus £1.50 for postage and packing from *Waterways World* on 01283 742970

Floors
For the main areas of the boat I used carpet tiles. These are very economical to use, are easier to lay in the relatively cramped confines of a boat and, if a disaster occurs, a damaged tile can be cleaned under a tap or completely replaced. They also allow easy access to the under floor space for inspection. DIY stores stock a number of different types but I was lucky in having a contact in the carpet industry who sold me some PVC-backed nylon tiles which are usually used in offices. Where these were required to be stuck onto steps or the bases of seating I once again used cork tile adhesive which gave an incredibly strong bond.

In the bathroom area I used cork tiles which, once varnished, give a warm but water resistant surface. The edges were sealed with clear silicon rubber sealant so that any splashes were contained and did not seep into inaccessible places.

A podged rug covers the carpet tiles in the boatman's cabin

Looking around, we have seen engine rooms floored with anything from chequer-plate steel to pink pile carpet (I kid you not). The latter seemed to be surviving quite well inspite of the presence of a Boxer dog on board but we decided something a bit more durable was needed for us. Carpet tiles seemed to offer a good compromise but the colour we had chosen for the rest of the interior did not really suit this area. We found some neutral coloured

Huega tiles in a sale and these were continued through into the boatmans cabin where they were partly covered by the attractive 'podged' or rag rug which Evelyn had spent many hours making.

Porthole trims
There are various ways of trimming around the insides of portholes. If you are very adept with a jigsaw the hole which you cut in the 18mm ply inner surrounds may be neat enough to leave showing and you can bring the cabin lining up to the surround, covering the junction with a moulding. If, like me, you are not so confident, the choice is between turned wooden surrounds and brass trims. Wooden trims are bulkier and therefore cut out more light whereas the brass ones actually reflect light into the cabin. The only snag with brass surrounds is that they need cleaning, and setting them into wallpapered walls, or even tiled ones, could cause a real problem. I overcame this by fixing them with screws, rather than the more normal adhesive method, so that they could be removed for cleaning.

Curtains
For the majority of the portholes we used Fenda Products' brass rods, brackets and rings. The system works well and gives a pleasantly 'period' look. The bottoms of the curtains are held back to the angle of the cabin side by similar brass rods.

The front door and windows were more difficult. Here we ended up with the windows dressed with fixed drapes held back by ties during the daytime and allowed to hang freely at night. The door has a roller blind made using a DIY kit and a length of curtain material stiffened with an aerosol spray stiffener. The boatmans cabin was, as always, a bit different. Old photographs show the bed area separated off from the rest of the cabin by lace-edged drapes, often with plates and framed photographs hanging against

Matching curtains and cabin side linings. Also note brass curtain rails, brass porthole trim, and 'coffered' oak panelling

them. We did not want to divide the cabin too much and limit its daytime use but felt that if we omitted the curtains altogether some of the essential character would be lost. So we compromised on fixed drapes projecting about 8in into the cabin from both sides and a lace pelmet attached to the roof beam. These were fitted with Rufflette tape into which normal curtain hooks were inserted at about 4in centres. A line of wire staples was then hammered part way into the beam at the same centres and the hooks dropped into them.

Porthole stoppers
For the portholes in the galley and bathroom, curtains seemed either inappropriate or dangerous and we considered using roller blinds as in the past. We decided instead

Upholstered porthole stopper used where curtains are inappropriate – as in galley, bathroom and boatmans cabin

to make 'pads' of plywood, edged with foam rubber and then covered in curtain material, which would fit exactly into the brass surrounds and provide a neater, less fire-prone solution. These seem to have caused a great deal of interest among boat owners so here is how they are made –

First, cut a disc of $1/2$in plywood, about $1/4$in smaller in diameter than the inside diameter of the porthole surround and then stick foam draught excluder all around the edge of the disc. At this stage it is a good idea to check that it just fits inside the surround with the foam squashed slightly – if it doesn't, you can reduce the size of the disc or add another thickness of foam.

Then drill a small, countersunk hole in the centre of the disc and screw the bolt from a brass knob through it until it grips tightly. Next, cut a circle of fabric, twice the diameter of the ply disc and lay it face down on a table. The disc is then placed, bolt sticking upwards, in the centre of the fabric circle.

The edge of the fabric at 'three o'clock' is then folded into the middle of the disc with just sufficient tension to start compressing the foam. Work your way round the edge – I usually go anti-clockwise – pleating the fabric into the middle as you go. A discreetly placed tack every six or

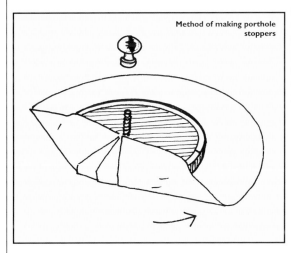

Method of making porthole stoppers

seven pleats will make the job of holding it all together easier. Trade secret – the first tack should be driven only half way in so that, when you eventually get back to the start point, you can remove it and tuck the last pleat under the first. Finally, check that all the pleats are the same width and screw the brass knob onto the bolt, trapping the loose ends.

Upholstery

Here I am pleased to be able to tell you of an easy way to ensure really professional looking cushions and covers – employ a professional. We would like to have done this job ourselves but, realising what a difference well made

upholstery would make to the whole interior we got Wilsons of Kinver to do the honours. I tend to agree with their advice that, no matter how good you are, unless you have an industrial quality sewing machine you face an uphill struggle on anything but the lightest fabrics. The foam density is important. For the beds I used 4 $1/2$in 40 grade and for the seats, 4in 35 grade. With today's firmer foams it is no longer necessary to make the foam dimensions slightly larger than the final cushion size as

Professionally upholstered seat in *Rome's* saloon.

we had done on *Bess*. It is not a bad idea to lightly button the cushions, especially the large seats, to avoid the covers moving after you have sat on them a few times.

Mirrors

Having combined the galley wall units and the arches I was left with the problem of how to finish the sides of the units which faced the saloon. The memsahib came up with the suggestion of filling in the arch with a fitted mirror which would make the solid panel appear transparent. Apart from the obvious drawback that I had not thought of this brilliant idea myself I could foresee problems getting a piece of glass cut to the precise shape. I made card templates of both panels (should have been the same but weren't quite) and took them with trepidation to the local Glass Merchant. He looked them up and down and asked me if I wanted to wait or call back in half an hour. Problem solved.

Lighting

You will have gathered by now that I am not the world's greatest fan of centrally placed light fittings, or exposed fluorescents in any situation. However, lighting is very much a matter of personal taste and it would be wrong of me to try to foist my ideas onto everyone else. All I will say is, if your chandler does not stock anything which appeals, don't forget that most of the hundreds of fittings, including table lamps, that BHS or any other lighting shop stocks can be pressed into service if you use a (low voltage) bus bulb. These can now be obtained in a high

Carefully designed valances under suspended cupboards and shelves in galley conceal indirect lighting

efficiency, long life version. A few pictures on the walls and some cushions on the seats and the whole boat took on a pleasant, homely look. It was hard to imagine that it had been my workshop for the past year or so.

CHAPTER 15

EXTERNAL TREATMENT

Temporary protection
Paint types
Putting it on
Roof finishes
Line techniques
Wood treatment
Cratches

EXTERNAL TREATMENT

It is said that there is nothing so boring as watching paint drying. This may be so, but the process of getting it on in the first place can be a very nerve-racking business. The reason is that most of us have to work outdoors and are therefore at the mercy of our changeable climate. If it isn't too wet it's too windy or too humid or the flies stick to it, and then it starts to rain again.

Temporary protection

Judging by the number of boats seen around the system in primer, a lot of owners do their fitting out first and leave the painting until last. This sounds sensible as you then don't damage the newly painted outside by dragging bits of plywood onto it or drilling holes through the shell. Unfortunately primer is what it says on the can – a medium for making sure that the rest of the paint system sticks to the bare metal. It is not weatherproof for any length of time and should be covered up as soon as possible.

Rome with two protective coats of paint to see her through the first winter

We took delivery of *Rome* in October and I was fortunate that two of the days of the fortnight's leave I took to get cracking on it were unusually fine and dry, so I was able to give the shell some protection. The first thing to do was to clean the outside of the boat thoroughly with a solution of sugar soap. This degreases the surface without leaving paint-rejecting silicones on it as washing-up liquid can, but it does have to be well rinsed off even so. It was then on with the painting before the condensation came down.

Paint types

As they are easily available, I have always used household paints on previous boats, arguing that if the manufacturer was happy to recommend them for a metal balustrade on the sea front at Brighton or wherever, they ought to survive on a narrowboat in the Midlands. This philosophy served me well but, partly because the ranges of available colours seemed to be getting more limited and partly because I wanted to see whether specialist paints were any better, I decided to give house paint a miss this time.

If you ask the owner of a really nicely finished boat what paint he has used the chances are it will be Mason's. This Derby-based company offers a range of vehicle finishes which can be brushed or sprayed so I sent for their literature and colour chart. The very high quality finish of Mason's is as much to do with the way it is put on as the paint itself. Painters often work in pairs with one applying the paint with a roller or pad while the other follows up very quickly laying it off vertically with a brush. At the time, the company had a legendary delivery service but its paints can now only be bought through one of its approved suppliers.

Then I got talking to a boat-fitting neighbour who had always used and sworn by Rylard Plus Enamel (made by Llewellyn Ryland Ltd) on his boats. His new shell had just arrived already finished in this paint and I had to agree that it looked very good. When I discovered that the factory was about a mile from where I worked I thought I would give them a try. Rylard is now owned by the self-confidently titled Indestructible Paint Company.

Rollers

I bought all the paint that I thought I would need for the whole job so that I would not be held up for lack of materials. The next question was what to put it on with. There is not much time in mid-autumn between it being too cold to begin and too damp to carry on, so brushing seemed to be a non-starter. I have never been a great fan of paint rollers but they seem to be used more and more by the building trade for gloss paint these days and, since I needed something which would cover large areas quickly, I thought it would be a good way to find out how they performed. I did not realise at the time that the normal fluffy rollers are not suitable for this work and that special short pile ones are available now. Fortunately the only rollers I had were well worn emulsion ones and these had worn down to about the right texture.

The undercoat went on very well in the time available and the boat was starting to look more like a boat and less like a hulk. The next question was whether to put on a second undercoat or a top coat to see it through the winter. Ryland's Technical Department was very helpful and advised a topcoat as this would seal the rest of the system against the elements. It went on just as well as the undercoat and I was starting to rethink my opinion of paint rollers. The surface had a slight orange peel texture but the coverage was good and for speed it was unequalled.

The proper job
By June of the following year I was well on with the bathroom, galley and boatman's cabin and it seemed a good time to finish the outside painting. A number of decisions had to be made before this could begin. First was what basic style of decoration to use. The choice was between looking like a traditional working boat with an elongated cabin, or going for a true tug style. It would have been interesting to try the tug style with its more formalised scroll work but we felt that, although the portholes gave a certain tug like appearance, the length of the boat and it's fairly fine lines looked more like a converted working boat. Besides, painting the name in large lettering along the side of a cabin full of portholes might have produced something akin to OR0MEO.

Colours
Next, and much more difficult, was the choice of colours. We looked through countless magazines and books trying

Scumbled outer sections on a cabin roof – attractive but seldom durable

to find a scheme that appealed and was different from the classic red and green which we had used in the past. Just when we thought we had found something we would discover that a hire company somewhere had beaten us to it, so we eventually agreed that *Rome* would be another of what the locals refer to as a 'grinanredun'. You can, of course, carry the converted working boat idea to its logical conclusion and paint the part of the superstructure which contains the boatman's cabin and engine room in a slightly different colour scheme from the rest of the boat. We decided to opt for simplicity at this stage, remembering that at least some parts of the boat will probably require a repaint in the not so distant future and any such embellishments can be reconsidered then.

One technique I would not contemplate on the exterior, even though I like it a great deal, is scumbling. Having tried it on the roof of *George,* and following all the rules as far as I could see, it was not a roaring success after the first winter. On the sides I might have stood more of a chance but it is still asking a lot of all the coatings which make up the whole system not to move differentially and start to peel.

For the record we picked Signal Red and British Racing Green – not because we were intending to do any speeding but because we wanted a really dark green to set off the red. In spite of what I have just said about painting the sides in different colours scheme, the front part of the roof is Dark Battleship Grey while the back part, over the Boatman's cabin and engine room, is Danboline Red bilge paint (a very close match to red oxide paint but weatherproof). There is also a strip of multicoloured diamonds between the slide and the pigeon box – well, you've got to have some fun haven't you? A word of warning on colour samples – most shade cards have small areas of colour surrounded by a white background. This has the effect of making the colour look about two shades darker than it really is. If you want to avoid disappointment ask for a larger sample of the colour you want or, better still, get a small tin of the paint and try it on the boat before you buy in quantity.

Putting it on
For putting the paint on there seemed to be three choices – brush, roller or spray. At risk of sounding like a large helping of sour grapes I have to say I don't think that spray finishes to automobile standards are entirely appropriate for canal boats. They look almost too perfect and must be very difficult to touch up when you have the inevitable scrape against an overhanging branch. They also magnify any slight distortion in the steelwork and even First Division builders are not immune from this. The boats which I admire are generally those with a really well executed brush finish that look as though they are the product of a human hand. Having said this I was so impressed with the roller which I had used the previous autumn that I thought I would give it a try on the final job – at least for the undercoats.

The first task was to hose off the muck that had accumulated over the winter and take stock. A few minor blemishes in the steel were filled with Plastic Padding and rubbed down with fine glasspaper. The screw fixings through the superstructure for door linings and the like were similarly dealt with. After a thorough clean down with sugar soap, a rub down with fine glass paper and a rinse to leave everything spotless, I was ready to start with a new gloss roller. The result was just as quick but the orange peel finish was starting to look more like an avocado pear. This was probably because of the build up of one textured finish on top of another, and because the drying time had reduced drastically in the warm weather, leaving the paint no time to level itself.

Fortunately I had started on the roof where this roughness was more appropriate but it would obviously not do for the sides. One answer would have been to put the paint on with a roller and then lay it off with a brush. The speed with which the paint was drying meant that I would have needed to have a roller in one hand and a paintbrush in the other so that the time advantage would be lost. It seemed more sensible therefore to forget about the roller and simply use a brush.

For the cabin sides and roof I used a 3in brush which is about the maximum size an amateur can reasonably cope with. For the green framing a 1in brush was used and for the decorative bits, an assortment of smaller artist type brushes. One type which I found particularly useful was what is known as a painter's flitch. This is a broad flat brush with the ends of the bristles cut to an angle so that you can block in largish areas and then follow a precise edge line without changing brushes. The Rylard paint looked good on the cabin sides, but I have used International paint for subsequent repaints as this was easier to obtain after I stopped working in Birmingham. International paint is also good and I find that it is easier to apply to a large area because it seems to keep its wet edge for a longer time.

Roof finish
Many builders provide a non-slip finish to their completed boats by adding sand to the undercoat. This can be done in two ways. You can sprinkle very dry, fine sand (International Paint sells it in little packets) onto a freshly applied undercoat, working in small areas to ensure that patches have not started to dry and become less sticky. Alternatively, you add sand to the paint, in which case you have to keep stirring it otherwise the sand settles to the bottom of the can. A two inch wide strip is usually left unsanded by the side of each hand rail. This stops you wearing your fingers to the bone – literally, and on solid handrails acts as a drainage channel.

Advantages and disadvantages of both are that they provide a safe walking surface and hide imperfections in the steelwork but they are difficult to keep clean and subsequent repaints tend to diminish their effectiveness. To overcome this last problem one builder actually topcoats with emulsion paint because it is gradually removed by foot traffic and cleaning but is quick and easy to replace. With both systems it is advisable not to use too much sand otherwise this layer will move independently of the steel beneath and start to break up. We found this problem with *Bess* so that I did *George's* roof simply in gloss paint. This meant being a bit more careful stepping on to the roof in locks but the pros outweighed the cons so *Rome's* roof was also just glossed.

Line techniques
The sides had one further undercoat and two topcoats. The trick here was to get the yellow lines between the red panels and the green framing an even thickness and in a dead straight line. This job would be a nightmare but for the invention of masking tape. The best method is to mark out the position of the lines on the undercoat using a home made template and either chalk or a pencil. The green

Creating the coachlines on the cabin side

framing was originally the structure of the cabin and was usually about 4in wide. Unless the height of windows makes it impossible it looks much better to make the imitation framing also about 4in wide – not, as sometimes seen, barely more that the width of the coach line. A coat of green undercoat was added between the lines. Where the two colours met I then painted a 1 $\frac{1}{2}$in to 2in line of white undercoat followed by two of yellow topcoat, making sure to feather out the edges and not form a hard ridge. When this was thoroughly dry I marked out the edges of the panels again and positioned the masking tape where the final yellow lines were required.

Getting the tape on is a bit of an acquired knack. As a right hander I usually place the left hand end of the tape at the start of the line and then pull out about an arms length of tape and let it 'relax' for a second or two. Holding the reel in the right hand, I then work along the tape from left to right positioning it accurately at about 10in intervals with my left hand. This process is then repeated until the other end of the line is reached. A quick check along the line to see that no wiggles have crept in and it is pressed down gently but firmly all over. Left-handers read the opposite.

The really important thing to remember about masking tape is not to leave it on too long – especially in very hot or wet weather. It has a nasty habit of sticking fast and your efforts in getting it off are likely to spoil the lovely paint finish you have just applied. I usually try to put it on the day that I do the first coats and then take it off the next day, immediately after the second coats have been completed. If you have to leave the second coats for the next weekend I would seriously consider removing the tape and retaping just before you do them. It is a lot of work but it could save you a lot more.

After you have completed all of this then comes the magic moment that makes the effort worthwhile when you peel off the tape – back on itself, not at right angles to the boat or the paint might come with it – to reveal a beautiful crisp yellow line. If you find that you have not been as accurate as you should with the roughing in and some red or green is visible it is a fairly easy job to touch this in with a small brush using the hard masked edge as a guide. The magic moment is short lived after the first side because you then have to turn the boat round and start all over again on the other side. It is as though someone has rubbed out all your hard work and told you to do it all over again.

Fancy bits

The rear bulkhead was painted in the same colours with the yellow dividing line forming the familiar 'crown' shape. Here, you are on your own and have to work freehand, refining the shape and thickness of the line with each successive coat. For this and the remaining traditional decoration I used *Narrowboat Painting* by Tony Lewery and *From Stem to Stern* by John M Hill for reference. The bow was treated in the standard Fellows Morton & Clayton way which most Allens seem to adopt, and the roof, as I have said, has a strip of diamonds between the slide and the pigeon box. To make sure that the patterns on the slides and hatches are symmetrical it's a good idea to cut a piece of newspaper the size of the hatch and then fold it into four. You then draw a quarter of the pattern on the top face and cut through this and the other three faces with a pair of scissors. When you open out the paper again, the pattern will be repeated exactly on all four sides. If you then want to put a design like a heart in the middle, fold the middle part back into two and then draw and cut out one side of the heart.

FMC boats rarely had barber's pole swan's necks but we like them and that was good enough for us. I did my first one on *Bess* and, just to prove it wasn't a fluke, did another one on *George*. Going for the hat trick I set to with string and tape on *Rome's* tiller. The technique is first to prime the tiller and undercoat it in white. Then tape pieces of thin string to the top of the raking section, just as it comes out of the bend, at front, back and either side. The strings are then wound round the tiller evenly spaced until the bottom is reached and the ends fixed on the quarter points with more tape. This is repeated for the shorter horizontal section and the spacing checked and adjusted if necessary. You then carefully follow down each string with a soft pencil so that the position is marked onto the white undercoat. The bent sections

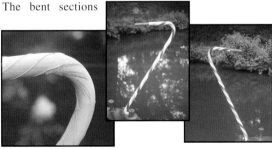

Method of marking the Barber's pole stripes on the tiller

are done freehand, slow bends being easier than the sharp ones some builders prefer. The white and yellow lines are then painted in on opposite sides with a small brush and then the blue and red added, refining the lines as you go like the rear bulkhead.

Hull protection

As you may recall from chapter 3, the hull had been painted by the boatyard using a thick two part epoxy paint which I hoped would last longer than standard bitumen paint. I had asked the builder to put the same paint above the top rubbing strake, except for the decorative bits at either end. This seemed a much better idea than the more usual gloss painted top bend as I could look forward to being able to moor, or be breasted up to, without the fear of irreparably damaging this vulnerable area. Who ever started the fashion for gloss painted top bends is probably the same chap who thought of mounting car indicator lights in bumpers.

Wood treatment

The only parts of the outside of the boat which are not steel are the hardwood front doors and windows which I have to admit I had made professionally. I have few pangs of conscience about this as I wanted a bit of instant security for the journey home, and they are arguably part of the shell anyway. To judge by the name, yacht varnish might seem to be just the thing for this job – and some years ago it would have been. Paint and varnish technology has advanced since then and there are now a number of microporous finishes to chose from. These allow the wood, a

Applying *Rome's* name on the aft cabin – not in tug style between the portholes, where it could have been misconstrued as **OROMEO**

natural material, to breathe and avoid the annoying habit of blistering off your beautiful varnish at the first change in the weather. They are generally tinted in order to filter out ultra violet light. One important thing to bear in mind is that the more coats you put on, the less microporous the system becomes so two or three is probably the maximum. When it comes to repainting time, be sure to rub down well to remove the top coat or two to avoid an excessive build up. Names to look for are Sikkens, Sadolin and Cuprinol.

Professional finish

And that's about it – apart from the signwriting that is. If done well this can drastically improve the appearance of a not so good boat. If done badly it can put a nice boat about ten points down the desirability stakes. When I described the *Bess* fitout I explained my rather laborious method of transferring the lettering onto the cabin side and I am still doing it that way. A similar method is described in John Hill's book and if you are really keen to have a go yourself I suggest you get yourself a copy. If, however, you are not totally confident of success, this is one job which I would advise you to leave to the professional.

Cratches

Of all the traditional details copied by modern narrowboats, the cratch is one of the most useful. The word cratch seems to come from the French *creche* – a manger or fodder store. On the working boats, a triangular shaped board attaches, with brackets, to the after edge of the foredeck. About three feet of the hold immediately aft of this is enclosed in a sort of wooden framed tent topped by the first of the running planks which is also supported by the box mast 10ft or so along the hold. Water is prevented from washing into the hold off the deck in locks or, when heavily loaded, by careful attachment of a deck cloth along the beam at its after edge. This is then folded up over the board and the wooden framework making a dry store for the horse's food or the rest of the canvas cloths required to protect perishable cargoes from the weather. Apart from the shorter run of top plank the major differences in modern cratches are the use of tailored vinyl covers and the variety of cratch board designs.

Modern steel self-draining forward cockpits don't really need the weather protection of a cratch so many start life without them. Then owners realise that they could do with a sheltered utility space between the muddy bank and the carpeted saloon, where wellies can be taken off, the dog/child/lockwheeler de-gunged, logs sawn, etc. With leeward cover rolled up, the cratch also provides a sheltered place to sit out when cruising. If you consider a cratch when planning the boat, you may be able to make better use of it – you might persuade yourself to set the forward cockpit deeper and longer. Deeper because, with cratch in place, the cockpit does not have to be self-draining. Without the need to keep the drain holes well above waterline, the deck can sit at a level that allows a decently high cabin door and avoids a major climb from cabin to cockpit (OK, additional steps may be needed from cockpit to side deck). The lower the deck, the greater the volume of space under the cratch. Any water falling into the cockpit can be drained by a separate bilge pump or by large diameter pipes that run back to the engine bilge. The ultimate in deck-lowering is to set it at the same level as the cabin floor. Then the cockpit takes on new potential as a major living space – like a cottage conservatory or caravan awning.

With visions of under-cratch dinner parties on balmy summer evenings, you may then be tempted to make the cockpit longer, effectively turning it into something like a working boat hold. 10ft seems to be a typical limit without additional masts. In this length you can also store a motor bike, make a safe play area for children, set up a workshop, or put occasional beds. Floor-level cockpits are used to link fore cabins with the main living area. The fore cabin, which also has traditional origins, makes an interesting semi-independent cabin for youngsters. Including a

cratch at the boat building stage should help it to fit more neatly.

The builder can add a low vertical flange on the inside of the cockpit coaming, to which the cockpit cover can be tailored, instead of hanging over the hull side, although this could trip you when getting on or off. Handrails and painted livery lines may be cut back to make the cratch look integrated rather than an afterthought. Cratch boards can be so diverse that the plain triangular board is almost a rarity. Here are some variations:

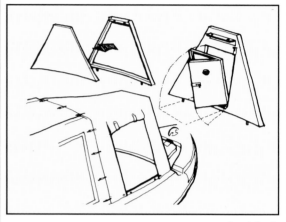

Cratch details

Glazed: a couple of triangular glazed panels or even just a porthole improves the view forward – particularly if you have gone to the expense of windows in the forward cabin bulkhead.

Steel: timber details on a steel shell seem to have an irritatingly short life. As a basic rule, whatever can reasonably be of steel, should be. While the top plank is protected by the cover, the board itself is exposed, and should not be difficult to fabricate in steel. If the board is to be demountable, a single steel board may be awkwardly heavy to lift and store – better to make it in two halves.

Steel framed: a steel 'A' frame is even easier to make; and a simple infill panel of ply or perspex can be inserted into it quickly. The panel can also be taken out on hot days, without demounting the frame or top plank.

With doors: a cratch makes access to the foredeck – and particularly the deck locker hatch – more difficult. So, if your gas bottles are there, a door set into the board allows you to reach through to operate the master valve.

With table: a bottom-hinged panel within the cratch could drop down to make a cockpit table. It might be combined with other cratch features – the aperture it leaves can be glazed. Or it could be combined with an inset side-hinged door. Disadvantage: unless the cockpit is shallow, the table may sit awkwardly high.

With wings: a central pillar supports the top plank, while triangular wings are hinged from it. The wings act as doors for reaching round to the deck cleat or locker; and can be removed quickly and stored.

Finally, you might ask your builder to construct the centre pillar and top plank as an integral part of the shell. That way the tunnel light and horn can be set into the pillar – rather than cling as excrescences on the bulkhead or perch on a vulnerable stalk.

Although some traditionalists prefer canvas, most cratch covers are made-to-measure in vinyl by boat canopy specialists. They fasten down with a combination of Dot fasteners or turnbuckles, and elastic thongs. Flexible windows can be inserted into the sides, although these seem less popular than a few years ago – perhaps because of the transparent material's limited life. Many have straps at the top to secure the sides when they are neatly rolled up. Zipped panels, set into the sides, make quick and convenient 'doors'.

If yours is a cruiser or semi-trad narrowboat you should consider fitting a cover to the aft cockpit. Against the cost you can set longer life of the deck, and less water entering the engine bilge – even if the deck boards sit on 'self-draining' bearers. Even tailored covers seem to collect pools of water unless supported from underneath. You might run an aluminium tube from tiller to cabin roof to serve as a stable ridge pole. This should also provide useful extra headroom when working on the engine in bad weather. The cover over a semi-trad cockpit will really be a tonneau. If a couple of short zips are set into it either side of the steerer's position he/she can steer in snug traditional mode (well, his/her bottom half can anyway). Finally, one major disadvantage of cratches and cockpit covers: they allow intruders to beaver away unnoticed at your padlocks.

We started without a cratch but, on acquiring our third Labrador, we joined the crowd and added one. It is made of hardwood to match the front doors and is of the 'winged' variety. I made triangular inserts so that the glazed wings could be blacked out for privacy or to stop the dogs waking too early in the morning. The cover is acrylic canvas – a compromise between the genuine arti-

Cratch with hinged wings to allow easy access to the front deck

cle with all its wayward ways and non-traditional looking vinyl – or 'canvas backed hooding' to give it its correct name. The sides roll up and are fastened to each side of a fixed triangular centre section rather than rolling right the way up to the centre board. This gives a useful 'porch' to the saloon, sheltering it from excessive sunlight or, more frequently, rain.

Easily lowered hood on a semi-trad rear deck. Flat 'tonneaus' are also useful

CHAPTER 16
CONCLUSIONS

Timely reminders
How long did it take
How much did it cost

CONCLUSIONS

With *Rome*'s bare shell now fitted out and ready to start cruising, it is time to add up the number of hours and the cost of the many components that went into it. However, before I do that, I would like to re-emphasise some of the general advice which I have found myself repeating to the many aspiring fitters I have spoken to since the first edition of this book was published.

- Hire several boats before you decide to own one in case you find that the canals are not for you. It's amazing how many people order a shell without ever having stepped onto a narrowboat let alone cruised it in a howling gale with rainwater dripping down their neck.

- Living on a boat may seem a cheap and attractive alternative to living in a house and, in the summer, it is very tempting. However, when you include all the costs, it is more expensive than you might think and it loses much of its appeal when you are frozen in two miles from the nearest pump-out point. Contact the Residential Boat Owner's Association (see appendix) for more details. Don't buy a boat which is designed for holiday cruising and expect to be able to live comfortably on it. Unless you really crave the simple life, residential boats require 230 volt electricity, more equipment and more storage space.

- Don't stint on the shell. The shell is the boat and, no matter what you do to it, the overall quality of the finished product will always be directly related to it. You can add a generator or a better galley at a later date – you cannot add a well proportioned bow or gracefully rising stern.

- Seek professional help for the parts you are not confident about and employ a properly qualified professional for the gas installation whether you are confident or not.

- Plan ahead. There are usually at least two ways of doing a job – one of which will be much easier or will make the next job easier. Think like a Snooker player and work out your moves in advance.

- Never build in services so that you can't reach them. There is a well known law which ensures that the pipes or wiring you can't get at are the ones that will fail.

- Finally, try to tidy up as you go. Working in a mess is dispiriting, can lead to mistakes and, possibly, accidents. Tidy up at the end of a weekend or every two or three days so that you start afresh next time. It's amazing how many lost tools you will find as well.

Having got that off my chest, we can look at how the project is likely to affect your social calendar and your bank balance.

Time

With the boat pretty well complete and lacking only a few minor items like the roses and castles in the boatmans cabin and some finishing off inside lockers, the total was 1,390 hours. This doesn't sound too much if you say it quickly but it represents every weekend for fifteen months plus two hours on workday evenings for half that time plus about ten weeks leave. I even did two hours of wallpapering on Christmas day, which gives a whole new meaning to the phrase 'Christmas decorations'. Had I been able to work only at weekends and perhaps two weeks a year leave time, the project would, in theory, have taken closer to two years.

The trouble is that the more you let the job drag on, the less efficient you become (you may decide to take a holiday on the part-finished boat which disrupts the logical sequence of operations) and before you know it you are thinking more in terms of years than months. Another disadvantage is that the boat is never 'new' because by the time you have finished the last part, the first parts are looking distinctly dog-eared. For these reasons I would definitely advocate doing the job in as short a time as possible as long as this doesn't mean that you have to rush it.

The chart is intended to give some idea of how long the whole project, and each part of it might take. I would reckon that I work at an average pace so somebody more skilled or better equipped in woodworking might be quicker while a more painstaking person, or one with fewer power tools might take longer.

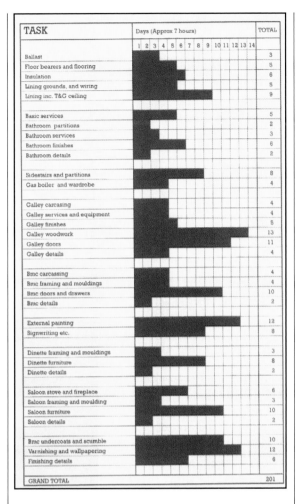

TASK	Days (Approx 7 hours)	TOTAL
Ballast		3
Floor bearers and flooring		8
Insulation		6
Lining grounds, and wiring		8
Lining inc. T&G ceiling		9
Basic services		5
Bathroom partitions		2
Bathroom services		3
Bathroom finishes		6
Bathroom details		2
Sidestairs and partitions		8
Gas boiler and wardrobe		4
Galley carcasing		4
Galley services and equipment		4
Galley finishes		5
Galley woodwork		13
Galley doors		11
Galley details		4
Bmc carcassing		4
Bmc framing and mouldings		4
Bmc doors and drawers		10
Bmc details		2
External painting		12
Signwriting etc.		8
Dinette framing and mouldings		3
Dinette furniture		8
Dinette details		2
Saloon stove and fireplace		6
Saloon framing and moulding		3
Saloon furniture		10
Saloon details		2
Bmc undercoats and scumble		10
Varnishing and wallpapering		12
Finishing details		6
GRAND TOTAL		201

The main tasks are presented in more or less the order in which they were done. Inevitably some of the jobs were done in dribs and drabs to occupy odd moments or to provide relief from more monotonous tasks. In these cases I have lumped the time in with the main heading. Other jobs had to be started before another operation could begin and then completed afterwards. Here I have shown two or three separate periods.

The order in which all the jobs are done is debatable. Obviously ballasting and lining have to be done first, but after that several approaches are possible depending on your circumstances. I tended to do the small, difficult areas like the bathroom and galley first, leaving the maximum amount of working space for as long as possible. This means a fairly hefty outlay on expensive pieces of chandlery at an early stage when you are still recovering from paying the builder for the shell – OK if you have just sold a boat, but not so good if you are a first timer. In this case you could do more of the basic woodwork first and perhaps leave some of it temporarily fixed so that you can still get the bath or fridge in when your finances recover.

Cost

I reckon that the cost of *Rome* is fairly average. We could easily have spent considerably more on equipment and fittings – a new Russell Newbery DM2 diesel would have added about £5000 to the total bill – but we could have spent less on timber.

The cost is broken down as accurately as I can but inevitably some small unidentified items are included in the 'pipework and fittings' sections. I have not included wiring as a separate item because, on *Rome*, it is not a significant sum and because of the piecemeal way in which it was done. If you are planning a floating version of Sizewell B then add an appropriate amount. All prices are at 1993 levels and include VAT at 17.5%

	£
Boatyard items	
Hull and superstructure	13,600
Engine	3,500
Fitting engine – parts and labour	3,100
Grit blast hull	600
Portholes, hatches and anodes – parts and labour	1,600
Hardwood front doors and windows	650
Batteries	210
Voltage regulator (original X-Alt)	75
Ballast	175
Lining out	
Polystyrene insulation	200
Ply floor and bearers	300
Ply lining and partitions	700
Bathroom	
Mansfield toilet	110
Holding tank	175
Vanitory basin	35
Bath	265
Water pump	70
Accumulator	30
Shower pump	75
Calorifier	290
Pipework and fittings	150
Tiles	150
Taps	200
Bathroom total	1,550
Galley	
Fridge	460
Hob	150
Oven	240
Sink	150
Taps	50
Filter	30
Pipework and fittings	100
Tiles	60
Galley total	1,240

Solid fuel central heating	
Little Wenlock	425
Flue	35
Collar	40
Chimney	35
Radiator	45
Feed and expansion tank	25
Pipework and fittings	50
Solid fuel c/h total	655

Gas-fired central heating	
Alde boiler	500
Finrads	115
Radiator	40
Brass cowl	40
Pipework and fittings	55
Gas-fired c/h total	750

Boatmans range	
Classic stove	250
Flue	120
Collar	40
Chimney	40
Boatmans range total	450

Gas installation	
Regulator	50
Pipework and fittings	100
Gas bottles	90
Gas installation total	240

Hardwood, oak faced ply, mouldings etc.	925

Interior fittings	
Porthole surrounds	250
Curtain rods	90
Brass grills, socket outlets	40
Light fittings	200
Fire extinguishers	110
Interior fittings total	690

Soft furnishings	
Carpets	200
Cork wall and floor tile	50
Wall coverings	60
Curtains	100
Upholstery	700
Loose cushions etc	100
Soft furnishings total	1,210

Exterior items	
Paint and varnish	250
Fenders	200
Horn	50
Headlight	80
Grand total	**33,000**

For the specialist equipment you will have to go to a chandlery. Some chandlers operate a discount scheme for people who spend over a certain amount with them in order to encourage them to buy all their equipment from them. If your local chandler does not operate a formal scheme you can probably negotiate a discount on the several thousand pounds worth of kit you might buy there. Another reason for getting to know one particular chandler is that you may be able to tap his valuable experience in fitting out.

When it comes to the larger items – £200 plus – it is worth phoning around to chandlers a bit further afield and comparing prices. I managed to save more than the price of the petrol by buying the fridge and the Alde from a more remote stockist, even allowing for my discount card with the local one.

For run-of-the-mill items it is usually, although not always, cheaper to buy from builders merchants and timber yards than chandlers. This is not because the latter are unduly greedy but because builders merchants buy in much larger quantities from their suppliers and can therefore pass some of this saving on to the customer. A cautionary tale – I needed about 500ft of oak moulding for which my supplier, a DIY supermarket, was charging over £3 per 8ft length. I was resigned to paying this until I discovered, just before I was about to buy the bulk of it, that he no longer stocked this line. This prompted me to contact the manufacturer who said that he could supply it through my usual timber merchant. My relief on hearing this was nothing compared with my delight when I discovered that I was now being charged only about £2 a length – a saving of £70.

CHAPTER 17

A YEAR IN *ROME*

How it worked in practice
Down to basics

When I had completed all the major tasks on *Rome* I had done about 200 days work. I must admit that finishing off the fiddly little jobs like fitting cupboard catches, varnishing inside lockers and adding the roses and castles took longer that expected and by the time she was ready to go to the Inland Boat Show in May 1993, the total was more like 250 days spread over 18 months – a lot of work. Inevitably, some details have been modified slightly as we have used the boat, while others have worked particularly well.

Getting into hot water

Quite a number of the modifications involve the calorifier and water system so we'll start with those. We found that the domestic hot water, heated by the engine, became very hot after a day's cruising but that it cooled down overnight to a luke warm temperature. This was not at all like our previous boat on which the water stayed piping hot overnight. I originally suspected that the lack of a non return valve on the cold water feed to the calorifier meant that warm water was being sucked back into the cold system every time a cold tap was turned on.

On further investigation, I discovered that the copper flow pipe from the engine to the calorifier, and indeed the engine itself, were remaining warm long after we had tied up for the night. This lead me to realise that reverse convection was taking place, robbing the calorifier of its recently acquired heat. I therefore tried putting a non-return valve into the flow pipe from the engine to try to prevent this.

I also felt that the mineral wool insulation, although safer in the event of a fire, was not as good at keeping in the heat as the expanded polyurethene of our previous installation, so I wrapped additional glass fibre loft insulation around as much of *Rome's* calorifier as I could get to.

The next cruise showed that some improvement had been made but it was still not as good as on *George*. I have concluded that part of the difficulty is caused by the design of the calorifier itself which lies horizontally rather than standing vertically. This means that, by the morning, there is only a thin layer of warm water at the top and a large area of contact between this and the cold layer below. The situation is not improved by the fact that the hot water draw off pipe is a little way down from the top of the cylinder so that the hot water above it never gets used. Another probability is that the Alde gas boiler is also taking back the heat when we stop, rather like the engine. However, I am reluctant to try the non-return valve solu-

tion in this case as I doubt whether the Alde pump would have the force to push water through the valve.

Fortunately we are able to overcome these problems quite easily by making sure that the first person to rise (usually myself) switches the gas boiler on for a short while which soon brings the water up to washing up temperature. Moral – use a vertical calorifier if you can.

Boiler plumbing

This brings us on to the next topic which is the plumbing in of the Alde. Because I wanted to ensure that the heat from the boiler always had somewhere to go, I had deliberately omitted the valve on the calorifier circuit. Fine in theory, until I came to commission the whole system. The calorifier, being on the shorter circuit heated up very quickly but the water just would not circulate around the radiators. I bled everything I could but still the heat petered out about a third of the way round.

The solution, I guessed, was to stop off the shorter circuit so that the water would be forced to go round the longer route, removing the air as it went. Having used Hep^{2}0 pipework it was a very easy matter to insert a gate valve where the flow pipe passed through a locker under the dinette. Closing this valve did the trick and the whole radiator system was soon pumping out the heat. Then I opened the new valve and was relieved to find that heat flowed to the calorifier while still keeping the radiators warm.

My intentions were thus slightly frustrated but the calorifier valve is in a far less accessible position than the radiator circuit valve, and, even if both were turned off at the same time, it would only cause the thermostat to turn off the boiler.

Free heat

On the credit side, the idea of putting a short length of fin-rad into the return pipe from the calorifier to the engine has worked very well and provides a gentle background warmth to the bathroom when the engine is running.

What a relief!

I soon discovered that the pressure relief valve on the hot water circuit allowed about a quarter of a pint of water a day to drip on to the tray onto which I had mounted pump and various other bits of plumbing. This was a surprise as the PRV on our previous boat never seemed to drip at all. In order to avoid mopping the water up I connected a length of plastic pipe to the PRV outlet and lead this into

Finrad elements heated by the engine and by the boiler

a milk bottle. All I then had to do was remember to empty the bottle every couple of days. Inevitably I forgot and was back to square one.

Then I hit on the idea of connecting the end of the pipe into the bath overflow which, because I had not been able to use the proper domestic waste outlet, was not linked to the waste pipe. A quick turn on the knob of the PRV produced a healthy squirt of water into the bath and proved that the idea worked. Now an occasional press on the bath waste pump switch gets rid of any surplus water. If I had been able to connect the pipe to the basin overflow the surplus could have drained away by gravity.

Cold comfort
The Batts fridge still amazes us with its efficiency and quietness. I have blended it into the other galley units by screwing a matching oak door to the front of the white fridge door. Not as easy a job as I would have thought, but possible if you pull the rubber door gasket aside and drill a few holes through to the front.

The 'Batts' fridge with door panel to match the galley cupboards

During the whole year it only beeped at us once to tell us that the battery power was too low. This was on the last evening of the third of the Black Country autumn rallies, after we had sat for a total of seven days with only two minimal cruising breaks in between – in short, we asked for it. Under normal cruising conditions the combination of three 'leisure' batteries, a voltage regulator and the recommended thickness of cable to the fridge seems to be a winner.

As noted earlier, Batts fridges are no longer available but the three makes mentioned in the appendix operate on the same principle and so should be just as good.

Even colder comfort
Two cold snaps at the beginning of November and the end of February gave me a chance to try out the frost resistance of the plastic pipework. It was not possible at the time to either drain down the domestic water system or to keep the central heating running or the stove ticking over. All I was able to do was to adopt plan B which meant switching off the water pump, opening all the taps and praying. This strategy worked, for in spite of temperatures down to minus 7 for a week, the system seemed to suffer no ill effects.

Too hot to handle
We anticipated that the bull's eye in the roof of the Boatman's cabin might be a fire risk so I tried grinding the top of the glass lens flat. This was obviously not effective, as we soon discovered to our horror a sizeable hole burned into the adjacent pelmet. The tiny porthole stopper which I made to stop the early morning sun waking occupants of the cabin has been firmly fixed in place under the glass ever since while I think of a more permanent solution. The current front runner is to fit a piece of obscured glass under the lens so that light can get in but the sun's rays are dispersed rather than concentrated. Since I haven't found time to do this yet, I can't say whether it works or not.

Paint topics
Moving to the outside of the boat, our decision to continue the hull paint up to gunnel level and not paint the top bend with enamel has done my blood pressure the world of good. I now actually enjoy breasting up to other boats and watching the anxious faces of their crews as they rush round with fenders trying to protect the mirror-like gloss on their topbends – just like I used to.

A load of bilge
I used Danboline red bilge paint for the decks and rear part of the main roof in order to give a reasonable, but more weatherproof likeness to the red oxide which was often

Roof in 'Danboline' finish

applied to the roofs of working boats. Its only drawback was that it was a bit too red and tended to clash with the signal red paint on the handrails. I noticed that Alvechurch hire boats paint their roofs in a semi-matt brown paint which also looks not unlike oxide so I enquired what it was. I was rather surprised to learn that it was Rylard 'non slip' light teak. As I had used Rylard paint everywhere else on the boat I was left wondering why I hadn't thought of that!

I bought a litre and set to enthusiastically. The result, I have to admit, is not altogether satisfactory. On Rome, the colour is a bit too brown and the paint itself is not easy to apply evenly – but at least it resists slipping and, being semi matt, is kinder to the line of the steelwork. I may overcoat it with oxide at some time, knowing that the real weather protection is under the surface.

Some builders use a secret formula of oxide and clear varnish to make up a semi-gloss roof paint but I have not used this myself so don't blame me if you try it and it peels off! Incidentally, I did eventually find a very good place to use the Danboline bilge paint – the engine bilge.

Happy landings

While on the subject of finishes, we needed a really good non-slip finish for the front deck to restore our not too nimble labrador's confidence when jumping on and off the boat. We opted for Trackmark – not cheap by any means but it has worked admirably. It took two sheets at about £25 a time and a pot of adhesive. There is a very expensive two pack adhesive and a not quite so expensive one pack type, made by Dunlop. I decided to take a chance with the latter and took all possible precautions to make sure that it worked.

If it was going to lift it would be at the corners or butted edges so I rounded all the corners to about $1^1/_2$in radius and, where two pieces met, I kept them about 2 inches apart to form a gutter. A similar space was left around the

Rome's front deck with non-slip finish

edge of the deck where it met the hull sides. The deck has two lengthways raised welds so I made sure that these came within the gutters – not under the Trackmark. With a bit of forethought I worked out a reasonable layout using the least number of pieces and covering the largest area with the material I had. It stayed down quite well to begin

with but started to succumb to the British climate after two or three years. I managed to get the pieces off without damaging them – not an easy job – and stuck them down again. This coincided with putting a cratch over the front deck which has protected the Trackmark and prevented any further problems.

Down to basics

So much for the smaller jobs. The one big maintenance job which catches up with us all eventually is dry docking. Although it is normally recommended every two years, and some really conscientious types do it annually, I was not able to do it until five years after *Rome* first went into the water so I waited with nervous anticipation to see the state of the hull as the water drained away. I was reasonably hopeful because the new hull had been grit blasted and then protected with an epoxy primer and a two part epoxy pitch. Periodic inspections showed that the critical area around the water line was in excellent condition for the first three or four years but more recently a few small blisters were starting to show just below the waterline.

Not knowing a great deal about this particular type of paint, I started to make some enquiries. The paint used on our boat was made by Jotun and, because I had never seen Jotun products in chandlers, I phoned International Paint to see whether their more widely available two part epoxy could be used instead. To their credit, the staff at International advised me that, since they had not tested their epoxy on top of Jotun, they could not guarantee that there would not be an adverse chemical reaction – even though it meant losing a sale. Their generosity even extended to supplying the telephone number of Jotun.

The Jotun staff were also very helpful, and the information they gave was not what I was expecting. In the case of one pack paints, especially coal tar pitch, my experience has been that a large proportion of the coating is removed either by rusting, abrasion on locksides or by the high pressure water jet commonly used to clean the hull once the boat is in dock. The answer is therefore to put back on as many coats as time allows so that this process is slowed down to a minimum before docking is due again. Two part epoxy paint is different. When I asked the staff how I should go about repainting the hull, their advice was "get the boat out, have a look at it and if it's alright, put it back in". They evidently felt that, even after five years, the paint system could well be intact. When I mentioned the slight blistering, they recommended either grit blasting the areas affected followed by epoxy primer and two or three coats of epoxy pitch, or a thorough derusting with a water jet and wire brush followed by two or three coats of epoxy pitch without the primer. A further coat over the rest of the hull was not reckoned to be necessary for anything other than cosmetic reasons.

Two part epoxy finish used on the hull

Only slight blistering around the anode after five years in the water

The author cleans *Rome's* hull using a high pressure water jet

I had fortunately made a note of the particular type of epoxy paint used as Jotun makes several sorts, and they are not all compatible. I was equally fortunate that the type used, Jotaguard 85, is available in 5 litre packs – with some, the minimum quantity is 20 litres. The price was also a pleasant surprise; it was less than some makes of vinyl modified pitch.

When the dock finally emptied I was relieved to find the hull in remarkably good condition. There was some slight blistering around the rear anodes which Jotun would not comment on without an inspection and the waterline blistering was evidently caused by abrasion, probably from a projecting bolt on a mooring somewhere. Apart from this there was just the usual scuffing around the bow area and that was it. The unpainted bottom plate looked as though it had never even been in the water.
The anodes were pitted, indicating that they were doing their job, but there was enough of them left to persuade me not to replace them this time. The reason for their longevity is probably that there were relatively few areas of rust to call upon their services so the rate of sacrifice was slow.

I opted for the water jet method and hired a machine for a day for £40. This was enough time to clean off *Rome* and a similarly sized boat sharing the dock with us. The machine was diesel powered, sucked its water from the drainage channel around the dock and delivered it at 3750psi. Next, I wire brushed and then applied two brush coats of Jotaguard to the damaged areas before finishing off with a rollered coat over the whole hull.

The paint itself is fairly user friendly provided you follow a few simple rules. It is advisable to use a clean mixing pot for each batch and brushes are difficult to clean or even preserve overnight due to the chemical action. Daz and boiling water have been recommended, but it is probably as cheap to buy some inexpensive brushes and use a fresh one each day. The pot life, once mixed, is reckoned to be eight hours so you can make up enough for a day's work in one go. In practice, the brush starts to drag after a couple of hours, especially in warm conditions, but this was not really a problem as you should be finished by then. Using a roller is much quicker but the rollered areas are thinner, and have a slightly different texture from the brushed parts.

It is important to allow each coat to dry for 12 hours before applying the next, and for longer, if possible, before putting the boat back in the water. For the two 60ft x 4ft hull sides of *Rome* I used about eight litres in all. Our docking partner, with a similarly sized boat, used just less than five litres of Comastic per complete coat.

You will have gathered by now that I am a great advocate of grit blasting and two part epoxy paints. Not only do they ease those nagging fears that your hull sides are starting to resemble the surface of the moon and make you the Mr Smug of your local dry dock; over a period of five years they are probably no more expensive than the reptile skin approach. Many builders claim that they can produce a satisfactory surface on the steel without resorting to grit blasting. They may be right but I suspect that they just don't want to do what is a very messy job.

APPENDICES

Shell builders
Engine suppliers
Electrical installation guidelines
Bibliography
General references

Appendix 1

SHELL BUILDERS

In the previous book, we asked builders to provide a great deal of detailed information and to quote for supplying a shell to a given specification. The price they gave determined their position in the table. Unfortunately there was evidence that some had not included VAT where they should have done and, in any case, the prices soon became out of date. The non-alphabetical order also made it very difficult to find a particular builder quickly. For this book, we have reduced the amount of information, asked builders to say which of a number of types of boat they normally build and placed the names in alphabetical order.

We sent a questionnaire to nearly 100 shell builders in 1998, and the following table is based on their answers.

Company	Experience Co / Fabr	No. of Shells	Shell types (See notes)	Plating thickness	Lined shells?	Preferred Engine type	CBA ?
Alexander Boatbuilders, Unit 1a, Chadwick Bank Industrial Estate, Stourport-on-Severn, Worcs							
DY13 9QW 01299 251471	25 / 25	400	A B C E F	10/6/4/4	No	Beta / Yanmar	No
Alvechurch Boat Centres, Scarfield Wharf, Alvechurch, Birmingham B48 7SQ 0121 445 2909	10 / 10	100	A B	10/6/4/3	Yes	Lister	Yes
A J Francis, Blakeley Lodge Farm, Etwall, Derbyshire DE65 6NQ 0797 077 8272	16 / 20	58	C D E	12/6/5/4	Yes	Any	No
Arcrite Fabrications, Fleming Road, Earlstree Industrial Estate, Corby, Northants NN17 4SW 01536 204969	20 / 30	200	A B F	10/6/4/4	No	-	No
P J Barber Boatbuilders, Sheet Stores Basin, Sheet Stores Ind Est,							
Long Eaton, Notts NG10 1AU 0115 946 1752	4 / 10	14	C E F	10/6/4/4	No	Any	Yes
Bettisfield Boats, Canal Side, Bettisfield, Whitchurch, Shropshire SY13 2LJ 01948 710465	8 / 23	18	A B	10/6/4/4	Yes	Beta Marine	Yes
Black Country Narrowboats, Prestwood Dr, Stourton, Stourbridge, West Midlands DY7 5QT 01384 872135	37 / 37	300	A C	10/6/5/4	Yes	Kingfisher	Yes
Branson Boats, Unit 4, Crowland Industrial Centre, Crowland, Peterborough PE6 0BN 01733 211966	15 / -	18	B E F	10/6/4/4	Yes	Beta Marine	No
Brent Wharf Services, Brent Wharf, 198 High Street, Brentford Middlesex TW8 8AH 0181 568 7041	18 / 35	70	B F	8/5/4/3	Yes	Perkins	No
Bridgewater Boat Builders, Unit 8, Highfield Road Ind Est, Little Hulton,							
Nr Worsley, Manchester M28 6ST 0161 703 8297	2 / 20	15	B	8/6/5/4	Yes	Lister	No
Brinklow Boat Services, The Wharf, Stretton under Fosse, Rugby CV23 0PR 01788 833331	8 / 18	14	C D	10/6/5/4	Yes	Any vintage	No
C T & P Fox, 10 Marina Drive, March, Cambridge PE15 0AU 01354 652770	25 / 43	86	A B F	10/6/4/4	Yes	Ford XLD	Yes
Canal Transport Services, Norton Canes Dock, Lime Lane, Pelsall, Walsall WS3 5AP 01543 374370	34 / 10	250	B C D	10/6/5/4	Yes	BMC / Perkins	Yes
Canalcraft (Boatbuilders) Ltd, The Wharf, Watling Street, Gailey, Staffs ST19 5PR 01902 791811	10 / 25	60	B C	10/6/4/4	Yes	Any	Yes
Castle Boat Builders, 22 Kilton Terrace, Worksop, Notts S80 2DQ 01909 478250	3 / 10	19	A B D	10/6/4/4	Yes	Beta Marine	No
Club Line Cruisers, Swan Lane Wharf, Stoke Heath, Coventry CV2 4QN 024 7625 8864	20 / 25	80	A B	8/6/4/4	Yes	Ford XLD	No
Colecraft Engineering, Southam Rd, Long Itchington, Rugby, Warks CV23 8OL 01926 814081	25 / 32	1000	B C F	10/6/4/4	Yes	Beta Marine	Yes
Cotswold Narrowboat Company, 8 Severn Road, The Docks, Gloucester GL1 2LE 01452 332772	1 / 5	6	A B C D	10/6/5/4	Yes	Yanmar	No
Dave Clarke (Boats), Unit 130, Boughton Industrial Estate, Ollerton, Newark, Notts 01623 835717	21 / 21	350	A B	10/6/4/4	No	Kubota / Vetus	No
Dave Thomas, The Trade Centre, Unit 2 Braunston Marina,							
London Rd, Braunston, Northants NN11 7JH 01788 890095	14 / 26	50	C E F	10/6/5/4	Yes	Phoenix	Yes
David Harris, 27 Blakeway Close, Broseley, Shropshire TF12 5SS 01952 882468	18 / 24	30	C D E	10/6/4/4	Yes	Any	Yes
Delta Marine Services, Nelson Wharf, Nelson Lane, Warwickshire CV34 5GB 01926 499337	14 / 34		C E F	12.5/ 6/5/5	Yes	Perkins	Yes
Eastwood Engineering, Old Mill, Station Road, Owston Ferry, Doncaster DN9 1AW 01427 728308	12 / 12	100	A B C F	10/6/4/4	Yes	Phoenix	No
Equinox Boatbuilders, Old Saw Mill, Sells Green, Nr Devizes Wilts 0976 301788	3 / 15	9	B C	10/6/4/4	Yes	Vintage	No
Evans & Son, New Road Industrial Estate, Hixon, Staffs ST18 0PJ 01889 270426	7 / 20	450	A B C D E F	10/6/4/4	Yes	Beta Marine	Yes
Falcon 5, Pritchard Street, Bristol BS2 8RH 07000 781309	35 / 15	800	B F	10/6/4/4	Yes	BMC	Yes
Floating Homes Ltd, Oak Farm Works, High Street, Stilton, Peterborough PE7 3RA 01733 240580	1 / 1	25	A B	10/6/4/4	Yes	BMC	No
Five Towns Boatbuilding, Navigation House,1 Whitebridge Lane, Stone, Staffs ST15 8LQ 01785 817506I	12 / 20	36	C D E	10/6/5/4	Yes	Beta Marine	Yes
French & Peel Boatbuilders, Station Works, Thorne North Railway Station,							
Selby Road,Thorne, S Yorks DN8 4HZ 01405 817954	10 / 44	42	A B C D E F	10/6/4/4	Yes	Any	No
Friesland Boating, de Tille 5, 8723 ER Koudam (FR), Holland 0031 514 522607	16 / 16	225	C D E F	25/6/4/5	Yes	Buhk, DAF, Deutz	No
G & J Reeves, Coventry Bridge Yard, Station Road, Napton, Warwickshire 01926 815581	7 / 23	300	B C E F	10/6/4/4	Yes	Beta Marine	Yes
GT Boatbuilders, Unit 10, Ladford Covert, Seighford, Stafford ST18 9OG 01785 282026	9 / 20	140	B	10/6/4/4	Yes	Beta marine	Yes
Heritage Boats, Evesham Marina, King's Road, Evesham, Worcs WR11 5BU 01386 48882	9 / 25	95	B C E F	10/6/4/4	Yes	Beta Marine	Yes
Ian Kemp, Dadford's Wharf, Mill Street, Wordsley, Stourbridge, West Midlands DY8 5SX 01384 485565	3 / 20	5	C D F	10+/6/5/4	No	Lister	No
Ivybridge Marine Ltd, Station House, Station Road, Watford, Northants NN6 7UL 01327 704847	12 / 20	45	C D E F	10/6/5/5	No	Beta Marine	No
J L Pinder & Sons, The Old Basin, 138 Hanbury Rd, Stoke Prior, Bromsgrove, Worcs 01527 76438	29 / 45	350	A B C D E	10/6/4/4	Yes	JLP (Kubota)	No
John South Boats, 89 Condover Industrial Estate, Dorrington, Shropshire SY5 7NH 01743 718415	25 / 25	170	B F	10/6/4/4	No	N/A	No
John White, Unit 17a, Weaver Ind Est, Blackburn Street, Liverpool L19 8JA 0151 427 7282	25 / 25	900	B C D F	10/6/5/4	No	N/A	No
Jonathan Wilson Boatbuilders, South Parade, Thorne, Nr Doncaster 01405 812500	15 / 17	300	B C D E F	12.5/6/5/4	Yes	Beta Marine	No
K H Ball, Industry Narrowboats, Orchard Cottage, Beffcote Lane, Gnosall, Staffs ST20 0EB 01785 824897	12 / 15	17	C D	10/6/5/4	Yes	Any vintage	No
Ken Bonikowski, Brookside House, 207 Bickershaw Lane, Abram, Nr Wigan WN2 5TA 01942 866367	15 / 20	60	A F	10/6/4/4	Yes	BMC	No
Ledgard Bridge Boat Co, Ledgard Wharf, Butt End Mills, Mirfield, West Yorkshire WF14 8PW 01924 491441	10 / 17	8?	B C D E F	10/6/4/4	Yes	Beta/Lister	Yes
Limekiln Narrowboats, r/o 4 Bridgnorth Rd, Compton,							
Wolverhampton, West Midlands WV6 8AA 01902 751147	12 / 24	45	B C D	10/6/5/4	Yes	Perkins	No
Littleborough Boats, 71 Gainsborough Avenue, Burnley, Lancs BB11 2PD 01282 455372	4 / 4	5	B	10/6/4/5	No	N/A	No
Liverpool Boats, Marina House, 25-29 Sefton Street, Liverpool L8 5SL 0151 707 0722	20 / 30	800	A B F	10/6/4/4	Yes	Beta Marine	No
Lower Park Marina Ltd, Kelbrook Road, Barnoldswick, Lancs BB18 5TB 01282 815883	10 / 10	35	B C	10/6/4/4	Yes	Vetus/Lister/AMC	Yes
Maestermyn Marine, Ellesmere Road, Whittington, Oswestry, Shropshire SY11 4NU 01691 662424	6 / 10	20	B	8/6/4/4	Yes	Lister	No
Measham Boats, Lower Rectory Farm, Snarestone Road, Appleby Magna,							
Swadlincote, Derby DE12 7AJ 01530 416098	2 / 7	6	B C E	10/6/5/4	Yes	Beta Marine	Yes

Company	Experience	Shells built	Shell types	Plating	Lining out	Engines	CBA
Mel Davis, Norwood Farm, Langwith, Mansfield, Notts NG20 9JA 01623 748592	5 / 24	32	B C	10/6/5/4	Yes	Beta/vintage	No
Midland Canal Centre, Stenson Marina, Stenson, Derby DE7 1HL 01283 701933	10 / 10	350	A B C D E F	10/6/4/4	Yes	Beta/Lister	Yes
Middlesex & Herts Boat Services, Winkwell, Bourne End, Hemel Hempstead, Herts HP1 2RZ 01442 872985	2 / 15	2	A B C D E F	10/6/5/4	Yes	Beta/Gardner	No
Norton Canes Boatbuilders, Norton Canes Docks, Lime Lane, Pelsall, Walsall, W Midlands WS3 5AP 01543 374888	12 / 20	66	C	10/6/5/4	Yes	Beta Marine	No
Orchard Marine, School Road, Rudheath, Northwich, Cheshire CW9 7RG 01606 42082	6 / 15	21	B	10/6/4/4	Yes	Beta Marine	No
Orion Narrowboats, Ashwood Marina, Kingswinford, West Midlands DY6 0AQ 01384 401464	6 / 22	30	A B C D E F	10/6/5/4	Yes	Lister	No
P M Buckle Narrowboats, The Boat Yard, Church Lane, Stibbington, Peterborough, Cambs PE8 6LP 01780 783144	12 / 15	300	A B F	10/6/4/4	Yes	BMC	No
PKB Narrowboats, Holme Road, Yaxley, Peterborough, Cambs 01733 243767	14 / 35	300	A B C E F	10/6/4/4	Yes	Perkins	No
Peter Nicholls, Braunston Marina Trade Centre, Daventry Road, Braunston, Northants NN11 7JH 01788 891823	23 / 23	350	B C D E F	10/6/4/4	Yes	Beta Marine	Yes
Phil Jones, 105 Griffiths Drive, Wolverhampton WV11 2JW 01902 710799	10 / 25	20	C D E	10/6/5/4	Yes	Perkins/vintage	No
Pickwell & Arnold, Unit 10, Nanholme Mill, Shaw Wood Rd, Todmorden, W Yorks OL14 6DB 01706 812411	7 / 20	50	B E F	10/6/4/4	Yes	Beta/Lister/BMC	No
Piper Boatbuilders, Red Bull Basin, Church Lawton, Stoke-on-Trent ST7 3AJ 01782 784754	30 / 24	550	B C	10/6/4/4	Yes	Vetus	No
R Tinker, Baytree Lane, Middleton, Nr Manchester M24 2EL 0161 643 3652	20 / 20	20	B E	10/6/3/3	Yes	Beta Marine	No
R & D Fabrications, Unit 65, Road A, Boughton Ind Est, New Ollerton, Newark, Notts 01623 862473	25 / 30	1400	B E F	10/6/4/4	Yes	Kubota	Yes
R W Davis & Son Ltd, Junction Dry Dock, Saul, Glos GL2 7LA 01452 740233	100+ / 30	100 +	C D F	10/6/5/4	Yes	RN / Kelvin	Yes
Sagar Marine, Victoria Works, Wharfe St, Brighouse, Yorks HD6 1PP 01484 714541	23 / 23	175	B E F	10/6/4/4	Yes	Beta/Lister	No
Severn Valley Cruisers, Boat Shop, Mart Lane, Stourport on Severn, Worcs DY13 9ER 01299 871165	23 / 25	160	A B C	8/6/4/4	Yes	Thorneycroft	Yes
Sirius Boat Builders, Redstone Wharf, Sandy Lane, Stourport on Severn, Worcs DY13 9PN 01299 871048	10 / 28	30+	A B C D E F	10/6/4/4	Yes	Yanmar	Yes
South West Durham Steelcraft, Front Unit, Old Colliery Buildings, Trimdon Grange Industrial Estate, Trimdon Grange, Co Durham TS29 6PA 01429 881300	9 / 9	130	B C E F	10/6/4/4	Yes	Beta/Lister	Yes
S M Hudson, Glascote Basin Boatyard, Basin Lane, Glascote, Tamworth, Staffs B77 2AH 01827 311317	7 / 7	50	C D	10/6/4/4	Yes	Beta/vintage	No
Stoke-on-Trent Boatbuilding, Longport Wharf, Longport, Stoke-on-Trent ST6 4NA 01782 813831	18 / 15	110	B C	10/6/4/4	Yes	Beta marine	Yes
Stone Boatbuilding Co, Newcastle Road, Stone, Staffs ST15 8JZ 01785 812688	25 / 35	100 +	B C	10/6/4/4	Yes	Any	No
Tayberg Steel Boats, Brookfoot Mills, Elland Road, Brighouse, W Yorks HD6 2QS 01484 400221	10 / 20	50	B C D E F	10/6/4/4	Yes	Any	No
Teddesley Boat Company, Park Gate Lock, Teddesley Road, Penkridge, Staffs ST19 5RH 01785 714692	30 / 16	20	B C	10/6/5/5	Yes	Lister	No
Walsall Boatbuilders, Old Birchills Wharf, Old Birchills, Walsall WS2 8QD 01922 722949	10 / 14	30	B C	10/6/5/4	Yes	Perkins	No
Warble Narrowboats, Warble Wharf, Broadway, Hyde, Nr Stockport, Cheshire SK14 4QF 061 367 9205	8 / 20	60	B C D	10/6/4/4	Yes	Beta Marine	Yes
Warwickshire Fly Boat Co, Shop Lock Cottage, Stockton, Rugby CV23 8LD 01926 812093	15 / 11	28	C D F	10/6/5/4	Yes	Vintage	Yes
Worcestershire Steel Boatbuilders, 13 Battens Close, Redditch B98 7HY 01527 522703	3 / 60	75	B F	10/6/4/4	Yes	Kubota	No

Experience: The two figures aim to reflect how long the company has been in business and the experience of its principal fabricator. The typical shell builder learns his skills by working for another narrowboat builder for several years before setting up on his own. (Incidentally, we didn't find any female shell builders but, if we missed any, we would be pleased to correct the omission).

Shells built: the figure is supposed to be the total output of the company – and should not include any shells built for previous employers. A few builders like Ian Kemp and Steve Priest spend much of their time restoring original working boats so their total of new shells appears low. Some long-established companies like Stone Boatbuilding Co produced hundreds of boats in the past but are now building fewer boats per year.

Shell types: The builders were asked to tick which of the following categories of boat they normally build. The categories shown on the chart correspond exactly to the answers given to our questionnaire. Some builders were surprisingly modest about their capabilities while others seemed more ambitious. If you are looking for category D shell in particular, you are advised to ask to see an example before ordering to make sure that both you and the builder are talking the same language.

A No-frills, very economically priced traditional, semi-trad or cruiser style narrowboats

B Mid-priced traditional, semi-trad, tug or cruiser style narrowboats with some traditional detailing – eg cants, shaped ends to handrails

C More expensive, heavier traditional narrowboats or tugs, just short of fully authentic replicas of working boats

D Authentic replicas of original working boats – eg double curved bow (See note above)

E Inspection launches, narrow beam Dutch barges or similar

F Wide beam boats (Not all builders build all styles of wide beam boat. Sagar Marine, for example, only builds Dutch barge types)

Plating: The figures refer to the thickness in millimetres of the base plate/hull sides/cabin sides/roof (in that order) for a standard 60ft boat.

Lining out: Some builders will line out the shell to give you a start, others do not have in-house boat fitters.

Engines : Most builders can fit any engine you specify but we asked them to state which one they would normally fit if you are undecided.

CBA Membership: Only members of the Canal Boat Builders' Association can offer to work under the British Marine Industries Association Federation contract mentioned in Chapter 4. Not every builder regards the CBA as a Good Thing, although more are joining as the European Recreational Craft Directive starts to bite. Some very good builders have their own personal reasons for not joining, so non-membership should not necessarily be seen as a reason for rejection.

The builders included on the list are all those which the author could identify at the time of publication of this book and who completed the questionnaire. *Waterways World* regrets that it cannot guarantee the quality of workmanship or financial standing of any of the companies listed and prospective customers are recommended to satisfy themselves on these matters.

Appendix 2

ENGINE SUPPLIERS

The following table of narrowboat diesels is also based on the replies of manufacturers/marinisers to our questionnaire in 1998.

MODEL	Power Hp @ rpm.	Torque ft lbs @ rpm	Tickover Rpm	Cubic cap./ cylinders	Weight in lbs	Recommended gearbox	Red'n ratio	Prop size	Alternator size - amps	Base engine	Price
E P Barrus Ltd, Launton Road, Bicester, Oxon, OX6 0UR 01869 363636											
Shire 20	18 @ 3,600	20.5 @ 1,600	900	636 / 2	251	Yanmar KM2C	2.21 : 1	-	55	Yanmar 2GM20	3590
Shire 25	27 @ 3,600	32.5 @ 1,600	900	954 / 3	304	Yanmar KM3A	2.36 : 1	-	55	Yanmar 3GM30	4225
Shire 1600	30 @ 2,400	69 @ 1,600	850	1,642 / 3	350	PRM 150	2.09 : 1	-	40 + 65	Yanmar 3TNE 88	5280
Shire 2000	35 @ 2,400	91.5 @ 1,600	850	1,995 / 4	400	PRM 150	2.09 : 1	-	40 + 80	Yanmar 4TNE84	6125
Shire 2000	40 @ 2,600	91.5 @ 1,600	850	1,995 / 4	400	PRM 150	2.09 : 1	-	40 + 80	Yanmar 4TNE84	6125
Shire 2200	45 @ 2,600	101 @ 1,600	850	2,190 / 4	400	PRM 150	2.09 : 1	-	40 + 80	Yanmar 4TNE88	6975
Shire 2200	50 @ 3,000	101 @ 1,600	850	2,190 / 4	400	PRM 150	2.09 : 1	-	40 + 80	Yanmar 4TNE88	6975
Beta Marine Merretts Mills, Bath Road, South Woodchester, Stroud, Gloucs, GL5 5EU 01453 835282											
BZ 482	13.5 @ 3,600	21 @ 2,400	900	478 / 2	196	TMC 40	2 : 1	12 x 9	40	Kubota	2551
BD 722	20 @ 3,600	36 @ 2,600	900	719 / 3	233	TMC 40	2 : 1	13 x 9	40	Kubota	3096
BD 1005	28 @ 3,600	45 @ 2,400	850	1,001 / 3	330	PRM 120	2 : 1	14 x 9	55	Kubota	3458
BV 1205	32 @ 3,600	53 @ 2,400	850	1,198 / 4	374	PRM 120	2 : 1	15 x 9	55	Kubota	3655
BV 1305	35 @ 3,600	60 @ 2,400	850	1,335 / 4	374	PRM 120	2 : 1	15 x 9.5	55	Kubota	3875
BV 1505	37.5 @ 3,000	74 @ 2,200	850	1,498 / 4	374	PRM 150	2 : 1	16 x 10	55	Kubota	4634
BV 1903	43 @ 2,800	97 @ 1,500	800	1,857 / 4	535	PRM 150	2 : 1	19 x 10.5	55	Kubota	5405
BV 2203	50 @ 2,800	115 @ 1,500	800	2,197 / 4	587	PRM 260	2 : 1	19 x 12	55	Kubota	6127
BF 2803	62 @ 2,800	140 @ 1,400	800	2,764 / 5	770	PRM 260	2 : 1	20 x 12	55	Kubota	6659
BV 3300	75 @ 2,600	180 @ 1,500	750	3,318 / 4	858	PRM 260	2 : 1	20 x 12	55	Kubota	6869
BD 3 Tug	35 @ 1,400	157 @ 1,400	400	3,150 / 3	1078	PRM 260	2 : 1	21 / 17	55	Ford	
Bubble Boats, Stenson Bubble, Stenson, Derbyshire, 01283 703113											
John Deere 2.9	40 @ 1,600	143 @ 1,400	600	2,900 / 3	696	PRM 260	2 : 1	17 x 11	70	John Deere	5405
Bukh TW Marine Ltd The Marina, Station Road, Furness Vale, High Peak, SK23 7QA 01663 745757											
DV 24 MEC	22 @ 3,000	42 @ 1,800	750	964 / 2	463	ZF/ISA BW7	2.5 : 1	17 dia	50	Bukh	6462 1 Aqu
DV 36 MEC	34 @ 3,000	66 @ 1,800	750	1447 / 3	628	ZF/ISA BW7	2.5 : 1	19 dia	50	Bukh	8413 1 Aqu
Calcutt Boats Ltd (CB Marine) Calcutt Top Lock, Stockton, Nr Rugby, Warwickshire, CV23 8HX 01926 813757											
BMC 1.8	36 @ 3,000	80 @ 2,400	700	1,800 / 4	585	PRM 150	2 or 3 : 1	17x12/19x14	55	BMC 1.8	4222
Matador	32 @ 2,900	82 @ 2,300	500	1,800 / 4	592	PRM 150	2 : 1	17x12	55	Hanomag (Merc)	3844
D3 152	42 @ 2,000	110 @ 1,600	400	2,500 / 3	680	PRM 260	2 : 1	20 x 15	55	Perkins D3	4578
Club Line Swan Lane Wharf, Stoke Heath, Coventry, CV2 4QN 024 7625 8864											
Ford XLD	43kw @ 4,800	108 @ 2,200	950	1,750 / 4	315	PRM150	2 : 1	-	70	Ford	5800
Darglow Engineering Ltd Upton Cross, Poole, Dorset, BH16 5PH 01202 624450											
Kingfisher											
Cadet	6 @ 2,000	12.5 @ 1,800	600	330 / 1	280	C3 Manual	2 : 1	12 x 9	8	Coventry	1730
Captain	14 @ 2,000	40 @ 1,750	500	707 / 2	480	MA 100	2 : 1	15 x 12	55	Coventry	2465
Tugmaster	26.4 @ 1,800	70 @ 1,750	450	1,630 / 2	946	MA 100	2 : 1	19 x 17	55	Ruston	3700
Tugmaster Sup.	26.4 @ 1,800	123 @ 1,650	400	2,445 / 3	1250	MA 125	2 : 1	21 x 16	55	Ruston	4230

MODEL	Power Hp @ rpm.	Torque ft lbs @ rpm	Tickover Rpm	Cubic cap./	Weight	Recommended	Red'n	Prop size	Alternator	Base engine	Price
Duffield Marine Ltd Salhouse Road, Norwich, NR7 9AB 01603 705111											
Phoenix 42	42 @ 2,800	98 @ 1,700	900	1,995 / 4	482	PRM 150	3 : 1	20 x 14	70	Perkins	6168
3 HD 46	46 @ 2,250	110 / 1,600	500	2,500 / 3	915	PRM 260	2 : 1	20 x 13	55	Perkins	6218
Ron Davis Marine, Castletown, Portland, Dorset, DT5 1BD 01305 821175											
RM 90	9.9 @ 3,000	18.5 @ 2,500	700	477 / 1	175	TMC 40	2 or 2.6 : 1	14 to 17	33	Ruggerini	2174
MM 150	14 @ 3,000	22.8 @ 2,800	800	654 / 1	187	TMC 40	2 or 2.6 : 1	14 to 17	33	Ruggerini	3384
MM 190	20 @ 3,000	33 @ 2,600	800	851 / 2	191	TMC 40	2 or 2.6 : 1	14 to 18	33	Ruggerini	3672
RM 270	27 @ 2,800	50 @ 2,300	600	1205 / 2	356	TMC 60	2, 2.5 or 3 : 1	14 to 20	58	Ruggerini	3672
MM 351	43 @ 3,600	62.5 @ 2,500	800	1566 / 3	375	TMC 60	2, 2.5 or 3 : 1	14 to 20	58	Ruggerini	4935
RoDa FNM 450	48 @ 4,500	59 @ 3,000	800	1366 / 4	341	TMC 60	2, 2.5 or 3 : 1	14 to 20	58	Ruggerini	4935
L. Gardner and Sons Ltd. Patricroft, Eccles, Manchester, M30 7WA 0161 789 2201											
2LW	28 @ 1,300	115 @ 1,000	400	2,800 / 2	1040	PRM 260	2 : 1	22 or 23 dia	50	Gardner	POA
Lancing Marine 51 Victoria Road, Portslade, Sussex, BN41 1XY 01273 410025											
XLD LP	40 @ 2,600	80 @ 2,600	850	1,753 / 4	405	PRM 120	2 : 1	19 dia	55	Ford XLD	4855
XLD MP	50 @ 3,400	80 @ 2,600	850	1,753 / 4	405	PRM 120	3 : 1	20 dia	55	Ford XLD	4855
FSD LP	51 @ 2,500	125 @ 2,000	800	2,496 / 4	578	PRM 150	2 : 1	21 dia	55	Ford FSD	5305
FSD MP	61 @ 3,000	125 @ 2,000	800	2,496 / 4	578	PRM 150	2 : 1	19 dia	55	Ford FSD	5443
NHD 450L	85 @ 2,000	248 @ 1,500	725	5,000 / 4	955	PRM 500	1.5 : 1	23 dia	45	New Holland	8000
NHD 450	105 @ 2,500	248 @ 1,500	725	5,000 / 4	959	PRM 500	2 : 1	23 dia	45	New Holland	8167
Lister Marine Diesels Long Street, Dursley, Gloucs, GL11 4HS 01453 544141											
LPA2	15 @ 3,000	29 @ 2,000	850	726 / 2	319	Hurth HBW 50	-	-	45	Lister Petter	3967
LPA3	23 @ 3,000	43 @ 2,000	850	1,089 / 3	374	Hurth HBW 100	-	-	45	Lister Petter	4579
Canal Star 18	18 @ 2,600	39 @ 1,800	800	930 / 2	330	PRM150	-	-	45	Lister Petter	5171
Canal Star 27	27 @ 2,600	59 @ 1,800	800	1,395 / 3	396	PRM 150	-	-	45	Lister Petter	5804
Canal Star 36	36 @ 2,600	78 @ 1,800	800	1,860 / 4	462	PRM 150	-	-	45	Lister Petter	6451
TS2	23 @ 2,600	49 @ 1,800	900	1,266 / 2	682	Hurth HBW 100	-	-	55	Lister Petter	6377
TS3	34 @ 2,600	74 @ 1,800	900	1,900 / 3	770	Hurth HBW 125	-	-	55	Lister Petter	7165
Marine Engine Services, Uxbridge Wharf, Waterloo Road, Uxbridge, Middlesex, UB8 2QX 01895 270422											
PM 12	16 @ 1,500	55	475	1,560 / 2	594	Hurth/PRM	-	-	45 or 55	Rigas	POA
PM 24	24 @ 1,800	66	525	1,560 / 2	616	Hurth/PRM	-	-	45 or 55	Rigas	POA
PM 32	32 @ 1,500	110	475	3,120 / 4	858	Hurth/PRM	-	-	45 or 55	Rigas	POA
PM 45	45 @ 1,800	138	525	3,120 / 4	858	Hurth/PRM	-	-	45 or 55	Rigas	POA
PM60T	60 @ 1,800	176	525	3,120 / 4	946	Hurth/PRM	-	-	45 or 55	Rigas	POA
Mermaid Marine Engines Ltd, 70 - 72 Cobham Road, Ferndown Industrial Estate, Ferndown, Dorset, BH21 7RN 01202 895882											
Meteor 2	56 @ 4,000	82 / 2,400	650	1,753 / 4	378	PRM 150	2.8 : 1	17 x 12	70	Ford XLD	5365
Nannidiesel A R Peachment Riverside Estate, Brundall, Norwich, NR13 5PL. 01603 714077											
2.50 KC	14 @ 3,600	20.5 @ 3,600	900	479 / 2	202	Hurth	2 : 1	12 dia	60	Kubota	3398
3.75 KC	21 @ 3,600	30.5 @ 3,600	900	719 / 3	231	Hurth	2 : 1	13 dia	60	Kubota	3902
3.100 KC	29 @ 3,600	42.5@ 3,600	900	1001 / 3	286	Hurth/TMC	2 : 1	14 dia	60	Kubota	4778
4.150 KC	37.5 @ 3000	65.5 @ 3,000	800	1498 / 4	320	PRM 150	2 : 1	16 dia	60	Kubota	5857
4.200 KC	43 @ 2,800	80.5 @ 2,800	800	2197 / 4	495	PRM150or260	2 : 1	17 dia	60	Kubota	6609
4.220 KC	50 @ 2,800	93.5 @ 2,800	800	2197 / 4	495	PRM 260	2 : 1	18 dia	60	Kubota	7396
5.280 KC	62 @ 2,800	116 @ 2,800	800	2746 / 5	620	PRM 260	2 : 1	19 dia	60	Kubota	7807

MODEL	Power Hp @ rpm.	Torque ft lbs @ rpm	Tickover Rpm	Cubic cap./	Weight	Recommended	Red'n	Prop size	Alternator	Base engine	Price
Russell Newbery (R W Davis and Sons) Sharpness Shipyard, Sharpness, Gloucestershire, GL13 9UD 01453 811261											
DM1	10 @ 1,200	47 @ 1,000	350	1,314 / 1	1008	Hurth 150	2 : 1	21 x 19	70	RN	POA
DM2	21 @ 1,200	95 @ 1,000	350	2,628 / 2	1456	PRM 260	2 : 1	24 X 21	70	RN	POA
DM3	31 @ 1,200	145 @ 1,000	350	3,942 / 3	1848	PRM 260	2 : 1	27 x 23.5	70	RN	POA
SABB UK Wixenford farm, Plymstock, Plymouth, PL9 8AA 01752 402286											
GG	10 @ 1,800	29 @ 1,600	350	760 / 1	440	SABB	2 : 1	16x14	75	SABB	4810
Sowester Ltd, Stinsford Road, Nuffield Industrial Estate, Poole, Dorset, BH17 0SW 01202 667700											
LDW 502 M	11 @ 3,600	15.5 @ 2,000	850	505 / 2	167	Hurth HBW 40	2.5 : 1	14 dia	30	Lombardini	3001
LDW 602 M	17 @ 3,600	24 @ 2,000	850	611 / 2	213	Hurth HBW 40	2.5 : 1	14 dia	45	Lombardini	3819
LDW 903 M	27 @ 3,600	41 @ 2,000	850	916 / 3	242	Hurth HSW 125	2.63 : 1	16 dia	45	Lombardini	5278
LDW 1204 M	33 @ 3,600	54.5 @ 1,800	850	1,222 / 4	297	Hurth HSW 125	2.63 : 1	16 dia	45	Lombardini	5660
LDW 1503 M	37 @ 3,000	71.5 @ 1,900	850	1,551 / 3	396	Hurth HSW 125	2.63 : 1	16 dia	65	Lombardini	6340
LDW 2004 M	48.5 @ 3,000	92 @ 1,900	850	2,068 / 4	506	Hurth HSW 125	2.63 : 1	16 dia	65	Lombardini	7045
LDW 2004 MT	82 @ 3,000	144 @ 2,200	850	2,068 / 4	567	Hurth HSW 250	2.63 : 1	18 dia	65	Lombardini	9074
Thornycroft Engines PO Box 61, Leyland, Lancs, PR5 1GG 01772 611144											
Type 33	16.5 @ 3,600	23 @ 2,500	750	635 / 2	236	TMC 40	2 : 1	13 x 9	40	Mitsubishi L	3484
Type 55	21 @ 3,000	37.6 @ 2,000	750	900 /3	343	TMC 40	2 : 1	14 x 10	40	Mitsubishi K	3508
Type 65	29 @ 3,600	46 @ 2,400	750	1,125 / 3	348	PRM 120	2 : 1	15 x 10	70	Mitsubishi SL	4465
Type 75	31 @ 3,600	53 @ 2,200	750	1,318 / 3	348	PRM 120	2 : 1	16 x 10	70	Mitsubishi SL	4661
Type 90	40 @ 4,000	58 @ 1,800	570	1,489 / 4	524	PRM 120	2 : 1	17 x 10	70	BMC 1.5	4398
Type 95	39 @ 3,600	62.5 @ 2,000	750	1,500 / 4	420	PRM 150	2 : 1	17 x 10	70	Mitsubishi SL	5307
Type 105	42.5 @ 3,600	73.5 @ 2,000	750	1,758 / 4	420	PRM 150	2 : 1	17 x 11	70	Mitsubishi SL	5594
Type 108	50 @ 4,000	78 @ 2,400	570	1,799 / 4	547	PRM 150	2 : 1	17 x 12	70	BMC 1.8	4577
Type 145	60 @ 3,600	99 @ 2,000	750	2,311 / 4	600	PRM 260	2 : 1	18 x 12	70	Mitsubishi SQ	6913
Type 155	67 @ 3,600	107 @ 1,900	750	2,505 / 4	600	PRM 260	2 : 1	19 x 12	70	Mitsubishi SQ	7109
Vetus Den Ouden Ltd, 39 South Hants Industrial Park, Totton, Southampton, SO40 3SA 023 8086 1033											
M 2.04	11 @ 3,600	15.8 @ 3,600	850	464 / 2	216	TMC 40	-	-	40	Mitsubishi	2890
M 2.06	15 @ 3,600	21.7 @ 3,600	850	635 / 2	216	TMC 40	-	-	40	Mitsubishi	3400
M 3.10	22 @ 3,600	31.6 @ 3,600	850	979 / 3	340	HSW 125 H	-	-	50	Mitsubishi	3930
M 4.14	33 @ 3,600	48.5 @ 3,600	850	1415 / 4	408	HSW 125 H	-	-	50	Mitsubishi	4630
P 4.17	42 @ 3,000	72.6 @ 3,000	875	1769 / 4	408	HSW 125 H	-	-	90	Peugeot	5740
P 4.19	52 @ 3,000	74.5 @ 3,600	875	1905 / 4	408	HSW 125 H	-	-	90	Peugeot	5869
D 4.29	65 @ 3,000	113 @ 3,000	875	2910 / 4	649	HSW 250 A	-	-	90	Deutz oil cooled	7155
Watermota Ltd, Abbotskerwell, Newton Abbot, Devon, TQ12 5NF 01626 333344											
WB 12 C	12 @ 3,000	30 @ 2,200	1200	630 / 2	225	PRM 120	2 : 1	-	50	Mitsubishi	3194
WB 20 B	18 @ 3,600	30 @ 2,200	1400	630 / 2	239	PRM 120	2 : 1	-	50	Mitsubishi	3306
WB 30 B	27 @ 3,600	43 @ 2,200	1400	950 / 3	274	PRM 150	2 : 1	-	50	Mitsubishi	3935
WB 35 B	32 @ 3,600	41 @ 2,300	1400	1118 / 3	368	PRM 150	2 : 1	-	50	Mitsubishi	4128
WB 38 B	37 @ 3,600	53 @ 2,400	1400	1305 / 4	419	PRM 150	2 : 1	-	50	Mitsubishi	4338
WB 42 B	42 @ 3,600	56 @ 2,500	1400	1490 / 4	419	PRM 150	2 : 1	-	50	Mitsubishi	4888
Canal Panther	30 @ 2,500	95 @ 2,500	1200	1753 / 4	410	PRM 150	2 : 1	-	55	Ford	4995
WB 55 A	55 @ 3,600	93 @ 1,920	1400	2180 / 4	470	PRM 260	2 : 1	-	50	Mazda	5559

Power: The message in WW's pages has always been that outright power is almost irrelevant to narrowboats. In most cases, the figures here do not refer to the engine's ultimate power output, but what it can produce when derated for narrowboat use.

Torque and cubic capacity: When comparing torque figures in brochures, be sure to check that they are taken at the flywheel and not at the prop shaft where they may be artificially magnified by the reduction ratio of the gearbox. If your brochure quotes torque in kilogram/metres (kg/m), multiply that figure by 7.233 to obtain ft/lb. If it quotes Newton/metres (Nm), divide by 1.355 for foot/pounds (ft/lb).

Tickover: Traditionalists seek slow running diesels because they make the right 'vintage' sound. Ordinary narrowboaters prefer them because they are generally less intrusive than busy, high revving engines. (although the smaller and lighter the engine the higher it will rev before becoming discordant).

Standard prop size: The exact size of prop to suit your narrowboat can depend on a large number of factors, including hull design. For conventional narrowboats, the three most important considerations are engine power, engine speed and gearbox reduction ratio. Using these basic figures, most engine builders/marinisers will quote a standard prop size. You can alter gearbox reduction ratio, trade-off blade diameter against pitch, and even specify a different blade area ratio to fit a suitable propeller against your available stern post height. For this reason, some manufacturers declined to give a suggested diameter and/or pitch.

Price: List prices of the larger manufacturers can be misleading. They are often pitched high to allow dealers to offer large discounts. The engine market is extremely competitive so, if you are concerned only with the cheapest price, try phoning a few rival companies when you are close to placing your order. This will not work with smaller canal-oriented marinisers because they cannot cut costs by building in volume and the special features of narrowboat engines – heavier flywheels and high output alternators – make them inherently more expensive to put together. The 'new vintage' engines, like Gardner and Russell Newbery, are built to the customers individual requirements and the price varies accordingly. These have therefore not been included.

Appendix 3

ELECTRICAL INSTALLATION GUIDELINES
By Peter Hopley

Unfortunately, it is not possible to reproduce all the information given in the British Marine Electronics Association (BMEA) Code of Practise (COP) and the two ISO standards. However, certain items should be mentioned because they are fundamental to the whole installation, and mistakes with these could be difficult, or indeed impossible, to correct at a later stage. But do remember that the following points represent just a few of the guidelines given, all of which are intended to ensure that good practice is followed at all times. I should also point out that some of the items below are the actual ISO standards, whilst others are 'guidance notes' provided by the BMEA, which are intended to clarify and expand upon the standard. The guidance notes are prefixed 'GN'

DC Installations

The system is to be insulated; 2 wire system or 2 wire system with negative ground. The hull must not be used as a conductor, but the engine block may be used as a grounded conductor.

If an AC system is installed, earthing (grounding) of the DC system is required, ie both the battery negative and the Craft's AC earth shall be grounded (see also the sections on AC below).

If a 'ground fault circuit breaker' (whole craft residual current device) is fitted in the protective conductor of the AC system, the negative ground terminal of the DC system need not be connected to the AC shore ground. The glossary of the COP provides a definition of a GFCB, but a note in the main body points out that such a device is not normally used in the UK!

GN – Equipment should be chosen which is capable of operating from 10.5 to 15.5volts (pro rata for 24v system). Cables should be sized so that volt drop at any appliance shall be not greater than 10% of the nominal battery voltage with all loads on that cable operating at maximum.

GN – It is recommended that there should be one single earth point in the craft where battery negative, all circuit negatives and the craft mains earth (if installed) may all be connected together.

Batteries shall be installed in a dry, ventilated location above bilge water level.

GN – Batteries should be in a well ventilated space so that no build-up of hydrogen can accumulate nearby. If the area is not naturally well ventilated, an automatically operated extractor fan may need to be fitted to remove gases (but then there are rules as to the type of fan that can be used!). Batteries should not be under a bunk/seat unless the battery box is sealed and fitted with a ventilated trunking.

Battery movement must be restricted to no more than 10mm in any direction when subjected to a force equal to twice the battery weight.
Batteries shall be installed or protected so that metallic objects cannot come into any unintentional contact with any battery terminal.

Batteries shall not be installed directly above or below a fuel tank or fuel filter.

Any metallic component of the fuel system within 300mm (1ft) and above the battery top, as installed, shall be electrically insulated.

GN – Batteries should be easily removable, and the top of

vented batteries be readily accessible for checking electrolyte level. They should be fitted in boxes of non-corrosive material so that leakage of all the electrolyte from every battery is contained within the box to a level not less than 75mm on all sides.

A battery disconnect switch should be fitted in a readily accessible location as close as practical to the batteries, in the positive line (more than one switch is allowed). Switch must be rated to the maximum system load or the feeder cable capacity whichever is smaller.

Remote controlled battery switches, if used, must also be manually operable at the switch.

Wiring shall be multi stranded copper conductors, with insulation being flame retardant (ie not supporting combustion in the absence of flame). *Author's note* – all reputable supplies of cables meet these requirements. Domestic 'twin flat and earth' should not be used – it is not multi stranded!

Single unsheathed conductors to be supported at least every 250mm, unless in conduit or trunking or on a cable tray.
Sheathed conductors and battery conductors (but excepting starter motor conductors) shall be supported at least every 450mm with the first support not more than 1m from the terminal.

GN – Cables should be run as high as practicable and wherever possible avoid bilges, proximity to cookers or other heat sources, fuel or LPG pipes, and avoid damage by abrasion and/or vibration.

Conductors to be sized in accordance with ISO standard, *Author's note* – these guidelines only relate to maximum permitted current, and minimum number of strands in any given cable, and do not calculate volt drop, which must be done in addition.

AC and DC conductors running together shall be sheathed and bundled separately from each other or shall be adequately screened (ie separated by a barrier or partition) and kept a minimum of 100mm apart.

Equipotential bonding conductors must be green or green/yellow stripe.
All DC negative cables must be Black or Yellow insulation. If an AC system is installed (which might use black for live conductors) then only Yellow conductors can be used for DC negative.
Black or Yellow shall not be used for DC positive conductors.
GN – metal conduit must be bonded to earth at the supply end.

GN – cable joins should be avoided, but where required, they must be identified and accessible.

GN – PVC insulated and sheathed cables must not run in direct contact with polystyrene thermal insulation.

A manually reset trip free circuit breaker or fuse shall be installed within 200mm of the source of power, for each circuit conductor. If not practicable, then the conductor must be contained within a protective covering (eg a conduit) from the source of power to the circuit breaker or fuse.

The main cable to a starter motor is an exception to the above, if sheathed or supported to protect against abrasion and contact with conductive surfaces.

GN – On metal hulled craft using 2 wire distribution circuits, the overcurrent protection device must be a double pole circuit breaker. Fuses must not be used.

AC Installations

The protective (earth) conductor shall be Green or Green with Yellow stripe.

The protective (earth) conductor shall be connected to the craft's DC negative ground/earth as close as practicable to the battery negative terminal (excepting where a ground fault circuit breaker (whole craft residual current device) is used – but note such a device is not normally used in the UK).
Metal hulls shall not be used as a conductor or protective conductor.

The protective conductor shall be connected to a metal hull at one point only (above any anticipated water accumulation).

The neutral conductor shall be grounded only at the source of power, ie the on board generator, the secondary of an isolation or polarisation transformer, or the shore power connection. The shore power neutral shall be grounded through the shore power cable and shall not be grounded on board the craft.

The craft ground/earth shall be connected to the ground/earth of the shore power source unless an isolation transformer is fitted, when the two must not be connected.

A manually reset trip free circuit breaker shall be installed within 500mm of the source of power. If not practicable, the conductor from the source of power to the circuit breaker must be contained within a protective covering (eg a conduit) from the source of power to the circuit breaker or fuse. If the conductor is over half the hull length, it must have a manually reset trip free circuit breaker installed within half the hull length from the source (ie shore connector, genset or inverter output terminals).
Double pole circuit breakers are required in conductors to the main power supply circuits.

In branch circuits, the live conductor shall have a circuit breaker or fuse.

(NB different rules apply for unpolarised systems, but most systems on narrow boats are not this type).

The main supply circuit shall have a double pole RCD breaker of 30mA sensitivity and 100ms maximum trip time (NB most RCD's encountered have a faster trip time of 40ms – these are fine as they are a higher standard).

GN – Heating and cooking appliances should be provided with their own local on/off switch that interrupts the live conductor.

Conductors shall have a minimum rating of 300/500-volt. Flexible cords shall have a rating 300/300-volt.

Conductors to be sized with reference to the ISO standard.

The connection from the earth circuit to the hull of a metal craft shall be accessible and by means of a screw or stud at least 6mm diameter.

For non metal hulls, an 'earth bar' should be made at the main switch board for the connection of all earth cables. This bar should be at least 64mm2 cross section (ie 8mm x 8mm or equivalent).

Non metal hulls should have an 'earth plate' of at least $0.25m^2$ (ie 0.5m x 0.5m or equivalent) well below water line. This should be connected to the 'earth bar' at the main switch board.

When a ring main or sockets are provided, their earth conductor shall be connected to the earth terminal on the AC main panel, which in turn shall be connected to the shore connector on the craft unless an isolation transformer is fitted.

An AC system panel board with a lamp indicating the system on/off function shall be installed.

A system voltmeter shall be installed on the panel board if the system is designed to supply motor circuits or if an on board generator is installed.

GN – When a shore supply is provided, a polarity indicator should be incorporated, which illuminates when the polarity is correct.

Mains sockets must not be interchangeable with DC sockets.

Having highlighted above a few of the important paragraphs mentioned in the two ISO standards, you may well be left feeling confused. Some of the wording leaves much to be desired, with statements which are frankly almost impossible to understand. For example, look at the 2nd paragraph I have given under DC installations, the one which starts 'If an AC system is installed, earthing (grounding) of the DC system is required ....' What I wrote is what I believe is intended by the standard. What is actually written in the standard is as follows (I quote):

'If an AC system is installed on the craft, earthing (grounding) of the DC system is required, ie connection to the shore ground of the AC system and the engine negative terminal shall be grounded'.

I bet you have read this at least three times by now, and still do not know what on earth it means. If you think this reads sensibly, then my apologies, but to me it just reads nonsensically. Unfortunately, this is just one example – there are others. I do know that at the time of preparing

this article, representations are being made to the ISO standards committee, to redraft the standards with a view to improving their readability, and also in some cases to make technical adjustments. 'Oh no' I hear you say, 'not more changes?' Well I'm sorry, but in all probability, yes, there will be changes. The best advice is to follow the standards as they are to the best of your ability, for the time being , and until such time as amendments are introduced.

Appendix 4

BIBLIOGRAPHY

Every month, *Waterways World* publishes articles which cover various aspects of boatbuilding. These generally go into greater detail than we can include in this book so the titles and dates of the more recent ones which are relevant to fitting out are shown below. Back numbers are available from Waterways World Back Numbers, The Well House, High Street, Burton-on-Trent, Staffs, DE14 1JQ or by ringing the Credit card hotline 01283 742970

Subject	Issue
Boat Safety Scheme	10, 11/96 and 09/97
Recreational Craft Directive	06/98
Boat lengthening	04/95
Diesel engines	05/99
Lister engines	02/96
BMC engines	03 96
Gardner Engines	07/95
Vintage engines	05/90, 05 and 06/94
Gearboxes	04/96
Generators	12/95
Windpower	02/96
Lighting	04/97
Cookers and fridges	10/94
Gasless cooking	01/98
Solid fuel stoves	10/95
Boilers	02/97
Toilet systems	06,07/97
Plumbing techniques	08/95
Door construction	05, 06 and 07/95
Galley worktops	05/96
Carpet	02 and 03/96
Tiling	10 and 11/95
Cratch construction	01 and 02/95
Canopies and cratch covers	07/96

The *New Inland Boat Owner's Book* is a companion volume to the *Narrowboat Builder's Book*. It contains information on the costs of boat ownership and covers topics such as living afloat, buying and selling boats and maintenance. it is available from *Waterways World* (address above) price £14.99 plus p&p.

Waterways World's sister magazine, *Traditional Woodworking,* contains articles on tools and construction techniques which are useful to boat fitters. It is published monthly, price £2.45, and is available at all good newsagents.

A large, well stocked chandlery

Appendix 5

USEFUL ADDRESSES AND CONTACTS

The following list is not claimed to be comprehensive but is intended to include a representative selection of organisations and companies that are likely to be useful to an amateur boat fitter.

British Waterways, Willow Grange, Church Road, Watford, Herts WD1
3QA (01923 226422) – Boat Safety Enquiries (01923 201278).

British Marine Industries Federation, Meadlake Place, Thorpe Lea Road, Egham, Surrey TW20 8HE (01784 473377).

Canal Boatbuilders' Association, via BMIF or:
Parkland House, Audley Avenue, Newport, Shropshire (01952 813572).

CORGI, 1 Elmwood, Chinham Business Park, Crockford Lane, Basingstoke RG24 8WG (01256 372200).

Inland Waterways Association, PO Box 114, Rickmanswowrth WD3 12Y (01923 711114).

Residential Boat Owners Association, PO Box 46, Grays RM18 8DZ (0370 785869).

Royal Yachting Association, RYA House, Romsey Road, Eastleigh, Hants SO50 9YA (023 8062 7400).

Drawings for DIY shell construction:

M&TBS, Hunters Park, Hernstone Lane, Peak Forest, Buxton, Derbyshire SK17 8EJ (0161 320 8023).

BOAT DELIVERY

R&J Dempster, Staffordshire (01785 814175).

Streethay Wharf, Staffordshire (01543 414808).

A.B. Tuckey, Warwickshire (01926 812134).

Wincham Wharf Boatbuilders, Cheshire (01606 44672).

CHANDLERS

The chandlers named below are included because of their size, their mail order service, or their strategic location – there are many more. Don't neglect your local chandler, who is an extremely useful contact for advice or when you are running short of brass screws.

Midland Chandlers, Teddesley Road, Penkridge, Staffs ST19 5RH (01785 712437).
Also at Junction Wharf, London Road, Braunston, Northants NN11 7HB (01788 891401).

And at Venetian Marine, Cholmondeston, Nantwich, Cheshire CW5 6DD (01270 528030).

Calcutt Boats, Calcutt Top Lock, Stockton, Rugby CV23 8HX (01926 813757).

Dobsons, The Wharf, Shardlow, Derbys DE7 2GJ (01332 792271).

Nantwich Canal Centre, Nantwich Marina, Chester Road, Nantwich, Cheshire CW5 6JD (01270 625122).

David Piper Boatbuilders, Red Bull Basin, Church Lawton, Cheshire ST7 3AJ (01782 784754).

Stone Boat Building Co, Newcastle Road, Stone, Staffs (01785 812688).

Rose Narrowboats, Stretton under Fosse, near Rugby, Warks CV23 0PU (01788 832449).

Uxbridge Boat Centre, Uxbridge Wharf, Waterloo Road, Uxbridge, Middx UB8 2QX (01895 252019).

VINTAGE ENGINES

Specialists in vintage engines tend to concentrate on a particular make although they may deal in others from time to time. A number of specialists are included below together with the makes they are normally associated with.
Paul Aldridge, Giggetty Wharf, Wombourne, Wolverhampton WV5 8EA (01902 892242) – Lister.

Brian Chisholm, Marine Engine Room, (0115 972 4311 [evenings]) – Lister, Ruston & Hornsby.

R.W. Davis, Junction Dry Dock, Saul, Gloucestershire GL2 7LA (01452 740233) – Kelvin, Russell Newbery, Dorman.

Tony Redshaw, The Locks, Hillmorton, Rugby, Warks CV21 4PP (01788 553417) – Gardner.

Seaward Engineering, 974 Pollokshaws Road, Glasgow G42 2HA (0141-632 4910) – Kelvin, Gardner.

Danny Williamson, Beechtree Bungalow, Roydmoor Lane, Hemsworth, West Yorkshire WF9 5L (01977 610329) – Gardner.

The Russell Newbery Register was originally formed to enable owners to exchange information about RNs but has since started to sell spares and some remanufactured engines – trading as the RN Diesel Engine Co Ltd it can be contacted at The Pippins, Staverton Road, Daventry, Northants NN11 4EY (01327 311724 or 01249 740277).

OUTBOARD ENGINES

Mini-narrowboats (i.e. up to about four tons weight) can be powered by petrol outboard motors. However only four-stroke outboards offer viable low speed reliability and fuel economy in canal use. Manufacturers of four-stroke petrol outboards are:
Honda Marine, Power Road, Chiswick, London W4 5YT (020 8747 1400).

Mercury Outboards, Sowester, Stinsford Road, Nuffield, Poole, Dorset BH17 0SW (01202 667700).

Suzuki GB, 46–62 Gatwick Road, Crawley, West Sussex RH10 2XF (01293 518000).

Tohatsu Marine, Portmore, Lymington, Hants SO41 5RF (01590 670787).

Yamaha Marine, Sopwith Drive, Brooklands, Weybridge, Surrey KT13 0UZ (01932 358000).

The Yanmar diesel outboard, which is suitable for boats of about six tons weight, is available from: E P Barrus, Launton Road, Bicester, Oxon OX6 0UR (01869 363636).

ENGINE MARINISING KITS

Calcutt Boats (address under 'Chandlers').

Lancing Marine, 51 Victoria Road, Portslade, East Sussex BN4 1XP (01273 410025) – (Publishes an invaluable guide/brochure).

Marine Mart, Blue Lias Marina, Stockton, Warks CV23 8HN (01926 811999).

GEARBOXES

PRM: Newage Transmissions Ltd, Barlow Road, Coventry CV2 2LD (024 7661 1845).

Hurth Great Britain Ltd, Marlborough House, Holly Walk, Leamington Spa, Warks CV32 4JB (01926 881285).

Borg Warner Marine, Kenfig Industrial Estate, Margam, Port Talbot, West Glamorgan SA13 2PG (01656 741001).

ZF Great Britain Ltd, Abbeyfield Road, Lenton, Nottingham NG7 2SX (0115 986 9211).

Technodrive, Ron Davis Marine, Castletown, Portland, Dorset DT5 1DB (01305 821175).

Marine Mart (address under engine marinisers)

PROPELLERS, STERN TUBES & SEALS

Crowther Marine, Eden Works, Honeywell Lane, Oldham OL8 2JP (0161 652 4234).

Calcutt Boats, (address under 'Chandlers').

Five Towns Boatbuilding, 1 Whitebridge Lane, Stone, Staffs ST15 8LQ (01785 817506).

Halyard (M&I) Whaddon Business Park, Southampton Road, Waddon, Salisbury SP 3HF (01722 710922).

Midland Chandlers (address under 'Chandlers').
Sea Otter Workboats Ltd, Unit 24, M1 Commerce Park, Markham Lane, Duckmanton, Chesterfield S44 5HS (01246 825750).

Teignbridge Propulsion, Forde Road, Brunel Industrial Estate, Newton Abbot, Devon TQ12 4AD (01626 333377).

Vetus den Ouden, 38 South Hants Industrial Park, Totton, Southampton (023 8086 1033).

FLEXIBLE DRIVE SYSTEMS

Angled cardan shafts:
Wilson Drive Shafts, Unit 1 Bennerley Court, Blenheim Industrial Estate, Bulwell, Nottingham NG6 8UT (0115 976 1202).

Aquadrive:
TW Marine, The Marina, Station Road, Furness Vale, Stockport SK12 7QA (01663 745757).

Hydraulic drive:
ARS Marine, 1 Langley Road, Chadgrave, Norfolk NR14 6BN (01508 520555).

ELECTRIC PROPULSION
Brimblow Engineering, The Old Mill, The Street, Catfield, Great Yarmouth, Norfolk NR29 5DH (01692 582707).

Electric Boat Association, 150 Wayside Green, Woodcote, Reading, Berks RG8 0QJ (01491 681449).

HFL Marine International, Lockfield Avenue, Enfield, Middlesex EN3 7PX (0181 805 9088) – (diesel-electric).

STEAM PROPULSION

Historic Steam, c/o Kew Bridge Steam Museum, Green Dragon Lane, Brentford, Middx TW8 0EN (020 8568 4757).

The Steam Boat Association of Great Britain, 54 Park Road, Chilwell, Notts NG9 4DD (0115 922 7654).

ENGINE INSULATION

TW Marine (under flexible drive systems).

CABIN SPRAYED FOAM INSULATION

ELF Urethane Ltd, 292 Whalley Road, Clayton le Moors, Accrington, Lancs BB5 5QX (01254 237066).

Insulair, 26 Wolversdene Road, Andover, Hants (01264 337777).

Warmways, Hurst House, Hurst Close, Crowthorne Road, Bracknell RG12 4EJ (01344 868489).

Websters Insulation Ltd, Crow Tree Farm, Thorne levels, Doncaster, South Yorkshire DN8 5BR (0800 581247).

TOOLS

Black & Decker and Bosch tools are found in most DIY stores.
Elu and Makita woodworking tools are available from local specialists. They are most easily found under 'Hire Services Tools & Equipment' in Yellow Pages and these, of course, will also hire out specialised equipment.

The Triton Workcentre is available from the manufacturer at:
Rock Mill Business Park, The Dale, Stoney Middleton, Hope Valley, Derbyshire S32 4TF (01433 630870).

The Kreg Mini jig is available from L.G. Supplies, The Old Bakehouse, Littlewick Green, Maidenhead, Berks SL6 3RA (01628 822028).

WINDOWS

Caldwell & Son, 1 Hartley Avenue, off Darlington Street, Wigan WN1 3BW (01942 826471).

Channelglaze, 21A Rushey Lane, Tyseley Birmingham B11 2BL (0121 706 5777).

Severn Yacht Marine, 146–156 Weston lane, Tyseley, Birmingham, B11 3RY (0121 706 0638).

Boatmans Cabin Co Ltd, The Boatyard, Mansion Lane, Iver, Bucks SL0 9RG (01753 651496) – Brass portholes.

Brenmarl Engineering (0121 503 0545) – Opening brass portholes. (Order via chandlers).

SACRIFICIAL ANODES

M G Duff, Unit 2 West, 68 Bognor Road, Chichester, West Sussex PO19 2NS (01243 533336).

ELECTRIC SYSTEMS & APPLIANCES

Acorn Engineering, 5 Turner Street, Denton, Manchester M34 3EG (0161 320 8023).

British Marine Electronics Association, Meadlake Place, Thorpe Lea Road, Egham, Surrey TW20 8HE (01784 473377).

Mastervolt, Unit D 5, The Premier Centre, Abbey Park, Romsey, Hampshire SO51 9AQ (01794 516443).

Electronic Alternator Controllers and Battery Management Systems:

Acorn Engineering (address above)

Adverc BM, 245 Trysull Road, Merry Hill, Wolverhampton WV3 7LG (01902 380494).

Driftgate 2000 Ltd, Little End Road, Eaton Socon, Cambs PE19 3JH (01480 470400).

TWC: Aqua-Marine, 216 Fair Oak Road, Bishopsgate, Eastleigh, Hants S05 6NJ (023 8069 4949).

Sterling Marine Power, Gregory's Mill Street, Worcester WR3 8BS (01905 26166).

Inverters/chargers:

Heart Interface: Los Angeles & Huddersfield Power Systems, Warble Wharf, Broadway, Hyde, Cheshire SK14 4QF (0161-367 9205).

Mastervolt (address above)

Victron, Jacknell Road, Hinckley, Leics LE10 3BZ (01455 618666).

PEL, Unit 2, Rectory Farm, Business Park, Meppershall Road, Upper Stondon, Bedfordshire SG16 6LJ (01462 851454).

GENERATORS

Honda Power Products (address under 'Outboard Engines').
Brownpower Engineering Ltd, The Wharf, Stretton under Fosse, Rugby, Warks CV23 0PR (01788 833383).

E.P. Barrus (address under 'Outboard Engines') – Yanmar portable diesel generators.

Beta Marine, Merretts Mills, Bath Road, South Woodchester, Stroud, Glos GL5 5EU (01453 835282).

Fischer Marine, The Loft, 108 Brassey Road, Winchester, Hants SO22 6SA (01962 841828).

Stephen Goldsbrough Boats, Knowle Hall Wharf, Kenilworth Road, Knowle, Solihull B93 0JJ (01564 778210).

Lister-Petter Marine, Thrupp, Stroud, Glos GL5 2BW (01453 885166).

SOLAR & WIND POWER

Wind & Sun, The Howe, Watlington, Oxford OX9 5EX (0149 1613859).

Ampair, PO Box 416, Poole, Dorset BH12 3LZ (01202 749994).

Marlec Engineering, Rutland House, Trevithick Road, Corby, Northants NN17 1XY (01536 201588).

CENTRAL HEATING

Gas:

Alde International (UK), Sandfield Close, Moulton Park, Northampton NN3 1AB (01604 494193).

Diesel, natural draught:

Harworth Heating Ltd, Blyth Road, Harworth, Doncaster, DN11 8NE (01302 742520).

Kuranda Marine, Canalside, Bridgemont, Whaley Bridge, High Peak, Derbyshire SK23 7PD (01663 734800).

Refleks, Cosalt International, Fish Dock Road, Grimsby, South Humberside DN31 3NW (01472 358881).

Diesel, forced combustion:

Eberspacher (UK) Headlands Business Park, Salisbury Road, Ringwood, Hants BH24 3PB (01425 480151).

Mikuni Heating UK, Unit 5, Second Avenue Business Park, Millbrook, Southampton SO15 0LP (01703 528777).

Water Travel, Oxley Moor Road, Wolverhampton (01902 782371) – Webasto.

WATER PUMPS

Cleghorn Waring & Co, Icknield Way, Letchworth, Herts SG6 1EZ (01462 480380) – Jabsco.

Aquafax, 27B Park Avenue Estate, Sundon Park, Luton LU3 3AE (01582 581222) – Johnson.

Shurflo Ltd, The Old Forge, 36 West Street, Reigate, Surrey RH2 9BX (01737 242290).

CABIN APPLIANCES

Narrowboat chandlers are the best place to compare cabin appliances – cookers, fridges, showers, washbasins, wcs, solid fuel stoves, lighting, etc. Calor Gas showrooms stock larger gas appliances for homes that rely on LPG. Caravan accessory shops are useful for smaller items like compact cooker/sink units. Domestic kitchen centres offer luxurious sinks with clever features but MFI and Homebase are where most narrowboaters buy their sink.

Further addresses:

Calor Gas Ltd, Appleton Park, Slough SL3 9JG (01753 540000).

Lee Sanitation, Wharf Road, Fenny Compton, Warwickshire CV33 0XE (01295 770000).

Gasless cooking

Blakes Lavac Taylor, 13 Harvey Crescent, Warsash, Southampton SO31 9TA (01489 580580) – Taylors diesel heaters and stoves.

Ouzledale Foundry Co, Long Ing, Barnoldwick, Colne, Lancashire, BB8 6BN (01282 813235) – Esse oil and solid fuel ranges.

Cookers

Stoves, Stoney Lane, Prescot, Merseyside L35 2XW (0151 426 6551).

Flavel, Clarence Street, Leamington Spa, Warks CV31 2AD (01926 427027).

Fridges

Brisk, North Lodge, Jeremy's Lane, Bolney, West Sussex RH17 5QE (01444 881620).

Ranger Refrigeration, 272a Long Lane, Halesowen, West Midlands B62 9JY (0121 422 9707).

Shoreline Refrigeration, Unit C4, Modern Moulds Business Centre, Harwoods Road, Littlehampton, West Sussex BN17 7AU (01903 733877).

FURNITURE & UPHOLSTERY

M.B. Bailey, The Wharf, Shardlow, Derbys DE7 2GJ. (01332 792922).

Contract Upholstry Services, 20 Station Road, Coleshill, Birmingham B46 1JG (01675 463747).

Elete Furnishings, Unit 2, Ariane, Lichfield Industrial Estate, Tamworth Staffs B79 7XF (01827 313334).

Foam for Comfort, 401 Otley Old Road, Cookridge, Leeds LS16 7DF (01532 678281).

Wilsons, 98 White Hill, Kinver, Staffs DY7 6AU (01384 872983) – upholstery and boat canopies.

TRADITIONAL BRASSWARE

Fenda Products, Hillmorton Boat Services, The Locks, Hillmorton, Rugby CV21 4PP (01788 578661).

Boatmans Cabin Co Ltd, address under 'Windows'.
Brenmarl Engineering, address under 'Windows'.

PAINTS

Blakes Marine Paints, Centurion Industrial Park, Southampton, Hampshire SO18 1UB (023 8063 6373).

Bradite Paints, Ogwen Valley, Bethesda, Gwynedd, North Wales LL57 4YP (01248 600315).

International Paints, 24/30 Canute Road, Southampton (023 8022 6722).

Jotun, West End, Albert Dock, Hull HU1 1DN (01482 329436).

The Indestructible Paint Company, (Rylard), Haden Street, Birmingham B12 9DB (0121 702 2485).

Joseph Mason Paints, Nottingham Road, Derby DE21 6AR (01332 295959).

Tekaloid, Croda Paints, Bankside, Hull HU5 1SQ (01482 41441).

Wales Dove, Mainline Building Products, South Sefton Business Centre, Canal Street, Bootle, Merseyside L20 8AH (0151 933 8446) – Hull Paints.

Wrights of Lymm, Wright House, Millers Lane, Lymm, Cheshire WA13 9RG (01925 752226) – Scumble, combs and rubbers.

J.H. Ratcliffe & Co, 135a Linaker Street, Southport, PR8 5DF (01704 537999) – Scumble.

Combs and knotting rubbers also from major chandlers and specialists.

SIGNWRITERS

Rob Beckinsale, Gloucester (0973 101790).

Chris Dumville, Upton-on-Severn (01684 569920).

Ron Hough, Braunston (01788 890910).

J.W. Mombrun, 9 Victoria Road, Bicester, Oxon (01869 253959).

Dave Moore, West Midlands (0831 243001) and (01384 571204).

D.J. Moseley 14, Old Acre, Brocton, Stafford ST17 0TW (01785 661726).

Steve Radford, 15 Northern Road, Heanor, Derbys DE75 7EP (01773 762408).

Andy Russell, 37 Barnaby Road, Poynton, Cheshire SK12 1LR (01625 850853).

Philip Speight, Wordsley Dock, Dadford's Wharf, Mill Street, Wordsley, Stourbridge, West Midlands DY8 5SX (01384 485554).

Tony Stephenson, 1 The Garth, Elslack, near Skipton, North Yorks (01282 843907).

John West, 103 Abbotswood Close, Winyates Green, Redditch Worcs B98 0QF (01527 516771).

INDEX